PEN PALS

PEN PALS

Edgar J. Hyde

First Printed 1997, reprinted 1999 (twice)

Text supplied by Joan Love

ISBN 1 90201 230 5

Printed and bound in the UK

Contents

Chapter 1

"Natasha Morris, will you please tell me, and the rest of your classmates, what on earth is so interesting outside?"

With a jolt, Natasha turned towards the teacher.

"I'm sorry Miss Harrison, I was just thinking about . . ." Natasha's voice tailed away.

She couldn't think of an excuse, and she couldn't possibly tell the truth – that this morning's long winded history lesson bored her senseless! After all, wasn't history supposed to be about Henry VIII and his six wives, romance, divorce and gory beheadings. Instead she was having to sit and listen to two hours about crop rotation! Crop rotation – who on earth cared?

"No. Don't even bother stuttering your way through an excuse, just do me a favour and pay attention. Remember you've got an exam coming up next week, and crop rotation just might be one of the questions!" Miss Harrison turned to the rest of the class. "Now, where we?" Her voice droned on and on.

Olivia turned and smiled at Natasha sympathetically. The two were best friends, and had been since they first met up as four-year-olds in the same nursery. They were now in their first year of high school, enjoying feeling all grown up, carrying their books from class to class round the massive, never-ending corridors, giggling as they frequently got lost only to arrive red and breathless at their next class. They had made new friends too, there was Ellis, with her dark curly hair and large brown eyes. How Natasha envied her looks. Then there was Marcie, though Natasha couldn't quite make up her mind about her just yet. She was the complete opposite of Ellis, pale with long, strawlike blond hair and rather on the quiet side. "Pale and interesting, I suppose, if one was being kind," thought Natasha.

She hastily scribbled a note, "Meet you outside the library at four," and passed it deftly to Olivia without Miss Harrison noticing. Olivia quickly pushed the note inside her notebook and gave no sign of having received anything.

Natasha looked at her watch. Ten minutes past four. Where on earth had Olivia got to? Just then, she saw Olivia, Marcie and Ellis wind their way up the long path from the front of the school.

"You took your time," she smiled as all three girls stopped just beside her.

"Sorry, Natasha, my fault," said Ellis. "I left my new lipstick in the loos and had to go and rescue it – never know who you might see on the way home."

Ellis was always experimenting with lipsticks and eyeshadows, always on the lookout for free samples and arriving in school after lunch simply drenched in perfume, having just spent the best part of her lunch hour in the perfume department of the nearest store!

"You should try some, Marcie, look – it's

quite a pale pink, it'd look really nice against your complexion."

"Gosh, no," said Marcie. "My mum would have a fit – she says there's loads of time yet to put all that 'muck', as she calls it, on your face. Anyway, I'd rather keep my money for important things. I'm going to buy some new CD's at the weekend, at least they won't wear out like your make-up will!"

"Hey, Ellis," someone shouted from behind them. The girls turned to see Scott Gregson almost opposite them. He was the best looking guy in their year, and everyone but everyone had their eye on him. "If you're going home, I'll walk with you."

Ellis smiled. "See what the 'muck' on your face does for you girls!" she muttered. "Sure, Scott, I was just saying goodbye to the girls – see you tomorrow everybody." And off she went, pink lips glistening, dark curls bouncing, school bag slung casually over her arm.

"Don't you just wish you had her confidence," sighed Olivia.

"Yes, and her hair and her teeth and her eyes," replied Natasha. "Never mind, 'Make the best of what you've got,' is what my mother always says. Now let's see, what could you make out of us three."

And as the three started to wind their way home, they laughed together, picking out the parts of each other that they thought were the 'best bits'.

"Okay, Natasha," said Olivia "you give me your teeny tiny waist, Marcie can give me her small perfectly formed feet, I can probably get away with using my own hands – if I paint my fingernails – and, with the help of a wig, there we have it, the perfect Barbie doll!" "

And so the conversation carried on until the girls were almost home.

"Oh, and Natasha," Olivia began, "next time you write me a note in class, you really don't have to write my full name on it – I do know who I am!"

Natasha looked at Olivia quizzically, "I didn't write your full name, Olivia, in fact I didn't even write your first name!"

"Yes, you did," Olivia laughed, as she fished in both jacket pockets for the note. "You wrote, 'Olivia Goulden, meet you outside the library at four.' Blast, I can't find the note – oh, look, here it is."

They had now reached Marcie's house and Olivia had emptied the contents of her school bag on to the pavement outside. She showed the hastily scrawled note to Natasha and, sure enough, Olivia's name was written just above what Natasha remembered writing.

"That's really weird, Olivia, I don't remember writing that, it doesn't even look like my handwriting."

"Marcie, where have you been?" the girls heard Marcie's mum shout from an upstairs window.

"Oops, got to run girls, Mum wants me to go to the supermarket with her today – see you tomorrow."

"Sure, bye, Marcie," called the two girls as she disappeared inside her front door.

Natasha was still staring at the note. "Go on Natasha, stop trying to be funny. I mean if you passed the note straight to me, and I didn't add my own name to it, then who did?" Olivia protested. "Anyway, look, I have to run too, I'm baby-sitting Mrs Winter's twins tonight and I have to try and get my homework done before I go. I'll see you tomorrow."

"All right," sighed Natasha, "but I still don't understand."

She left Olivia at the end of the street where the road leading to her house forked left.

Weird, she thought, she must have been in more of a bored stupor than she realised this morning. How could you write someone's name and not remember?

"Suzanna Craigson," she read aloud from one of the gravestones in the cemetery. She had to pass the cemetery every day and night going to and from school and, though was never comfortable with this, she found the best way round it was to make up stories about the people lying beneath the rows and rows of tombstones. That way it seemed to take the scariness out of things.

"Born 2 November 1906, cruelly taken from her beloved parents 1 November 1920."

Natasha had never noticed that particular stone before, or maybe it was just that she had never actually realised how young Suzanna had been when she died.

"Just a year older than I," she thought. "Wonder what happened to her."

The use of the word 'cruelly' seemed to indicate murder or something gory and horrible.

"Better stop thinking about it," she decided. "Mum always says my imagination's too vivid – it'll end up getting me into trouble one of these days."

"Here comes fatso, here comes fatso."

Her young brother's chanting soon stopped her daydreaming.

"Come here, Tommy, you little brat," she laughed, chasing the bubbly little three year old into the back garden. "I'll give you fatso."

She grabbed the little figure and hugged him tightly round the waist, lifting him right off his feet. She kissed him loudly on the lips and came away covered in green sticky stuff.

"What have you been eating now?" she smiled.

"Gooey monsters," he said and showed her the empty packet.

"Green Slimey Guts," she read aloud. "Made from jelly and packets of sugar and full of additives," she added, "your teeth will fall out," and poked him in the tummy playfully.

"Don't care about teef," he retorted. "Like gooey monsters!"

How did the rhyme go, she mused as she went inside to change. Sugar and spice and all things nice, oh yes, frogs and snails and puppy dogs' tails, or something like that anyway. Tommy was that, all right, and she adored every last little inch of him. She wondered if Suzanna Craigson had had a brother?

Chapter 2

Next morning Natasha simply couldn't believe they were having to play hockey outside in the muckiest conditions she had ever seen. It had started to rain last night and had hardly let up from then until now so that the pitch was virtually unplayable! Their gym teacher, however, had insisted that they don their gear and, "get on out there, gels – a bit of rain never hurt anyone!" So there they were, trying desperately to hit the puck into the opposing goal, but usually ending up sprawled on the ground with sticks and legs flying every way but the right way! She sidled over to where Olivia was standing on the pitch. Both Olivia and Marcie hated sport of any form and were both trying to look small and insignificant so that Miss Starrs wouldn't notice they were taking no part in the game!

"Managing to get away with it so far, then?" she hissed to the pair.

Olivia raised her eyes heavenwards, "I'm so wet and dirty I'll have to soak in a hot bubble bath for at least three hours tonight!"

Natasha laughed. Just then, one of the girls at the far end of the pitch started to run towards them. As she drew nearer, Natasha realised that the girl was Ellis, wearing a brand new bright orange and green headband. Ellis drew her stick back and swiped the puck as hard as she could.

The puck seemed to be heading straight for Olivia. Natasha moved forward to try and stop it but, to her surprise, Marcie moved out in front of her. She took a swipe at the puck but, misjudging the wet conditions, leant too far forward, causing herself to skid in the mud. She slid for some distance, turning round to face the opposite direction, while the stick was wrenched from her hands with the sheer force of the fall. The stick flew through the air. Natasha grabbed Olivia.

"Quick, Olivia, down!" she shouted as both girls lay close to the earth waiting for the sickening thud.

The stick landed just beside Natasha's right foot, narrowly missing hitting either of the girls, on almost the exact spot where Olivia had been standing a few short seconds before. Miss Starrs was running down the field, wet hair standing on end, eyes wide with horror, unsure whether or not anyone had been hurt.

"Natasha, Olivia, are you all right? Oh, thank goodness!" she said as both girls stood up. Both their faces were streaked with mud, their gym shorts and tee-shirts dirty and sodden. "Go inside and have a hot shower, girls," she said gently, "while I attend to Marcie."

Marcie too was on her feet. "I'm sorry, Olivia, Miss Starrs, I was only trying to block . . ." She was crying now, her pale cheeks even paler than normal.

"Go inside, Marcie," said Miss Starrs. "On you go, follow the girls in and have a nice hot shower. I'll come and see you all in a minute or two."

Miss Starrs gently herded the girls into the

school then went back to the top of the field. She checked her watch – only about ten minutes to go. She'd let the three girls have some time to themselves and then get the rest of the class inside and cleaned up. She blew the whistle for the girls to play on, and heaved a sigh of relief. She'd thought her recently completed first aid course was going to come into its own that time! She looked around to see where Ellis had gone; Miss Starrs knew she hadn't meant any harm, but since she was the one who hit the offending shot, she was sure she'd be concerned about Olivia.

She finally spotted her, standing on her own at one side of the field. Now isn't that strange. Miss Starrs shook her head. She'd thought Olivia and Ellis were friends – maybe she was wrong. She tried to shake some of the rain from her hair and ran up the pitch to make sure nothing more untoward happened!

Ellis admired her new trainers. She thought the green flash at the side matched her new headband really well.

Marcie was towelling herself dry after her warm shower. The girl was shaking from the shock of what had almost happened.

"I really am sorry, Olivia," she kept repeating. "I was only trying to block the shot. I could see from where I was standing that Ellis was going to make a direct hit, I mean, I don't mean that she meant to hit you, just that I could see, that it looked as though . . . Oh, I don't know what I mean anymore. I really am so sorry," she finished.

Olivia put her arms round the, by now, tearful girl.

"Look, Marcie, I really appreciate what you did out there just now. You didn't hit me with your stick, though I don't know how you managed to miss!" She winked at Natasha. "But the truth is that no harm was done and I'm eternally grateful to you for getting me off that cold, wet pitch and into this lovely warm shower, so no more tears, eh?"

Marcie smiled. "Okay then, if you're sure you forgive me."

"And, hey," joked Natasha, "aren't you the dark horse, then? I thought you were supposed to hate hockey, yet there you were, diving in front of people, swinging sticks for all you're worth – quite the little sporting heroine, eh? Just shows what friends will do for you – lucky you, Olivia," she finished.

Marcie looked a bit apprehensive but when

she realised that Natasha was genuinely congratulating her she visibly relaxed.

"Let's get dressed and get out of here," said Olivia, "before the rest of the class arrive and we're caught up in the stampede. And remember we have to pick up our class photographs today I can't wait to see how awful we look, and who has the worst acne!"

Chapter 3

Marcie volunteered to pick up all three photographs and joined the queue outside the head's office. Ellis was two in front of her.

"Hey, Marcie, how are you doing now?" she smiled. "That was some display you put on this morning."

"I'm okay," Marcie replied. "You must have got a shock yourself when you realised the direction the puck was taking."

"Next," came the loud voice from just inside the headmaster's office.

Ellis stepped forward.

"See you later, Marcie," she said as she picked up her photograph and walked off down the corridor.

Marcie sighed. Why was she the one to feel so guilty in this whole incident when Ellis had played an obvious part and yet seemed to be shrugging the whole thing off. Maybe that was what happened when boys became interested in you – hockey fields became insignificant parts of your life and new 'stays put – even after kissing' lipstick took over. She wondered if she'd ever feel that way, but couldn't help but question whether boys would ever be interested in her – maybe she should dye her hair.

She handed the small package to Natasha.

"I've given Olivia hers," Marcie was out of breath from hurrying up the corridor. "She says she'll see you in class – I've got double geography, so I'll catch up with you later."

"Thanks, Marcie, see you." Natasha stuffed the photograph in her rucksack – she'd have more time to look at it later. She took her place in Mr Jenkins' French class, as usual sitting somewhere near Olivia. She liked French, and even more so since Mr Jenkins was more than a little good looking. She could listen to his almost perfect accent and look at his ruggedly handsome face for two periods every day, and not fall asleep once! She smiled briefly at Olivia before opening her text book.

Just before four o'clock, Natasha realised she'd forgotten to pick up the dry cleaning her mum had asked her to pick up when she was half asleep this morning. She'd have to run into town if she was to make it before the shop shut. She hoped Olivia remembered they had plans for this evening – she'd pass her a note, just in case. The bell rang and Natasha jumped up straight away. She pressed the note into Olivia's hand.

"Got to run," she said, "see you later."

Olivia clasped the note as she tried not to drop her books, pens, rucksack and watched Natasha almost run from the classroom.

"Where is she going in such a rush?" she wondered. "Find out tonight, I suppose."

"Did you pick up the dry cleaning?" her mum shouted, as the front door slammed.

"Yes, Mum, I remembered," she shouted

back, breathing a sigh of relief that her memory hadn't failed her!

She gave Tommy's sleeping face a quick kiss as she passed his room – he took so much out of himself he still needed a short afternoon nap – and went into her own room to change out of her dreaded uniform. Jogging bottoms and tee-shirt donned, she flopped onto her bed, hands behind her head.

"Suppose I'd better check if I have any homework now, as I probably won't get round to doing it later," she thought, picking up her ruck-sack.

As she rummaged around in the bag, the forgotten class photograph came to hand.

"Oh, the class photo," she smiled. "This should be good for a laugh, if previous years are anything to go by," she thought.

She tore off the cellophane paper and searched the sea of faces for her own. There she was, hair pushed untidily behind her ears, little wisps escaping from either side. She could never get it to look even remotely tidy, apart from the year her mum had taken her to the hairdressers to have it put up for a school dance she was going to. The girl at the hairdressers had taken such care over it, but even she had a hard time getting it under control. There had been so much hairspray on it, though, that Natasha decided she preferred it to look unruly rather than stuck together on top of her head!

But look, there were Ellis and Olivia standing together, and Marcie in the row in front. She was smaller than the others, so the photographer had suggested it would be better for her to be nearer the front of the class. Marcie said later she should have worn her new platform shoes, then she wouldn't have had to be split from her friends, and Paul had laughed and said it didn't matter where you stood in a photograph, you could still be the greatest of friends after the camera had flashed! Ellis had smiled at this too, though not as widely as she had smiled for the cameraman. She was so photogenic; just look at the way she played to the camera.

Natasha's eyes scanned the rest of the photograph quickly. Her eyes came to rest on the right hand side of the back row. A small, fair girl stood slightly apart from the others, her eyes not looking into the camera at all.

"Who on earth is that?" thought Natasha.

She'd never seen the girl before. Was it someone from another class who'd been put with theirs at the last minute? She didn't remember anyone being brought in, or possibly it was someone new at school altogether, but no, new starts always caused such a lot of interest, she couldn't possibly have missed out on that happening. Who was she? Olivia would surely know – she looked at her watch – only five-thirty. Olivia was due to come over about seven that night, they were going to discuss their costumes for the Halloween Ball on Friday night. Natasha wanted to go as Cleopatra, the Queen of the Nile, and her mum had promised to help make her wig. It would also be a good excuse to paint lots of make-up on, and wear jewellery half way up her arms! She propped the photograph against her CD player and went downstairs to see what was for tea.

Chapter 4

Olivia looked again at the note.

"See you at seven at the cemetery – look for Suzanna Craigson's stone."

Olivia was utterly puzzled by the note – she thought tonight was for discussing costumes – not an eerie night at the graveyard! It was so unlike Natasha, too, she wasn't exactly brave when it came to anything to do with graves and old churchyards, and especially not at seven o'clock at night just when it was beginning to get dark. She sighed and stuffed the note into her jacket pocket. After she'd helped Mum clear the dinner dishes she'd get changed and go and meet her friend, no doubt all would be revealed once she'd met up with Natasha.

Five minutes past seven. Natasha was late. Olivia had found the tombstone fairly easily as it was positioned near the front of the graveyard and could be seen quite clearly from the road. Olivia was grateful she'd worn her heavy jacket as it was beginning to get quite cold. She pulled up her collar and dug her hands deeper into her pockets.

Ten past seven.

"Olivia," she heard from behind her. She turned and saw a figure come from the direction of the cemetery gate.

"Hurry up, Natasha," she said. "Whatever were you doing in there?"

It was at that split second, she told Natasha afterwards, that she realised "Natasha" wasn't in fact Natasha at all. The person coming towards her was smaller and slighter than her friend, and she walked with a pronounced limp. Olivia tried to see the girl more clearly, but dusk had just started to fall and she couldn't quite make out her features just yet. As she approached, slowly, hindered by the limp, Olivia was able to see that the girl had long, almost golden, hair, curled in ringlets which framed her face and cascaded down her back, and she appeared to be in some distress.

"Are you okay?" Olivia ventured.

The last thing she felt like doing was standing there offering help; for some reason the approaching girl frightened her. Olivia gave herself a shake.

"Don't be so stupid," she thought, "it's merely the fact that you're right beside a cemetery, it's getting dark and the trees are casting dark shadows."

This little talking to only served to make her feel worse, though, and she found herself willing Natasha to hurry up. A bit of moral support wouldn't go wrong!

The girl had stopped now, almost directly opposite Olivia, and Olivia was aware of the strange clothes the girl was wearing. Her dress was long and frilled at the cuffs and she wore a little matching bonnet over her fair curls. She wore a funny sort of built up shoe on her right foot, and this was the leg which had seemed to drag behind her as she walked.

The girl looked directly at Olivia and Olivia noticed for the first time there was an almost ethereal quality about her. Her skin was so pale as to be almost translucent and her eyes seemed to be wet with tears.

"Are you Olivia Goulden?" she almost whispered. "I must find her, please help me. She is in great danger, I must warn her!"

She reached out her hand as though to clasp Olivia's but no touch was made. Instead, the girl's hand seemed to go right through Olivia's, bringing with it the sensation of a cold, cold wind which chilled her very soul.

Olivia was by now quite literally frozen to the spot with fear. She was so cold her teeth had begun to chatter and all she could think of was getting out of there.

"Please, you must listen to me," the girl said again. It was at this point that Olivia was unfrozen. She turned from the pale haired girl, took to her heels and ran as she had never run before. All the way along the pavement she ran, stumbling sometimes over broken paving slabs, until at last she could see Natasha's house, warm and welcoming in the distance.

She didn't even knock on the door, just burst in and ran straight upstairs to Natasha's bedroom, pushing Natasha aside as she jumped up to see what the commotion was.

"Olivia, what on earth . . . ?"

Olivia was standing to one side of the window, and had pulled back the curtain.

"Put out the light," she instructed Natasha.

"Not until you tell me what's happening," Natasha replied from the bed where she had fallen.

"Put out the damn light!" Olivia almost screamed "or I'll do it myself."

"All right, all right," answered Natasha as she jumped up to put off the switch. "Keep your voice down, you'll wake Tommy." She joined Olivia at the bedroom window to look outside, although she had no idea what she was supposed to be looking for.

"Look, there she is!" Olivia was almost hysterical. Natasha looked out of the window to see Marcie approaching the house.

"It's Marcie," said Natasha. "She rang just after six o'clock tonight to ask if she could come over and help with either of our costumes. What's the problem with that?" It was then that she noticed that Olivia's hands, and practically her whole body, were shaking.

"Olivia, you have to calm down and tell me

what happened out there – I have no idea what's going on. Come on, come and sit on the bed with me."

Olivia allowed herself to be led to the bed where she promptly sat down and burst into tears. Marcie had arrived, and knocked on the front door. Tommy woke up and started to cry. Mrs Morris answered the door and brought Marcie in.

"Do me a favour, pet," she said, "go and start heating some milk for Tommy – he likes a hot milky drink if he wakes at this time – and I'll go and bring him downstairs."

"Sure, Mrs Morris," agreed Marcie. She just adored chubby little Tommy and didn't mind helping out with him before she joined her friends upstairs.

Olivia, meanwhile, had just recounted her story to her friend.

"But what on earth were you doing standing about at the cemetery?" asked Natasha.

Olivia turned, aghast, to Natasha. "Because you told me to meet you there, in your note," she replied.

"In my note. What note? The one I passed you in French?"

"Oh no, not again," thought Natasha. Was she going mad? "Let me see the note, Olivia, please. I know I didn't ask to meet you at the cemetery, I just know I didn't, let me see the note, please."

Olivia took the now tattered note from her jacket pocket and handed it to her friend. Sure enough, the note said what Olivia had said it did, except that, for Natasha, it was even more frightening.

"See you at seven at the cemetery – look for

Suzanna Craigson's stone." Suzanna Craigson! The grave Natasha had noticed for the first time the other day.

Natasha shook her head in disbelief.

"I have no idea what on earth is going on here, Olivia, I swear it. I did not write 'at the cemetery' on that note, I merely wrote 'See you at seven'. I mean, you know how I feel about graves and things, there's just no way I would have asked you to hang around there waiting for me." She sighed deeply. "I don't know what to do here, Olivia, you do believe me don't you?" She looked at her friend.

Olivia lifted tear-stained eyes.

"Yes, Natasha, but only because it's you and I've known you too long to think you would ever deliberately frighten me. But it still doesn't solve the puzzle. What on earth is happening here? First, my full name was written on the initial note, then words are seemingly added to the second note and then that, that *person* outside just now . . ." Olivia started to shake again.

"We'd better get ourselves together before Marcie joins us – we don't want to frighten her half to death with some half-baked story about notes and ghostly apparitions," said Natasha.

"Half-baked story?" protested Olivia.

"Yes, I know what you saw, and I believe you," said Natasha "but will anybody else? Honestly, we should keep this whole thing under wraps until we know exactly what's going on."

"So, what's Ellis coming to the party as?" asked Marcie as she deftly glued some more sequins on Olivia's dress. Olivia had decided to go as a gangster's moll – she was a real old movie buff and had just finished watching a season of gangster movies where all the molls wore sequinned dresses, fur stoles, and lashings of glossy red lipstick!

"Don't know – she hasn't mentioned it at all," replied Olivia.

"Don't suppose for a minute it'll be anything unglamorous, though. Can't imagine Ellis doing anything remotely unglamorous, can you?" Natasha smiled. "Well, we're not exactly dressing down for the event, are we girls?"

She looked at Marcie. "What are you coming as, Marcie. Hey, listen, if you don't have a costume yet why don't you come as Al Capone, you know, the infamous Chicago gangster, then you could partner Olivia. You could borrow my dad's braces, and I'm sure we could get a violin case from someone, you know, to pretend it was a machine gun – Marcie, are you listening to a word I'm saying?"

She turned to the other girl who still sat, head bowed, gluing sequins on Olivia's dress.

"Yes, Natasha, I hear you," she replied. "And thanks. It's just that my mum said she would find a costume for me – something about family tradition." Marcie lowered her head again and returned to the task in hand.

Natasha and Olivia exchanged glances but said nothing. Sometimes they wondered about Marcie's family. She seemed to have a very strict upbringing – perhaps because she was an only child they supposed. Better to say nothing, anyway.

Olivia threw a rolled up leather belt in Natasha's direction. "Made you this, Natasha, it's an asp, remember, Cleopatra needs a snake."

Natasha screamed loudly. "Get that away from me, Olivia, there's no way I'm putting an asp near me – Cleopatra or not!"

Natasha's room door was pushed open to reveal Mrs Morris standing in the hallway.

"If you girls wake Tommy again you won't be going to the Halloween Ball," she threatened. "Now keep it down, please."

Chapter 5

Next day at school, Natasha, Olivia and Ellis stood chatting in the playground.

"Still seeing Scott, then Ellis?" Olivia asked.

"Yes, we went to the cinema last night – saw a really scary film, you know the one about the Zombies in the shopping mall?"

"Zombies? – are you mad?" laughed Natasha. "I thought young lovers were supposed to go see romantic movies and sit in the back row?"

Ellis laughed too. "I know, I don't actually think Scott and I are romantically suited – I'd rather sit and watch a good scary film than snog in the back row. Olivia, is something wrong?"

Olivia had turned from the two girls and was staring at Marcie who was walking slowly towards them. Except that she wasn't walking – she was limping and dragging her leg behind her.

"Wh—what have you done to your leg?" she stammered.

Marcie drew alongside the girls.

"I fell over when I came out of the shower last night – the floor was a bit wet and I slid," she finished. "I have to go," she said, "I've got social studies first period and you know what Mr Livingstone's like for timekeeping."

"Bye, Marcie," the girls shouted as they watched her disappear up the steep stone stairs and through the front doors of the high school.

"I have to run, too," said Ellis. "See you at lunchtime."

"Bye, Ellis," said Natasha. "Olivia, are you all right?" she asked her friend. Olivia gave herself a shake.

"Yes, I'm okay, Natasha. It's just that with the colour of Marcie's hair, and then the limp, she looked just like . . ."

"It's okay, Olivia, I know who you mean. Suzanna Craigson's uppermost in my mind too, though I'm trying hard not to think about her."

Just at that moment the bell rang summoning the girls to that morning's classes.

"Let's go," Natasha took her friend's arm. "We can talk more about this at morning break."

Break was a long time coming. Natasha spent the whole of the first two periods decorating the front of her book with drawings of eyes. Cleopatra's eyes with thick black liner and gold lashes, Cleopatra's eyes with thick green liner and blue lashes, Cleopatra's eyes with thick silver liner and gold lashes! She was just debating whether or not to paint her nails two different colours when she was startled by the bell ringing. She stuffed her books into her schoolbag and, as she did so, came across the class photograph she had put into her bag the previous evening so that she could ask Olivia who the mystery girl was.

She joined Olivia in the queue for the tuck shop.

"Wait till I show you this!" Natasha took the class photograph from inside her bag and showed it to Olivia. "Notice anything strange?" she asked her friend.

Olivia scanned the photograph.

"Oh my God, it's her!" she stammered, "Natasha, that's her, the girl at the graveyard, the one at the top right of the photograph." She turned to Natasha, "I don't understand – just what's going on here?"

People were turning round to stare.

"Shh, Olivia," Natasha again took her friend's arm and guided her away from the queue towards the quietness of the cloak room.

"What on earth do you mean, it's her? I can't believe what I'm hearing," said Natasha. "Do you mean the girl in the photograph is Suzanna Craigson?"

Olivia was no longer listening instead she was rummaging inside her own schoolbag.

"Here it is," she said triumphantly as she pulled out her own copy of the class picture. She pulled the cellophane from the print and thrust it in front of Natasha's eyes.

"Look," she cried, "she's not in my photograph, there's nothing weird about mine, who's been tampering with yours? None of this is making any sense. Who would want to paint a face into your photograph? Who is this Suzanna Craigson?" She started to cry.

Natasha took Olivia's photograph and looked at it long and hard. Sure enough, the girls in the back row of this photograph were all classmates and well known to them and there was no sign of the slight, fair haired girl who stood at the top right hand corner on her own.

"I don't know the answers to any of your questions, Olivia, but I want to find out just as much as you do. Whoever Suzanna Craigson is, we're going to find out, and find out soon.

Come on, don't cry any more, it's all right now."

Olivia wiped at her eyes with the sleeve of her jacket. Natasha held both the photographs in her hands. She must try and stay calm, for Olivia's sake, as well as her own. She turned the photographs over and saw that Olivia's name was written on Natasha's copy, and vice versa. Marcie must have mixed up the prints when she picked them up the previous day.

"Olivia, it looks as if you've had my copy," she said. "Look, your name's on mine," and she showed the backs of both photographs to the girl. "Not that it matters one little bit," she finished.

"Oh, but it does," Olivia rejoined. "Don't you see, Suzanna said she had to talk to me, that I was in great danger. She seems to be trying to contact me somehow, adding things to your notes, appearing outside the cemetery, and now this, appearing in my picture! I don't know if I can take much more of this." Olivia was ashen white.

Natasha tried to appear reassuring.

"Come on," she said purposefully, "we have two more classes this morning then at lunchtime, you and I, my friend, are going to the library."

"We're meeting Ellis, and probably Marcie, at lunchtime, though Natasha."

"Blast," said Natasha, "well, we'll just have to wait until four o'clock then. No more notes," she smiled, "we'll make our plans face to face from now on!"

"Why are we going there anyway?" asked Olivia, puzzled.

"Because they keep old newspapers, things of interest which have happened in town for the last hundred years or so, and if there's anything of any interest there to do with Suzanna Craigson we're going to find it."

Olivia shuddered. Thank goodness Natasha was so brave and sensible, or at least pretending to be, because Olivia wasn't coping with this thing very well at all. Natasha replaced the two photographs inside her school bag as both girls made their way to their next class. Neither she nor Olivia noticed that the girl at the top right corner of Olivia's class photograph had completely faded out of sight.

Mrs Florence looked at both girls over the rim of her glasses.

"Not usual to see you two young ladies in the library after school," she stated.

Natasha sighed. "I know, Mrs Florence, but we've decided to take part in a new project – life back in the 1900s right here in our own little town, and we thought you'd be the best person to help us out. Not that I'm insinuating that you're old, or anything," she continued, "just that maybe you could point us in the right direction for any news cuttings, history books, old pictures, etc, that could help us out – you know the kind of thing I mean."

The seemingly frosty, but kind-hearted librarian almost smiled.

"This way then, girls," she led them towards the narrow winding staircase of the old library, "and hurry, before any other potential knowledge seekers come in looking for assistance."

The girls had never been upstairs in the library before. Indeed, it wasn't one of their most favoured haunts at all. They could always find much more exciting things to do outwith school hours, or at least up until now they had!

"When you reach the top, the books on your left will help with the history of the actual town of Chalmersville, then the shelves below have hanging files which should contain old newspapers – in chronological order, which I don't want messed up!" she added before returning to the main desk. "If you need any help, you'll have to come down, I really can't leave the desk unmanned in case it get busy."

Her words faded into the distance as the two girls climbed higher and higher up into the top part of the old library.

Natasha and Olivia exchanged glances.

"Busy?" Natasha raised her eyebrows.

"When was the last time you saw a queue form outside the library?"

Olivia giggled. "Shh, she'll hear you, and we may need her help later, you never know."

"She won't hear us," replied Natasha, "listen, can't you hear her – 'stamp, stamp', she just loves putting that 'overdue' stamp on the returned books."

The girls had by now reached their destination.

"Gosh, what a musty smell," said Olivia as she plonked herself down on the dusty floor.

"It'll get even worse by the time we've finished," returned Natasha. "Just look at how thick the dust is on top of this book."

She pulled a large brown book from one of the top shelves and opened it on the top of the desk in front of her.

Chapter Five

"Okay, Olivia, you start on the newspapers. Now let's see, if I remember correctly Suzanna lived from November 1906 to October 1920, so see if you can find anything about her from the papers. Here," she drew two bags of crisps from inside her jacket pocket, "sustenance."

Two hours later, the girls had made little progress. The name Craigson, Natasha had discovered, was relatively new to Chalmersville. New, being a couple of hundred years old, that is. The family had settled there in a house, the description of which meant nothing to either of the girls. They decided that the house must no longer exist or, if it did, it had been changed so much by the present owner that it bore no resemblance to the description in the book.

"Wait a minute," said Olivia excitedly. "Look at this!"

> Tragedy within Craigson Household. A young girl was today recovered from the boating pond outside her home at Gatefells after a fatal drowning incident.

Natasha slammed her book shut and gave her full attention to what Olivia was reading.

"That's where Ellis lives, Gatefells, go on Olivia, don't stop there."

> Mr and Mrs Craigson, who today lost their only child, are understandably distraught and have asked that they be left alone with their grief.

There the story stopped, though in a later article the girls were able to read more about the family. Apparently not much was known of the couple, being relative newcomers to Chalmersville, although Mr Craigson was fast becoming a well known figure in the community through his tireless work helping charitable organisations. They found that the girl who had drowned had, indeed, been named Suzanna. She had gone out on her own in the boat, despite having been warned by her parents on previous occasions that she should always be accompanied. If she had been accompanied by someone, there was no evidence of this. The article also said that she was of poor health and wore a built up shoe as she had been born with one leg shorter than the other. Olivia gave a sharp intake of breath.

"It's just got to have been the same person, Natasha, the girl in the photograph and at the graveside. But why is she trying to reach me now? Oh, I wish I understood what was going on. It's not so long ago I didn't even believe in ghosts!"

Natasha continued to flick through several newspapers.

"At least we've found out some information, Olivia, the day's not been completely wasted. I mean, we now know that Suzanna Craigson did live in a house in Chalmersville, that she was killed in a boating accident and that she was an only child." She stopped.

"So what, Natasha? I mean, I'm sorry, but how exactly does that help us to discover why on earth she wants to get in touch with me?" Olivia sighed.

"Patience, my dear, we'll get to the bottom of this little mystery soon enough," Natasha replied. "And, hey, did you work out those dates? 2 November to 1 November 1920 – that means she died the day before her birthday, the day after Halloween. That's just got to have some significance. It's too creepy not to. Come on, let's get out of here, before we get put back up on the shelves with the rest of the old relics here! I feel so dusty I can't wait to get home and have a shower."

The two girls climbed back down the winding staircase, dusting themselves down as they went.

"Thanks, Mrs Florence," they shouted to the librarian.

"Shh, girlies," she held her finger to her lips.

"Sorry," they giggled, "didn't think there was anyone here to disturb," as indeed there wasn't. Luckily for them, Mrs Florence didn't hear their last remark.

She followed them to the door.

"I hope you put everything back in chronological order," she bent over to speak to the two girls. "I put in a lot of hard work organising those papers, you know," she finished.

"Yes, of course we did," smiled Natasha, "and thank you for all your help, Mrs Florence, we might need to come back another day, and it's great to know you'll be here for us to rely on," she gushed.

Mrs Florence pushed a loose tendril of hair back behind her glasses.

"Always a pleasure to see you both," she flushed. "Any time, girls." She closed the door gently behind them both.

"Natasha?" said Olivia as they crossed the road outside the library to begin the journey home.

"Yes?" said Natasha absent-mindedly.

"What's chronological?"

Chapter 6

Olivia was excited about the Halloween Ball tonight and felt as though her geography lesson would never end. She and Natasha both had their costumes ready and couldn't wait to get home and dressed up.

"I wonder what Marcie and Ellis are doing? Maybe they told Natasha and she forgot to say, or maybe it's a big secret," Olivia mused.

Both she and Natasha had made a pact to forget all about Suzanna Craigson for this one night and simply go to the Halloween Ball and have just that – a ball! The bell began to ring and, as one, the pupils threw books, pens and anything else that came to hand into their bags. Olivia caught up with Natasha outside the class.

"Thought that was never going to end!" she smiled at her friend.

Natasha smiled back. "Hey, Ellis," she called.

Olivia looked in the direction Natasha was facing and saw Ellis' retreating back as she left the school building. Her dark curls bobbed as she flounced out of the door but she seemed not to hear her friend's shout as she carried on walking.

"Strange," said Natasha, "I could have sworn she saw us, and I'm almost positive she's not far enough away that she wouldn't have heard me shout." She looked puzzled for a second or two. "Ah well, never mind, let's get out of here. We've got a lot to do before we meet up tonight, and then we'll discover the secrets behind Marcie's and Ellis's costumes!"

The school hall was brightly lit, not just by lights but by strategically placed pumpkins with the insides removed to make room for short, dumpy candles. One by one the pupils arrived, exclaiming over the others' costumes, guessing the identity of those who wore masks. Loud music filled the hall from the disco set up on the stage and banners suspended from the ceiling carried the words "Welcome to the 1997 Chalmersville Halloween Ball". Natasha was just arriving and was trying to adjust her wig as she got out of her mother's car.

"For Heaven's sake, Natasha, leave it alone, will you, or you'll end up with no wig on at all!" her mother sighed.

"Bye, Cleo," Tommy smiled from the back seat, his little fingers opening and closing over his chubby little hand as he waved her goodbye. He couldn't quite get his tongue round Cleopatra so Natasha had said Cleo would do very nicely.

"Goodbye, sweetheart," she blew a kiss as she stepped out onto the street.

"Now, Natasha," her mother began.

"I know, Mum," she interrupted, "I won't be late." Mrs Morris smiled as she put the car into gear and made to draw away from the kerb.

"Have a nice time, Natasha, goodbye."

Natasha waved at Tommy as he waved out of the back window then, with one last pull at her wig, she joined the other party-goers as they entered the hall.

"Over here, Natasha," she heard Olivia call.

She turned to see her friend, cigarette holder in silken gloved hand, wearing her beaded, sequinned dress and topped by a small hat with a very large feather.

"Olivia, you look terrific," she laughed as she joined her friend.

"So do you, Nat, your make-up's fantastic. You look like a dead person reincarnated, your eyes are so black!"

The two girls laughed together and went in search of the rest of their classmates. There was to be a prize for the best costume and most of the pupils had made a bit of an effort to get in the running. A passing gorilla growled at Olivia. Olivia laughed.

"Unfortunately I'll never know who he is. There are at least six different gorillas here."

The girls made their way towards the end of the hall where soft drinks were being served.

"Hey, look, there's Batman over there," smiled Natasha, "and Catwoman's with him. Just look at the length of her claws, and I thought my false nails were long!"

A rather fat Indian squaw stood at the side of the soft drinks table, smiling now and again at a sequinned Elvis.

"Isn't this just the best fun?" Natasha nudged Olivia. "Olivia – what on earth's wrong with you?"

Olivia looked to be in some sort of trance, but the look of fear on her face told Natasha there was something very wrong. She followed Olivia's gaze to the far side of the hall they had just left and saw immediately what had caught her friend's attention. A slight, fair haired girl had just entered the room. She wore a long, cream coloured gown which was very old fashioned and, had frills round the cuffs and hem. On the back of her head she wore a small matching bonnet.

"Oh my God!" Natasha breathed. "It can't be – can it?" The two girls stood as though they were rooted to the spot. Then Natasha felt a tug on her arm.

"Hi, girls."

Natasha turned round.

"It's me, Marcie."

She was dressed in a pale blue dress with a short white apron tied around it. In her hair she wore a large Alice band and under her arm she had tucked a white rabbit. Natasha tried to regain her composure. She had hoped that the girl they had been looking at in the distance was in fact Marcie, but if the girl standing beside her was Marcie dressed as Alice in Wonderland then that ruled that possibility out!

"Hi, Marcie," she said. "Olivia," she pulled on her friend's arm. "Look, isn't Marcie a brilliant Alice."

Olivia turned. "Oh, yes, yes," stumbled Olivia. "Your costume's just great."

She tried to show some enthusiasm, but kept feeling her eyes being dragged back to the slight figure at the other end of the room.

"Told you – family tradition," Marcie continued. "Apparently my great, great, great aunt, or someone, actually I'm not sure how many greats it is, knew Lewis Carroll, you know the person who wrote *Alice in Wonderland* and

Through the Looking Glass and based Alice's sister on her character. I mean I know she only played a small part, the sister, that is, but our family became very Alice-orientated after that. Every Halloween we use it as an opportunity to indulge a little in the book's characters. I've gone as a white rabbit before, though that can get very hot and stuffy . . ."

Marcie's voice droned on and on in the background and by this time Natasha was paying her as little attention as Olivia had been.

"Marcie, I hate to be rude, but there's someone we must see at the end of the room. We'll be back in a minute or two – excuse us."

The two girls moved away and hurried to the far end of the room. Marcie turned away, feeling slightly miffed, and limped towards the drinks' table. As Natasha and Olivia approached, the fair haired girl turned towards them with a smile on her lips.

"Hello, Natasha, Olivia," she murmured. "What do you think, then?"

Natasha and Olivia stopped in their tracks. Olivia looked quizzically at the girl.

"Ellis?" she questioned.

"Blast!" said Ellis. "I knew you'd guess it was me – it's the dark eyebrows, isn't it?" Natasha and Olivia started to breathe again. Natasha's eyes travelled to Ellis' feet, but she wore normal shoes, not a built up one like the real Suzanna.

"But who are you supposed to be?" the girls asked.

"Well, I know I'm not anyone famous, really," said Ellis, "but Mum found a trunk in the attic and this was one of the outfits inside. It was just such a good fit, and I haven't had time to make anything, what with seeing Scott and everything, so I decided I'd just come looking as a young Chalmersville girl would look about 100 years ago! You two look very glamorous though, maybe I made the wrong choice," finished Ellis.

"No, you look really great," Natasha managed. "Listen, we left Marcie by the drinks', we'll have to go back and get her – are you coming?"

"Yes, in a minute or two, I just want to find Scott. He said he was dressing as a gorilla – I don't suppose you've seen him, have you?"

Olivia and Natasha rejoined Marcie.

"Marcie, I'm really sorry," said Olivia. "Let me have a proper look at your costume."

Marcie smiled.

"Well I have to admit I was a bit hurt earlier, but I'll forgive you both," she twirled, showing the full flounces of the skirt, with the stiff net petticoat underneath. "Don't know how they ever wore these things though," she said "give me a pair of good old jogging bottoms any day!"

The girls laughed. Natasha and Olivia smiled at one another.

"Come on," said Olivia as they went on to the dance floor, "let's have what we said we were going to have – a ball!"

All too soon, as is wont to happen when you are enjoying yourself, the evening was over. The pumpkins had lost their glow, as had most of the guests, and parents' cars were drawing up outside to pick up their children. The four friends stood on the top step outside the school hall.

"Oh, I almost forgot," said Ellis. "Mum said I could invite you three over tomorrow, seeing it's Saturday, for some lunch. Pleeee-ease say you'll come. She and Dad are going out for the day and the house will be ours to do what we want. Come on, girls, you've never been to mine before, say you can make it."

The girls looked pleased at the invitation, Ellis was right, they hadn't been to her house before.

"We'll be there," they returned.

"Great," smiled Ellis, "be there for twelve o'clock – you too, Alice," she nudged Marcie. "And bring your white rabbit if you like!" Ellis ran off down the steps.

"Wait, Ellis, don't you want a lift?" shouted Olivia.

But Ellis was gone, fair ringlets streaming behind her as she ran off into the darkness.

"Ah well, seems like she didn't want a lift,"

Olivia finished as her father's car pulled up at the kerb side.

The three girls clambered in, stifling yawns as they pulled on seat belts and yanked at annoying wigs, stiff petticoats and tutted at sequinless patches of dress.

"Not turned into pumpkins yet, then?" joked Mr Goulden.

"No, Dad," returned Olivia, "nor did any of us meet our handsome princes."

Natasha leaned her head back against her seat and closed her eyes for the short car journey in front of her.

Chapter 7

"Monkey nuts? You can't be serious, Natasha, you want to take monkey nuts with you?" Olivia couldn't believe she was hearing her friend.

"It's just for fun," Natasha laughed down the phone. "I mean it is the day after Halloween – maybe Ellis was planning on having us bobbing for apples – you never know. Anyway, my mum bought in loads of nuts and she still has them in the kitchen. I'll fill a few bags and bring them."

Olivia had gone rather quiet on the other end of the phone.

"Are you still there, Olivia?" Natasha asked.

"Yes, I'm still here, Natasha. It was just with you saying this was the day after Hallow-een and I remembered the date. November the first. It was on this day in 1920 that Suzanna died – remember?" Natasha had momentarily forgotten.

"Yes, I do remember, Olivia. Look, shall we do what we did last night? Go to Ellis' house, have a good time and put Suzanna to the back of our minds for now? I mean, let's face it, nothing strange has happened for a couple of days – maybe the whole thing was in our imagination."

Olivia started to protest.

"No, okay, I know you're right, we couldn't

have imagined the things that happened. Let's say then that after today we look at this whole thing again, go back to the library, maybe ask Mrs Florence some direct questions. You never know what she might be able to help us with."

Olivia took a deep breath.

"Okay, Natasha, I guess you're right. I'll meet you at the bottom of the lane next to the new Health Centre – I'll give Marcie a call and tell her we'll wait for her there, too. See you in half an hour or so."

Olivia hung up the phone. Natasha was right. She must put this thing to the back of her mind. Suzanna Craigson was dead, and there was absolutely nothing she, Olivia Goulden, could do about that. She picked up the phone and dialled Marcie's number.

There was no reply from Marcie's home.

"Strange," thought Olivia, "maybe she's already gone up to Ellis's house, though I'd have thought she would have wanted to meet up with Natasha and me and all go up together. Maybe she's gone to the shops to pick up some things before she goes and we'll meet her en route."

Olivia ran up stairs to pick up her warm jacket. It could be quite chilly outside these days, and she wasn't sure if Ellis planned for them to spend the day indoors or out. Better to be prepared.

"Come on, slowcoach," shouted Natasha. "It's freezing standing about here."

Olivia hurried along the pavement towards her friend.

"Sorry, I kept trying Marcie's number before I came out, but I can't get a hold of her," replied Olivia.

Natasha shrugged.

"She's maybe already at Ellis's house – who knows? Let's hurry up, anyway, hopefully she'll have something hot to drink waiting for us."

The girls began their ascent towards Gatefells, for the house was situated almost at the highest point of the town, and they climbed together in companionable silence – the silence that comes only from knowing someone your whole life.

Olivia broke the silence to ask, "Do you know what Ellis's father does for a living, Natasha? The family certainly seem to be very well off."

Again, Natasha shrugged.

"No, I kept meaning to ask my mum, but I

never did. All I know is they live in a large, posh house on the top of this hill and that Ellis never wants for anything!"

The girls were now in the grounds of the old house and Natasha was struck not only by the beauty of the large gardens which surrounded the house, but by the sheer size of everything.

"Wouldn't it just be a dream to live here, Olivia? Look at the grand scale of everything."

Olivia didn't answer. Since she had entered the grounds of the house, she had been feeling ever so slightly on edge.

"Didn't there used to be gates here?" she asked Natasha, pointing to the edge of the lawn. Natasha turned to look at her.

"Now, how would I know that, Olivia? I've only passed in this direction once or twice before, and both of those times I was in the car. As far as I know there weren't any gates."

"Then, how is it that I remember large wrought iron gates, supported on either side by stone pillars?" asked Olivia. "And I know that that oak tree over there used to hold a swing in the summertime"

Olivia was becoming more and more animated now as she spoke. Her eyes were bright as she looked all around her.

"There, look, the window I used to sit at while Ellen prepared dinner. If you sat in a certain position just before dusk fell you could see Papa dismount . . ."

Natasha was staring very hard at Olivia. This whole thing had affected her friend more than she could have imagined. Natasha took both Olivia's hands in her own.

"Olivia, you have to calm down! Olivia, please!"

Olivia's eyes were wild, darting in every direction. She was smiling, laughing almost, but it was a hollow laughter which chilled Natasha's very heart.

"Olivia, please, you're frightening me. Who is Ellen? Papa dismounting? I don't know what you're talking about."

"Natasha, Olivia, over here," both girls turned. Ellis was standing in the doorway to the house, waving frantically. "Come on, you two," she shouted "I thought you'd never get here."

Natasha turned back towards Olivia, still holding both her hands. The wild eyed look had gone, and her own Olivia again stood beside her.

"I'm, I'm all right, Natasha, honestly, I don't know what happened just then. I had the strangest feeling that . . . oh, never mind, come on," she rubbed at her eyes as though she had just woken from a deep sleep and pulled the collar of her jacket up even further. "Ellis is waiting for us, let's go."

Both girls walked up the short path which led to the front entrance of Gatefells, each of them trying to put aside their uneasy thoughts.

Ellis led them into the enormous kitchen. There was a blazing log fire in the large fireplace and she had just boiled the kettle.

"Okay, chocolate and peppermint, chocolate and orange, chocolate and coconut, chocolate and chocolate?" she held up the little sachets of drinking chocolate one at a time.

"Oh, anything, so long as it's warm," smiled Natasha. "It's really cold out there today."

Ellis turned to pour the boiling liquid into the waiting mugs and Natasha stole a glance at Olivia. She seemed to be completely back to normal. She took the hot mug from Ellis gratefully and cupped both hands around it.

"Thanks, Ellis. Is Marcie not here, then?" she enquired.

"Haven't seen her yet," Ellis joined the girls at the oak table. "I thought you were all coming together."

"Well, yes," said Olivia, "that was the plan, but I couldn't reach her on the telephone and assumed she'd come up earlier on her own. Never mind, maybe we can phone her again in a while?"

Ellis nodded.

"Sure, why not. Listen, if you've started to heat up, give me your jackets and I'll hang them up for you just now, then you'll feel the benefit of them once we go back outside."

"We're going outside?" asked Natasha. "My toes are just beginning to thaw out and you're talking about going back outside?"

"Oh, don't be such a wimp, Natasha." Ellis dug the girl playfully in the ribs as she walked past her to hang up the jackets. "It's only November, for Heaven's sake, there's a lot colder weather to come. I thought you two would love to have a bit of a forage around the grounds later, since it's your first time here."

Olivia shifted in her seat.

"I, for one, would love to have a look round, Ellis. I'm quite interested in the history of the place – perhaps you can fill us in on the details."

Ellis smiled.

"Well, Mum and Dad would probably be better at that, though I do know some things, I'll try my best."

Natasha raised her eyebrows in Olivia's direction.

"Oh well," she thought, "perhaps it's for the best to find out more about this place. After all, it seems to strike a chord of recognition with Olivia, and maybe Ellis can explain away some of the morning's weird events."

She helped herself to a chocolate biscuit and pulled her chair closer to the open fire.

Chapter 8

"Ellis, I need to use your bathroom," said Olivia.

"Okay, go back out the way we came in, take your first left then first right – you can't miss it," Ellis replied. "Meanwhile, Natasha and I will go down to the library – if you want to find out about the history of Gatefells, that's the place to do it! I'll take Natasha first, then meet you back in the kitchen."

Natasha and Ellis made their way from the

kitchen down some winding stairs that led to a long narrow corridor.

"Wow!" exclaimed Natasha, "are these your ancestors?" She looked at the rows of paintings that lined the corridor.

"Yes, some of them are," Ellis replied, "that's great uncle Nicholas, and that's his wife in the small painting above his own. Don't think they had any children. Okay, not far now."

The passageway was getting darker and darker the further the girls travelled. Suddenly Ellis stopped in front of a door. She tried to turn the handle.

"It's a bit stiff, I'm afraid – not used very much these days." She gave it a hefty push and the door slowly opened.

"Where's the light?" asked Natasha as she peered into the darkness. To her utter surprise and amazement she felt a tremendous push from behind. "Ellis, what are you doing?" she almost screamed. Ellis seemed to smile in the dark passageway and gave one final push.

"Sorry, Natasha," she muttered as she bolted the door from the outside. "No hard feelings, and all that, just need to get you out of the way for now."

Natasha, plunged into blackness, had fallen down the small flight of stairs inside what appeared to be some sort of cellar.

"Ellis," she cried, "let me out of here! If this is some sort of a game . . ."

She tried to stand but had hurt her ankle in the fall. Her hand felt wet when she lifted it to brush the hair from her eyes. She must have cut it on the rough edge of the stairs when she tried to break her fall. And what was that noise?

Something scuttled past her, and she could just about make out its shape in the darkness.

"Oh God," she thought, by now terrified and hurting, "not rats, please God, not rats."

"Where's Natasha?" Olivia asked as Ellis returned to the kitchen.

"Oh, she's looking something up, she said, then she's joining us outside. Here, I brought your jacket."

"But aren't we going to the library with Natasha first?" asked Olivia.

"No, no," Ellis reassured her, "she said she'd only be a minute or two then she'd come and get us. Come on, let's go, and I'll show you around. I thought you were curious. Aren't you?"

Olivia took her jacket from Ellis's extended hand.

"Oh, yes, I'm curious all right, where shall we start?"

The two girls made their way outside and round the back of the house.

"The boating lake – it's still here!" cried Olivia.

"Yes, it's still here," returned Ellis "and why wouldn't it be?"

"Well, I just thought, you know, with Suzanna being drowned here and everything, that maybe the lake would have been drained and filled in," said Olivia.

Ellis did not register surprise at the mention of Suzanna's name

"Oh, no," replied Ellis. "These old boating lakes have their uses, you know," she smiled at Olivia. "Let's go out in the boat, it looks a bit old, I know, but it's quite safe really."

Olivia started to follow her, then stopped in her tracks.

"Ellis – do you know the story of Suzanna, then? It's just that you didn't stop me just now to ask how I knew about it."

Ellis turned to face her.

"Of course I know the story – she was a relative, you know. Come on, you first. I'll hold your hand while you step into the boat."

"I'm not very sure," Olivia started. "I mean, do your parents allow you . . ."

"Just get in, Olivia," Ellis snapped, almost pushing the girl into the boat.

"Ellis, don't push, you'll rock the boat."

Ellis laughed.

"Don't push, Ellis, you'll rock the boat," she mimicked in a childish voice. "Always the helpless little baby, aren't we, hiding behind

Natasha. Well, Miss Goulden, I've had just about enough of your whining little ways."

She began to unfasten the boat from its moorings.

"She's gone mad," thought Olivia. Where on earth was Natasha? "Ellis, please stop this," she pleaded.

"Oh no," returned Ellis, "I can't stop now – I've waited years for this, don't you see, I have to avenge Suzanna. Suzanna Craigson, you remember, the girl who died here. Except she shouldn't have died. Let me turn the clock back for you. Are you sitting comfortably? Then I'll begin."

Ellis cleared her throat, while the boat started to drift ever so slowly away from the lake's edge.

"The Craigson family – mother, father and

Suzanna, that is, settled here over 100 years ago. Suzanna was their only child, deeply loved by both. The girl was introverted, and did not make friends easily because she was self-conscious about a slight disability. But the townsfolk frowned on incomers in those days, especially those who were a little different. One day, however, a woman knocked on the door of Gatefells to enquire whether or not the Craigsons needed a housekeeper. Mrs Craigson was unsure at first, having managed so far to keep house very well on her own, but when she invited the woman in and opened the door wide, she saw the woman, too had a daughter, roughly the same age as Suzanna. There was no mention of a husband, however, and Mrs Craigson took pity on the two and engaged the woman as a housekeeper, probably thinking at the same time that the young girl would be company for her own daughter.

"Ellen, the housekeeper, worked diligently from morning till night. At first, she kept her daughter with her in the kitchen but then, finding that Suzanna would sit outside, staring into the kitchen, as though waiting for the girl, she gradually allowed Jemma to spend some time with her. The two girls soon became inseparable and the Craigson household rang with their laughter. Mr and Mrs Craigson were delighted with the way things were progressing and told Ellen, as she served up their evening meal, how it had been a fortuitous day when she came to Gatesfell. Of course, these things are never what they seem, are they?"

Ellis paused and glared at Olivia.

"Just as you're probably not what you

seem, either, Olivia, little miss goody two-shoes. Are you frightened? Wish your friend was with you?"

She gave a little laugh and pushed the boat out a little further with the paddle.

"Anyway, to get back to the matter in hand. Jemma, underneath it all, really carried a big chip on her shoulders you see. She had started off life as an illegitimate child – and it was a big deal then, you know – she felt inferior to Suzanna, and she hated having to watch her mother slave from morning to night, making sure everything was done for the Craigsons' comfort. So she hit upon a plan. Very straightforward and logical, I suppose, if you need to get rid of someone, and they happen to have a boating lake right on their doorstep, to simply take them out on the lake one day and drown them.

She planned it right down to the finest detail. She believed, you see, that if Suzanna was out of the picture then there was the possibility that Mr and Mrs Craigson would become even more attached to her, and possibly even adopt her! Though she didn't exactly want to be parted from her mother, being adopted would mean she would inherit, and she and her mother would never have to beg, borrow or steal again.

"She knew Mr and Mrs Craigson were fond of her, and she did everything in her power to wheedle her way even more into their affections. There used to be a boat house here at that time, and she put dry clothes there on the fateful day in preparation for what was to come. Mr and Mrs Craigson had gone into town to pick up the new dress they'd had made for Suzanna's birthday party. She would be fourteen years old the next day, and they were planning to take the girls to a fancy new restaurant that had just opened in the next town. Jemma had been given one of Suzanna's castoffs to wear, a perfectly good dress which fitted very well, but to Jemma it was the final straw.

" 'Today's the day, then,' she decided. As Mr and Mrs Craigson made to set off that morning, Jemma made sure they saw her dress in her outdoor clothes. 'I'm just going to visit old Mrs Lawrence,' she told them, 'Mama says she's not been very well recently, so I'll take over some of her herbal cough remedy to ease her chest a bit.' 'What a kindly girl,' they both thought as they waved goodbye.

"Great how you can just fool some people, isn't it?" said Ellis, again coming back to the present.

Olivia was as white as a sheet. Slowly, the boat was drifting steadily to the centre of the lake and Olivia could feel that her feet were wet.

"Oh, didn't I tell you?" laughed Ellis. "There's a hole in the bottom of the boat. Just a small one, mind, but big enough to let the boat fill up in about half an hour. Just long enough, I think, to make sure you're frightened half to death – then you'll know what poor Suzanna went through!"

Olivia looked down and, sure enough, there was a hole just at the far end of the boat and a small puddle had gathered there.

"Ellis, please," she begged. "I don't understand, really I don't. What does all this have to do with me? Why are you making me pay for Suzanna's death? I didn't have anything to do with it. I couldn't have, it was before I was born! Ellis, please help me!"

But Ellis just seemed to stare right through her. Her eyes, which Natasha had thought so beautiful, looked now to be cold as steel. Olivia knew, deep in her heart, that Ellis would never help her, she seemed to have completely lost her sanity.

"Natasha," Olivia whispered almost silently, "I need you. Please help me."

A single tear started to roll down her cheek.

Chapter 9

Natasha had managed to drag herself to an upright position. Her eyes were becoming accustomed to the dark and she could see there was a deep cut in her hand. She took off one of her socks, slipped her sneaker back on, and wrapped the sock around her hand as best she could. The rats she thought she had heard earlier had either scuttled back into the blackness, or were maybe just small mice, which were no doubt more frightened of her than she was of them. She tried to think. She had absolutely no idea why Ellis was doing this. All she did know was that she had to get out of here, and fast. Who knew what sort of trouble Olivia was in? It was beginning to get even colder in here, there were no windows so no sunlight permeated the room. Then, with a start, Natasha saw the reason for the sudden onset of cold. The slight figure of Suzanna Craigson had appeared in the corner of the room. Natasha limped back in fear until her back was already pressed hard against the wall, and she could move back no further.

"Natasha, please don't be afraid," Suzanna started. She held out her hand towards the terrified girl. "Please, believe me! I'm here to help you. You must get out of here, and quickly. She has Olivia."

"Ellis has Olivia – where?" Natasha asked.

She tried to move.

"Oh blast, it," she kicked at the wall in frustration, momentarily forgetting her swollen ankle, and drawing back in pain. "How can I get out of here?" she asked. "There aren't any windows. I can't budge the door. What am I supposed to do?" Somewhere in the back of her rational mind, she was thinking "I'm conversing with a ghost, I've completely lost it now, I'm talking to a ghost."

For now though, rational thoughts took second place to the crisis at hand: getting out of this dark cellar and finding her friend. Suzanna spoke again.

"Natasha, you must listen to me, and listen carefully. I lived in this house once upon a time, and I know the passageways. If you follow my instructions, I can get you out of here, but you must listen very carefully."

Natasha nodded.

"I'm listening," she said.

Suzanna turned towards the wall opposite the door and pointed to a large stone which jutted out more than the others.

"If you press this, it will open out on to a passageway which leads to the kitchens. Just inside the doorway before you proceed down the passage, put your hand in to the left and you will be able to feel a candle and some matches. They have been there since my time in this house, and now you must make use of them."

Suzanna gave more directions as Natasha listened intently, trying vainly to ignore the pain in both her hand and her ankle.

"Quickly, Natasha," Suzanna's figure started to fade. "You must hurry, there's no time to waste."

Chapter Nine

As the girl disappeared completely from view, Natasha moved towards the stone and pressed hard. As Suzanna had said, the wall began to move, slowly, not having been moved for years, and opened out on to a large passageway. She felt to the left of her, picked up the candle and lit it with a match, then began to limp as fast as she could along the passageway.

The boat was almost a quarter full by now. Olivia was desperately trying not to panic as she knew any movement she made in the boat would merely worsen the situation. Ellis, meanwhile, had resumed her story.

"And so Jemma waited, waited until the Craigsons were out of sight, before she went indoors, discarded her outer garments and went to seek out Suzanna. She found her outside, and quickly set her plan into action. She invited her out in the small rowing boat which was always moored to the side of the small lake and, when Suzanna showed some fear, for she could not swim, quickly dispelled her doubts and reassured her that everything would be just fine. Would she, Jemma, let anything happen to her dearest friend? Suzanna smiled. She was being silly, of course. Jemma would take care of her, hadn't she always?

"The two girls went to the lake and helped one another into the small rowing boat, each taking hold of a paddle. Jemma started to sing 'Row, row, row your boat,' and Suzanna joined in, both girls laughing together as they neared the centre of the lake. Then, just at the centre and deepest part, Jemma dared Suzanna to stand up, saying that she also would stand. After some hesitation the trusting young girl did as she was bid, but when Jemma stood it was to grasp the girl roughly and push her out of the boat and into the dark murky waters. Suzanna bravely tried to fight her off, her eyes wild with both fear and disbelief, but remember she was a slight girl, weakened by illness and her disability, and her strength could not compare with that of Jemma. One final push and she was in the water. Jemma didn't wait to see whether or not her friend's head would bob back up, instead rowing to the other side of the lake as quickly as she could in order to retrieve her dry clothes from the boat house where she had placed them that morning.

Suzanna did surface, at least twice, struggling to breathe, trying to call out for her beloved parents, fighting for her life. The last sight she saw, just before her lungs filled completely with water, was that of her friend clambering from the boat at the lake's edge, and the last emotion she felt was that of betrayal."

"Betrayal, Olivia. Is that what you're feeling now that I've betrayed your friendship? I hope you're feeling that, Olivia, I hope you're feeling terrible, terrible, fear, because you know that I will never help you."

Olivia, crying silently, looked at the girl on the other side of the lake, and said nothing.

Ellis had started to speak again.

"Of course it didn't work," she continued. "The Craigsons were so distraught at the loss of their poor daughter that they couldn't even bear to look at Jemma, she reminded them of Suzanna so much. The final straw came one day, a few weeks later, when Jemma dressed in Suzanna's new dress, the one she was to wear to her fourteenth birthday party, thinking maybe Mr and Mrs Craigson would like to see her wear it, that their hearts would soften would soften maybe when they saw her dressed and looking so beautiful in it. Of course the silly creature only distressed them even more. Mrs Craigson was almost hysterical with grief and Mr Craigson shut himself away in his study. Downstairs, in the kitchens, Ellen chastised her daughter for being so vain and unthinking. She was aware of her daughter's faults, and that the girl could be vain, greedy and spiteful. Although she tried to banish the thought from her mind, she wondered sometimes if Jemma had been in any way involved with the boating accident. The Craigsons' grief was such that she felt like a complete outsider, and that her daughter's presence was a constant reminder to them of Suzanna. She left some weeks later and settled in a town a few hundred miles away. Ellen Goulden – name mean anything to you, Olivia?"

Olivia started. "Goulden – it's a common enough name, Ellis, why should it mean anything to me?"

"Because she was your relation, that's why, Olivia. She wormed her way into poor Suzanna's affections and then disposed of her when she felt like it. Do you know what my mother's maiden name was, Olivia? Craigson. Yes, that's right, Craigson. Suzanna was, or would have been, her great, great grandmother, but your greedy relation decided to snuff out her life, do away with her in order to try and inherit her money. Sad, isn't it, that it didn't work, Olivia. Us Craigsons, though, are made of sterner stuff. Suzanna's father had sisters and brothers scattered throughout the county and one of the younger brothers and his wife came her to Gatesfell to settle, and make sure that the family line was continued. So here I am. And there you are."

Ellis glanced in Olivia's direction. "Not long now," she thought. The boat was just about to topple.

"Olivia, hold on, I'm coming."

Olivia turned in the direction of the voice. Marcie was running towards her with an older man – her father – Olivia later realised. Ellis looked up, dismayed, only to see that Natasha, too, had escaped and was limping towards the lake. Marcie's father though was the one who dived into the lake and swam out towards the almost capsized boat. He was the one who pulled Olivia from the boat and half-dragged, half-swam with her back towards the bank. And he was the one who held her gently in his arms while she cried.

Chapter 10

The girls found out the next day that Ellis had rung Marcie at nine o'clock to tell her that the lunch at Gatefells had been cancelled and not to bother coming.

Marcie, however, returned from a shopping trip with her mother and telephoned Natasha to meet up with her that afternoon only to be told by Mrs Morris that Natasha and Olivia were at Gatefells! Never having trusted the girl much, anyway, Marcie suspected something was afoot and asked her father to take her to Ellis's house.

Natasha and Olivia placed small bunches of flowers on the grave and sat quietly for a few moments before getting up to leave the cemetery.

"Goodbye Suzanna," whispered Olivia, "and thanks for everything."

Natasha linked arms with her best and dearest friend.

"What a shame nobody could have saved her in time – guess it just wasn't meant to be," she sighed. "At least we've still got you," she smiled and hugged her friend.

Natasha still limped slightly from her fall in the cellar. The doctor said it was just a very bad sprain and she should rest as much as possible.

"No more hockey for a few weeks," she joked with Olivia.

"What do you think will happen to Ellis, then?" asked Olivia.

"Who knows," Natasha replied. "Probably a remand home or something. No more than she deserves."

Olivia turned to close the gate to the cemetery and noticed one of the graves was strewn with fresh flowers. She raised her eyes to look at the tombstone. There were only two words inscribed there – Jemma Goulden.

We hope you have enjoyed this story from the pen of Edgar J. Hyde. Here are some other titles in the Creepers series for you to collect:

Rag & Bone Man
Payback Time
Cold Kisser
Noisy Neighbours
The Sold Souls

This series was conceived by Edgar J. Hyde and much of the text was provided by his minions, under slavish conditions and pain of death! Thankfully, none of these minions defied their master and so we can say 'thank you' to them for toughing it out and making this series possible.

Edgar J. Hyde, however, has yet more plans for these dungeon-bound slaves. 'No rest for the wicked' is his motto!

Creepers

NOISY NEIGHBOURS

A seemingly puritanically-minded family move to a big run-down area in a big city.

They refuse to talk to their new neighbours as they regard them as inferior. But something doesn't quite fit with this family. At night all the wild, partying noises come from their house and through the blinds, the neighbours see shadows of what looks like inhuman forms.

Killjoys during the day – fun lovers at night, this Jekyll and Hyde type family come under the scrutiny of three teenage would-be ghost busters!

Creepers

PAYBACK TIME

A family's life is made a misery by loansharks who then discover that they have bitten off more than they can chew. The family pay back the moneylenders in carefully worked out instalments and with interest!

Mysteriously, the family is helped by the sympathetic previous tenant of their home, who was forced out by the same loansharks in the past

This tenant disappeared under unexplained circumstances and now seems to appear only at the moments of most need!

Creepers

RAG & BONE MAN

In a small village the night after every funeral, an apparition of a rag and bone man, with his horse and cart, reputedly makes his way down the high street.

The trouble is, the person reporting the sight is normally the next person in a coffin!

Thus a conspiracy of silence prevails among the locals and the legend remains unconfirmed. Until, after the death of an elderly relative, Bryan Codie and Dave decide to investigate . . .

Creepers

THE SOLD SOULS

A collection of overambitious high school children who, through dabbling in the occult, sell their souls to a harmless, minor demon who poses as the Devil! They would do anything for success, not knowing that by selling their souls to an impostor, they have incurred the wrath of the real thing!

Now the real Devil gets his own back by posing convincingly as people they know. They are then led, in blissful ignorance to untimely ends.

Will any of them survive?

Creepers

COLD KISSER

All the boys at school want to kiss the new girl until one boy does. Word then gets around about her cold kiss which seemed to freeze him in time, like a temporary kiss of death.

Another boy, Tommy therefore does all he can to resist kissing the new girl, Sally Anne.

Strangely, he feels as if he's known her before. But when and where?

easyJet

The story of Britain's biggest low-cost airline

Lois Jones

First published 2005 by
Aurum Press Limited
25 Bedford Avenue
London WC1B 3AT
www.aurumpress.co.uk

A catalogue record for this book is available from the British Library.

ISBN 1 84513 093 6

10 9 8 7 6 5 4 3 2 1
2009 2008 2007 2006 2005

Text design by Roger Hammond

Typeset by SX Composing DTP,
Rayleigh, Essex

Printed and bound in Great Britain by
Creative Print & Design (Wales) Ltd, Ebbw Vale

This book is dedicated to
my dear father – thank you
for showing me the way
on the journey through life.

Contents

Acknowledgements

THIS IS AN unauthorised account of easyJet and how the bright orange airline has transformed peoples' lives by making flying affordable for everyone. The story is the result of numerous interviews with key players in the airline industry, people associated with the airline and many passengers.

I would like to thank many for their help in creating this book. Individuals who deserve a particular note of thanks include: David Bryon, managing director of bmibaby; Chris Buckley, senior vice-president Europe at Airbus; Professor Rigas Doganis, industry expert; Tim Jeans, managing director of Monarch Scheduled; Philipa Kane, former easyJet employee; Andrew Lobbenberg, airline analyst at ABN Amro and of course my editor Graham Coster. The biggest thanks of all goes to Barnaby, my wonderful, loving husband, and to my family.

1. How it all started

easyJet

VISITORS TO LUTON Airport in the autumn of 1995 regularly gawked at two of the Boeing 737s parked outside on the tarmac. Someone had painted human-sized, bright orange digits along the fuselages of the aircraft. A closer look revealed that the digits made up a telephone number. People who dialled it found they could fly between Luton and Glasgow for £29 each way with an airline called easyJet.

EasyJet first took to the skies on 10 November 1995, just five months after its conception, flying to Glasgow with a plane normally used by British Airways. One passenger on flight EZJ 11, on what he described as a 'wet, miserable, lousy day in Luton', was its founder, Stelios Haji-Ioannou; he may not have known it at the time, but his venture would change not only the world of aviation but the culture we live in.

Stelios was a bear-like figure, tall and broad with dark curly hair and a marked Greek accent. He wore a loose, open-necked shirt, slacks and a Swatch watch, even though (as he later admitted) he owned a Patek Philippe. He came from a background of dazzling wealth, with a shipping tycoon father who enjoyed cruising the Mediterranean on a floating gin palace capable of carrying some 180 people. Stelios himself was worth more than £100 million, with homes in London, Athens and Monaco, but he was less interested in showing off his fortune; embarrassed by his vast wealth, he made a conscious effort not to stand out. 'Nobody likes fat cats,' he once commented. 'People are always suspicious of people in grey pinstriped suits with a Rolls-Royce and a chauffeur.'

Stelios's attitudes were key to his imaginative approach to air travel, an approach that was to make him popular with all ranks of society. He realised from the start that it was hard to make short-haul air travel make glamorous, and he had no intention of trying. Instead, the self-proclaimed entrepreneurial Robin Hood wanted to declare the end of 'rip-off Britain' and offer consumers an airline with low-fare flights. The philosophy was simple: cut out the travel agent, the in-flight meals – even the peanuts – and pass on the massive savings to the customer. Instead of wearing a uniform, flight attendants were dressed casually in black jeans and orange polo shirts. 'No frills, no extras,' said Stelios. 'You pay for the flight and nothing less. That's what people want. The so-called freebies that other airline offer aren't freebies at all. They're a rip-off. I look at it like this. If someone came up to me with a plastic tray of airline food and said, "Will you give me a tenner for this shit?" I would say "no". There's no such thing as a free lunch so we don't pretend to provide one.'

It was a strategy that was bound to make Stelios popular with the travelling public. Unsurprisingly, the airline establishment was less enthusiastic, but Stelios was not slow to take up the cudgels. When Swissair opposed easyJet's plans to fly to Barcelona from Geneva, insisting that the airline obey an obscure rule that its cheap flights must come with accommodation attached, Stelios responded by pitching a tent on a rocky hillside north of Barcelona and inviting easyJet passengers to stay there. Stelios was a fierce critic of his rivals, particularly British Airways. When BA launched its own no-frills airline, Go, he tried to hijack the event by booking a seat and turning up in a boilersuit in his company's trademark orange. EasyJet eventually bought Go.

Shrewd business sense accompanied the PR stunts. The essential elements of the easyJet business model have always been fast turnarounds, no free lunch and enticingly low fares that rise as flights fill up. Nine out of ten easyJet seats are now sold via the Internet, a far higher proportion than for any traditional airline. The company squeezes the maximum possible revenue from each flight; even its airsickness bags convert into envelopes to send away camera films for processing. And it differs from the average low-cost airline operators, which fly on routes between secondary airports, by operating competitive routes between major cities.

EasyJet's cost control is legendary, as I learnt during my first interview with Stelios in 1996. At the time, I was a young reporter working for *Airline Business* magazine. I had been swept away by the glamour of the airline industry, the champagne receptions and the luxurious press trips to exciting destinations. EasyJet's larger-than-life chairman soon brought me down to earth. He didn't offer me a sandwich, never mind a lavish lunch when I interviewed him at easyLand, a tin shed at Luton Airport 30 miles north of London which serves as easyJet's headquarters. Instead, I was handed a plastic cup of instant coffee from an automatic machine. The coffee tasted awful and didn't even come with a plastic swivel stick to stir it with.

I hated the coffee but liked Stelios's candour. The tycoon was open about almost everything, even the failure of his diet. The only exception was his love life, which remained off-limits. By the end of the interview, Stelios had given me an excellent set of quotes for my story and fired me up with his vision of how no-frills flying would change the skies over Europe. He was right. The airline led the low-cost revolution in the UK, and Britain, in turn, has spearheaded the introduction of no-frills flights throughout Europe.

Since that first interview, I've watched easyJet grow to become the largest no-frills airline based in Britain, operating 92 aircraft on 89 routes from 36 European airports and beginning to eclipse the traditional carriers who once estimated its survival in days or weeks. 'It's not rocket science,' Stelios is fond of saying. EasyJet flies the same expensive tubes of metal as its competitors, but manages to do it more cheaply, luring passengers away from the established airlines and making travel affordable for everyone, even those who had never flown before.

Thanks to easyJet, the British are flocking to buy second homes in Spain, Italy and France. Fashionistas now refuse to pay retail for Gucci in London when they can fly to Milan for a weekend, buy the real deal at the factory outlet and take in a night of opera for roughly the same price. Prague, Budapest and Amsterdam have replaced Blackpool or Brighton as the most popular destinations for a stag party or hen weekend. For the many young Europeans working abroad, a weekly commute between London and Rome or Barcelona has become possible for the first time. It may not be rocket science but it's still clever stuff. Stelios claims to be redistributing the population of modern-day Europe. 'I meet a lot of people on our flights that don't have to make the stark choice between the sun in the south and business in the north,' he says. 'In the time of my father, this would have been impossible.'

Of course, no boom is all good. Europeans are feeling the effects of commodified travel on the continent's fragile infrastructure. In the clubbing mecca of Ibiza, business people love the budget airlines. Yet years of mass tourism are clearly taking their toll. Much of the tap water tastes salty and has a funny odour: the result of seawater infiltrating the overused wells. Splendid eastern Europe cities such as Prague and Tallinn are having a hard time adjusting to the hordes of English lads who parade through their streets dressed up in women's clothes, screaming and, most of all, getting drunk.

Aimée, the manager of Café Anglais on Tallinn's town hall square, is still struggling to comprehend the behaviour of some of the easyJet passengers who are shipped in each weekend. 'Their behaviour is incredible,' she complains. 'I don't know if they behave like that at home. Maybe they see us as some sort of second-hand, cheap country and think we don't deserve any better because they have money. It seems as if they think they can do whatever they want. They pee on the wall near us or are sick outside and then I have to clean it up. It happens twice a month or even more. For us, it's quite hard to understand.'

But overall the advantages of cheap flights outweigh the disadvantages. Since that first flight in 1995, easyJet, with its lurid orange brand, has become a household name. Nowadays the British flying public has lowered its expectations of on-board service. Sometimes people get on the wrong plane, are stranded for hours at airports or lose their luggage. As for the others, they don't care, as long as they get a cheap deal.

Stelios was born in Athens on Valentine's Day in 1967, the younger son of a wealthy Greek-Cypriot couple, Loucas and Nedi. His father, the eldest of thirteen, left his home village in Cyprus in 1950 with nothing. He made his fortune buying old tankers cheaply when no one wanted them, twice cashing out when there was a shortage of tanker capacity. He called his business Troodos, after the mountains in Cyprus where Stelios's grandfather scraped a living as a poor hill farmer. Talented and ambitious, Loucas made himself the 'Tanker King', the billionaire owner of one of the world's biggest tanker operations.

Shipping, shipping and more shipping was Loucas's philosophy. 'My father was a great advocate of focus,' Stelios has said. 'He decided what he wanted to do in life and stuck with it. He was very disciplined in not investing in anything else. My brother reminds me increasingly of my father. He thinks anything other than shipping is a rubbish business.'

Loucas had a profound influence on his son, and despite their occasional disputes there is no doubt that Stelios recognises his debt to his father. At home in Athens the talk was always business. It was in Stelios's genes. He describes his mother, Nedi, as the 'calming influence in my life' and thanks her for keeping his feet on the ground. She certainly keeps hers there, being so frightened of planes she has not flown for years. At the age of seven, Stelios was also scared of aeroplanes. Fortunately, his phobia didn't last very long.

Stelios enjoyed a privileged childhood: 'It was probably what you would call upper middle class.' As a child, he dreamed of playing football for AEK Athens, and his room, like that of many ten-year-old boys, was full of football posters. He attended private school and learnt English from an early age, later taking private tuition to complete two English A-levels in Mathematics and Economics. He was a 'good student, but not excellent', but his business sense was apparent at an early age. Even in the sixth form Stelios was managing other people's money, when he ran the students' union.

In 1984, aged seventeen, Stelios moved to London for his higher education. He was familiar with the country already: 'I was always coming to England. My father is an Anglophile.' His parents never kept him short of money – by eighteen he owned his own Porsche – but he developed a work ethic very early on: 'I didn't sit on my backside doing nothing. I decided I wanted to make a difference.' He studied at the London School of Economics, graduating in 1987 with a BSc in Economics. The next year, 1988, he also graduated from the City University Business School in London with an MSc in Shipping Trade and Finance.

For years, Stelios's ambition was to take over the family business. He worked for his father in his student holidays, and after graduating in 1988 joined his older brother at Troodos Shipping. Two years later, Loucas made himself chairman and his younger son the chief executive. But it was only on paper. 'Every morning,' said Stelios, 'my father used to wake up, pick up the phone and shout a bit at people, go to lunch and then shout a bit more.' When Stelios tried to move Troodos from old-fashioned typewriters to computers, Loucas interfered with his negotiations with outside suppliers. 'As the son of a father who is active in business, you're never really in charge.'

Stelios was growing more aware of the obstacles to his ambition. His father wasn't ready to retire. His older brother was also involved in the business and he was flanked by what he has described as 'lieutenants of his father', who weren't ready to let a twenty-three-year-old boss them around. Besides, Stelios didn't want to hang around in the shadow of his father and act the Greek playboy. 'Because I had a successful father, I had to prove to myself and the world that I wasn't just the son of a rich father. I was driven by the need to prove myself.'

A tragic event fed Stelios's growing restlessness and marked a turning point in his career. On 11 April 1991, the *Haven*, a Troodos tanker anchored outside Genoa, exploded, the fiery ball killing five crew members and swamping the Italian coast with 35,000 tons of crude oil. Stelios was in the office in Athens when the disaster struck. 'I slept there that night and tried to look after the people and everything else. But once the wreck itself was over, the ship was on the bottom of the sea, pollution was cleared up to the best of our ability, the whole thing became a legal saga instead of a real saga. I was facing criminal charges: a foreigner, a ship owner, and a villain in a foreign country.'

An Italian prosecutor, eagerly backed by the *Haven*'s first officer, went after Stelios and his father on criminal charges that included manslaughter, extortion and attempting to bribe a witness. If the Haji-Ioannous were found negligent they would be personally liable for the $1 billion claims; if human error by the crew was the cause of the accident, the family's liability was limited to $200 million, all paid for by insurance. As it turned out, the *Haven* had been completely refurbished and certificated just prior to the accident, and Stelios and his father were twice cleared of all charges and then finally exonerated.

The traumatic experience shaped the way that Stelios looked at life. He decided that his long-term aspiration was 'to build businesses that people like rather than businesses that people dislike'. He told his father that he was too ambitious to spend his life working for him and persuaded him to help him start his own business. Before he left Troodos, Stelios negotiated a $35 million payout from his father, with the hope that the funds would grant him his longed-for independence: 'If I had to go back and ask for funds every time, he would have been in charge.' Loucas imposed one condition, which Stelios accepted: if he became financially successful, his brother and sister would benefit too. 'My father was hedging his bets,' Stelios has said. 'He had two sons. He wanted to see who would do better.'

In 1992, at the age of twenty-five, Stelios set up Athens-based Stelmar Shipping. 'I had enough of being accused of running an old fleet,' he said later. 'I wanted to run a company with modern ships that focused on operating, not the buying and selling of assets.'

Stelios soon set about proving himself to his father. He built up the shipping line into a multi-million pound business that was comfortably profitable and listed on the New York stock exchange in 2001 at $12 a share. But he still wasn't satisfied. Within three years, he realised that he wasn't the person to run Stelmar. But at least he now knew what he wanted: to be an entrepreneur and start, not run, businesses. 'I was desperately trying to get rid of the "daddy's boy" image. I had to do something away from home, in an industry that my father knew nothing about, where my surname meant nothing to anybody.'

It was on a Virgin Atlantic flight between Athens and London in the early 1990s that Stelios had the idea that launched his empire. He happened to sit next to a friend, who offered him an opportunity to invest in a Virgin franchise. The airline, South East European Airlines, had started flying between London and Athens with just one plane. Stelios researched the deal; in the end he declined the Virgin opportunity, but in the process, he caught the aviation bug. He decided to enter the airline business on his own terms instead. 'Europe was being deregulated and I thought, if anyone is going to do this, it's me,' he recalled. Two years after he founded Stelmar, Stelios once more delegated himself out of a job and directed his attentions towards the airline business.

His first plan, perhaps because it was all he had ever known personally, was to set up something along the lines of Virgin's Upper Class service. Then a trip to the US impressed him with the low-cost business run by Southwest Airlines. 'I saw a winning formula. An internal flights company called Southwest Airlines was carrying 50 per cent more than British Airways with a cheap and cheerful service. I don't mind admitting I copied the idea. But I took it one step further. Southwest give away peanuts – we don't! But you can buy them on board for 50p if you want them.'

Stelios may have spent his privileged youth behind the wheel of a light-blue Porsche and at the helm of a 33-metre yacht by the name of *Gee Whizz*, but he understood the value of a pound. 'The world's biggest companies, such as Wal-Mart and McDonalds, got that way because they sell low-cost products.' His subconscious might have made the additional calculation that the low fares would make him popular. 'The cheaper you can make something, the more people there are who can afford it,' he has said. 'People like you if you give them what they like. And what they like is a low price. As soon as you get into the business of making things cheaper, then you are on the side of the little guy, you become their friend. I enjoy that. I could have chosen many careers. I could have gone into, I dunno, arms dealing or something. But I decided consciously to do something that was likeable.'

As a start-up carrier facing Europe's most highly regarded airline, British Airways, easyJet knew it had to focus on its competitor's soft spot: price. 'I spotted a gap in the market. For many years, BA and the other big airlines conditioned people into believing that air travel had to be expensive. If you give people a good fare they will jump on an aeroplane like they would jump on a bus. You just have to convince them that, if the price is right, they should take the benefit and see other places.'

Whether you're interested in ships, airlines or even stationary objects, having a billionaire shipping magnate as a father always helps when it comes to starting a business, as Stelios is the first to admit. He approached his father again for cash, while starting negotiations with a British Airways franchisee, GB Airways, about leasing aircraft. 'Banks would have laughed at me for trying to set up a low-cost airline with no backing.' He also arranged to operate his new venture under the Air Operating Certificates of GB Airways and the Luton-based Air Foyle, run by the Foyle family of bookshop fame, which flew BAe 146 planes on behalf of passenger airlines before later moving into air cargo and chartering giant Antonov 124s.

The crucial conversation with his father took place over dinner in the family summer house south of Athens, during the summer of 1995. He told his father he wanted the capital to set up a cheap, no-frills airline, designed to attract customers from coaches and trains as well as from other airlines.

'If I set up a marketing organisation and I don't buy the aircraft yet, I think I can make it take off with £5 million,' Stelios told his father. 'That's all I'm asking for at the moment. If it doesn't work, I'll pull the plug.' Stelios's father opened his chequebook, signed a cheque for £5 million and gave his son his blessing.

Loucas had one stipulation: he instructed Stelios not to base the airline in Athens, since he considered the Greek market too small and seasonal. So Stelios started looking around for a suitable base. London was the obvious choice. As a Greek Cypriot, he was born with a British passport, he spoke English and, besides, London served the biggest aviation market in Europe. 'It wouldn't have worked in any other country, with their red tape and state-owned airlines.'

Stelios settled on London Luton Airport. It was the cheapest of the four London airports, the others being Heathrow, Gatwick and Stansted. In June 1995, Stelios turned his back on his luxury yacht and a languid Greek summer and set up shop next to the toilets in a small, prefabricated building in Luton. He believed that offices should be spartan and perks should be banned. The office housed one PC, two desks, three phones and a big round wastepaper bin, with a note from Stelios saying, 'Scan documents, then throw them in the bin. This is a paperless office.' Stelios never relaxed the paperless rule. Finance director Nick Manoudakis, his first colleague and another son of a rich Greek magnate, resorted to keeping a hidden stash of documents in the ladies' toilets, the only place in the airline where they were safe from the boss's eyes.

Stelios worked 100-hour weeks, but his style at work was very relaxed. Colleagues called him by his first name, not least because, as he joked himself, 'the surname is unpronounceable anyway'. His casual approach extended to office attire: 'If anyone turns up for work in a tie, we suspect them of having been for an interview for another job.'

There was one key problem: the airline still didn't have a name. Stelios hired an expensive brand consultancy and offered them £100,000 to come up with one. A month later, the consultants turned up at easyLand with magazine clippings attached to pieces of cardboard. Unimpressed by their efforts, Stelios promptly fired them. In the end, he came up with the airline's name himself. He remembers going to Harry's Bar in Mayfair, London, and scribbling 'CheapJet', 'No-Frillsjet', and other such variations on a napkin. The word 'easy' kept on coming into his head, so he decided to christen the airline easyJet. For the company logo he went to a small local design consultancy, White Knight, which gave the airline its famous shade of orange, known as Pantone 021C, used by no other airline at the time or since. The design consultancy then created a simple set of graphics for the airline's first advertising campaign. EasyJet has always resisted creatives who have wanted to change the original colour and simple design.

The next step was to decide on destinations. The new airline's executives chose Glasgow and Edinburgh as its first routes. The logic was simple: southern Scotland was the biggest domestic market from London for which air was a sensible alternative to road or rail.

The airline opened a telephone reservations centre and took its first booking on 23 October 1995. The phones at the easyJet telephone reservation centre started ringing and never stopped. They were in business.

2. Taking off

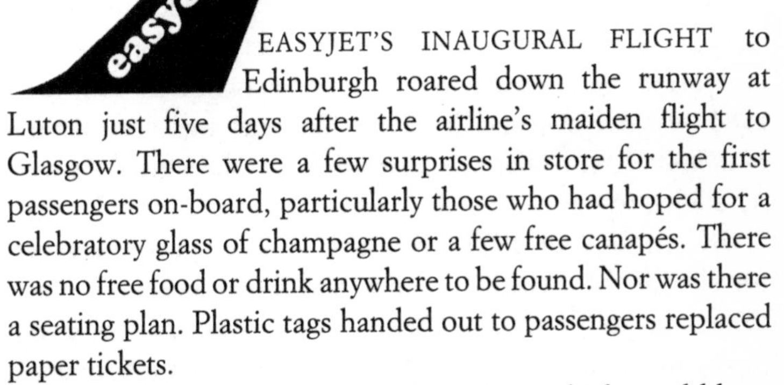

EASYJET'S INAUGURAL FLIGHT to Edinburgh roared down the runway at Luton just five days after the airline's maiden flight to Glasgow. There were a few surprises in store for the first passengers on-board, particularly those who had hoped for a celebratory glass of champagne or a few free canapés. There was no free food or drink anywhere to be found. Nor was there a seating plan. Plastic tags handed out to passengers replaced paper tickets.

The whole concept was novel. Ryanair, which would later become easyJet's greatest rival in the no-frills stakes, was still a commuter airline in Ireland; the idea that it would one day sell tickets for as little as £5 and become Europe's most profitable airline would have seemed ludicrous. The other low-cost airlines that fill our skies today hadn't even made it to the drawing board. Stelios was about to change the face of aviation. Of course, it wasn't all down to the larger-than-life

Greek entrepreneur. As well as brains, cheek, charisma and a cheque from Dad, Stelios owes a lot to Sir Freddie Laker, Southwest Airlines and deregulation of the skies.

Laker was probably the first entrepreneur to offer low-cost flights. In 1966, he formed Laker Airways Limited, a charter airline which soon became Britain's first all-jet air carrier. He invented the concept of 'time charters', whereby tour operators bought flight hours, a major factor in the explosive growth of the UK package tour business.

Laker then fought a six-year legal battle in both the UK and the US for the right to fly people cheaply across the Atlantic. At the time, carriers were national emblems and fiercely protected by governments. Laker eventually won his battle to get a licence for a new airline and set up a service he called Skytrain, which allowed passengers to fly between the UK and the US without reservations and at revolutionary cheap fares as low as £32.

On 26 September 1977 the first Skytrain flight left London Gatwick for New York. The service was expanded in 1978 to include a London to Los Angeles service. Miami and Tampa in Florida were added to the route network in 1980 and 1981 respectively, and by 1982 Skytrain was also serving Manchester and Glasgow Prestwick; in all, a total of nine scheduled routes.

By the end of 1981, over two million passengers had travelled on Sir Freddie's planes, and the airline was looking to expand its route network to the Far East, Australia and Japan for what would become Sir Freddie's next venture, Globetrain, a daily, round-the-world air service carrying people from all nations at fares that were substantially lower than anything that had been offered before.

But those plans never materialised. In February 1982, Laker Airways was forced into receivership and subsequently liquidation. Laker filed a $1.5 billion anti-trust action in the US District Court of Washington, claiming that twelve major international and US airlines and others had conspired to put

Skytrain out of business by offering equally low fares, which they could subsidise from more lucrative routes. The action was eventually settled out of court, but it was the end for Laker's innovatory company.

Meanwhile, however, another no-frills airline was already in mid-flight. Southwest started operating in the US in 1971. Stelios and Ryanair boss Michael O'Leary have both dubbed Herb Kelleher, Southwest's founder, their role model. Kelleher eliminated anything superfluous to a safe, cheap and reliable flight: he kept his aircraft in the air for as many hours as possible, ditched pre-assigned seating and served no meals. The airline offered low fares and what is more, it made money in the process, never recording an annual loss in its existing history.

Southwest's concept transformed the US airline industry. 'When Southwest was founded in 1971, only one in four Americans had actually flown,' said Linda Rutherford, head of public relations at Southwest Airlines. 'Air travel was considered a luxury experience, rather than a commodity. Nowadays four out of five Americans have flown. Southwest has democratised the skies in the US. We've made it affordable for people to consider air travel as a choice.'

The US carrier employed a single type of aircraft, the Boeing 737, which meant that maintenance and inventory costs were lower. It kept costs low by high utilisation of aircraft and operating economy class only, making boarding easier and turnarounds quicker. 'As Herb Kelleher says, you're only making money when in the sky,' said Rutherford.

As well as offering low fares, Southwest was favoured by the US flying public for its good service and friendly cabin crew, who were happy to laugh and make jokes with passengers; as Rutherford commented, 'Just because the fares are low, it doesn't mean that customer service shouldn't be high.'

Southwest Airlines was the first carrier to seize upon US airline deregulation in 1978 when it started flying between states, showing that low costs and low fares could stimulate profitable growth in new and existing markets. And its European counterparts were keen to follow its example. Deregulation of the airline industry in Europe became fully effective in April 1997 following a process of reforms which began in 1987. Unrestricted cross-border flying had been permitted since 1993. The deregulation was meant to fell entry barriers and end restrictive practices, which allowed airlines to keep flying despite inefficiency and massive losses. Liberalisation brought about numerous advantages to European travellers, in terms of both higher quality offered by airlines and drastic price reductions.

The free market also permitted any EU airline to operate domestic flights in any other EU country plus Norway and Iceland. Although competition on most major routes was limited by the lack of airport capacity, there were many opportunities for innovative low cost carriers to step in. 'We owe it all to deregulation,' said Tim Jeans, managing director of Monarch Scheduled and previously sales and marketing director at Ryanair. 'There would be no low-cost airlines were it not for deregulation. It would have meant perpetuating flag carriers if deregulation hadn't come about. It is difficult to understate its importance.'

Back in 1995, before deregulation had changed the skies, Stelios was just as unfamiliar with the idea of no-frills flights to Scotland as everyone else. Accustomed to holidaying on Greek islands and flying business class, he had never even been to Glasgow until two weeks before easyJet's first flight there took off. 'My biggest break was shedding my own prejudices and preferences about what an airline should be,' he later commented.

In its first months easyJet was a virtual airline. The carrier contracted in everything, including two leased Boeing 737-200 aircraft, the pilots and check-in staff. It was the fastest way for the airline to get started. Everyone who booked a flight with the airline did so by phone. They could hardly miss the

'0582 445 566' booking number, painted in 20-foot orange letters on the side of the planes. The booking staff prided themselves on picking up the phone after only one ring.

Refusing to sell tickets through travel agents or computer reservation systems allowed easyJet to save 25 per cent on the cost of each ticket. 'I was only capable of cutting out the travel agents because I knew nothing about the travel business,' Stelios has said. 'I had no allegiances, I had no friends in that industry, I just said, "This doesn't make sense, we will not do it."'

The first flights were accompanied by a brash advertising slogan stating that easyJet was as 'affordable as a pair of jeans'. And not even Levi's. Stelios used to walk around carrying a pair of jeans and tell people that they cost £29 at Tesco, exactly the same as a one-way flight with easyJet – and one-tenth of the full fare that British Airways charged from London Heathrow to Scotland.

But it took time for the message to get across to the paying public. Two months after the first easyJet flight, the airline commissioned a survey to see how many people had heard of the company. Only three out of a hundred people surveyed had. Stelios nearly cried. Some of the early flights flew to their destinations with just flight attendants and pilots and without any paying passengers, or with a scant four or five scattered across the cabin. The maximum number of passengers on-board each aircraft was twenty-six out of a possible seventy or so for the first few months.

So Stelios opened his chequebook and spent a million pounds on marketing within three months. The world started to turn orange as easyJet placed full-page ads in the news-papers and paid for wall-to-wall radio advertising as well as a television advertising campaign thrown together in a matter of days.

Lack of awareness wasn't the only problem. Used to high prices, people couldn't understand how they could fly any-where for just £29, and worried that easyJet was compromising on safety. It took time for them to realise that despite its low fares easyJet was as safe as any of its competitors.

But the advertising, and the lack of any accidents, began to take effect. Stelios was perceived by the airline's first passengers as a curious type of folk hero offering value to the masses. 'I don't think people could believe the prices we were charging,' Stelios has said. 'But once they got on to the planes and saw for themselves that they were clean and had the requisite number of wings, they were pleasantly surprised.'

EasyJet's rivals also started to take notice. British Airways had at first treated the new airline with scorn and derision, but before long the flag carrier realised it had a threat on its hands. BA and British Midland, the UK's other large airline, both chose to offer return flights between London and Scotland for £58 – curiously enough, exactly the same price as easyJet's return fare.

Stelios was initially flattered by the established carriers' reactions. 'You can jump up and down as much as you like, but it's only when your opponents recognise you and fight back that you have become a brand. It's a sign you've arrived.' But BA's and British Midland's fare cuts soon placed easyJet under pressure. The company's executives worked long hours as they battled to make easyJet viable. Stelios did everything from greeting customers to dashing out to buy rubbish bins at the local cash-and-carry, and spent flights going up and down the aisle talking to his passengers. This commendable public relations exercise had its drawbacks. As one stewardess said, 'The passengers loved meeting him, but it did mean he was always getting in our way.'

Philipa Kane, née Ripley, was one of easyJet's first twelve flight attendants, whom the airline employed after contracting in crew for the initial weeks of operations. Philipa witnessed Stelios's eagerness to get involved in every aspect of the airline's day-to-day running alongside its fifty-five employees. 'It was like one big family and everyone mucked in and helped each other, including Stelios,' she recalled. 'He would check out everything from the catering to the advertising. He used to man the phones taking bookings in the call-centre if someone was taken ill, or even if they were understaffed. He couldn't fly the plane or act as a flight steward because of safety standards. He would do absolutely everything else though! I've even seen him hoovering the cabin and cleaning the planes in between flights.'

Philipa had applied to the airline after seeing an advert in the local newspaper. The annual starting salary of about £9,000 was a lot lower than those offered by other airlines, which would pay as much as £12,000, but the airline was based near her then home in Stevenage and only operated a couple of aircraft, meaning that flight attendants had to work just four hours a day, two or three times a week, with no stopovers. She would be back at the airport by 9.30 a.m. after the morning flight.

EasyJet was looking for experienced cabin crew who could help boost the airline's reputation. Philipa had gained lots of experience from working for Gulf Air, Saudi Air and Qatar Airways. She knew what to expect from the job. Or so she thought.

British Airways trained the easyJet flight crew, to the same level as their own staff. The surprises started when Philipa discovered that she wouldn't be dressed in high heels, tights and skirts, as she had at previous airlines. Rather than a well-cut designer uniform, Philipa's on-board attire comprised black jeans, an orange polo shirt, an orange bomber jacket and a baseball cap. What's more, she was told she had to shop for her own jeans at Tesco and pay for them herself. She was also asked to buy a pair of plain black boots to wear for work. EasyJet bought a pile of orange polo shirts of various sizes from Benetton and supplied the baseball cap and coat for Philipa and the rest of the crew. Philipa wasn't allowed to keep the duffel coat when she left the airline eight months later to return to the Middle East, although it still evokes fond memories: 'The lettering on the back of the duffel coat said "easy" in big letters, followed by "jet" in small letters and then "cabin crew" in big letters. From a distance it looked like "easy cabin crew" was written on the back, which caused much amusement.'

The easyJet girls and their informal wardrobe were the source of much entertainment at Luton Airport. 'We would turn up at the airport, dressed in our jeans and orange polo shirts. Then the crew for Britannia, a charter airline based at Luton, would turn up dolled up in their skirts and make-up. We were the absolute laughing stock at the airport. EasyJet just wasn't taken seriously at the time.'

After the initial shock, Philipa soon grew to appreciate her unconventional uniform. 'It was a relief to be able to run around and get on with your work in jeans, rather than tottering around in high heels. It was practical too as we were constantly kneeling down or picking things up from the floor. Cabin crew who had worked for other airlines particularly liked it. We all felt very comfortable and had fun and enjoyed our casual uniform. You didn't have to put up any pretence. That was one of the best things about working for easyJet.'

As well as a casual new look, Philipa and the other flight attendants had to adapt to an informal atmosphere on-board. EasyJet was keen to emulate its US role model, Southwest, whose cabin crew would make jokes throughout the flight. The easyJet cabin crew was encouraged to be spontaneous and have fun with the passengers. Flight attendants were encouraged to play games, such as asking which passenger was wearing yellow socks that day, who was the oldest or youngest passenger, or even who had the most points on their driving licence. The winner would normally be rewarded with a free flapjack. A member of the senior cabin crew might read out the *Sun* newspaper to the passengers during the flight and give them an update of the daily news, or ask them to complete that day's crossword with him.

Not all members of the British flying public appreciated the American-style approach. 'Some of the passengers loved it and thought it was funny but others were plain embarrassed,' Philipa recalled. 'The gay flight attendants were best at having fun with the passengers. It wasn't me at all, though, and I didn't make jokes. I had been strictly trained and it was too difficult to switch roles and suddenly become all American. I think nowadays easyJet would probably look for more outgoing, bubbly cabin crew to do that kind of thing.'

Philipa's most memorable experience was the run-up to easyJet's first Christmas. 'The flight deck was playing Christmas carols and songs and the crew and the captain ran around wearing flashing Christmas lights. We were diverted to Edinburgh on the Christmas Eve flight back to Luton from Glasgow. But it was like a big party on-board and the atmosphere was absolutely fantastic. The passengers were merry after a few drinks and quite happy. We didn't land in Luton until after midnight but no one cared as we were having such a good time.'

The games and merriment on-board translated into a pleasant working environment. 'It was a lot of fun,' said Philipa. 'Everyone just enjoyed his or her work. I used to look forward to getting up at 4 a.m. and going to work, and I haven't felt like that working anywhere else. We didn't need much motivating, as it was fun to do. We were all really enjoying being part of this exciting new thing.'

Some of easyJet's early employees weren't convinced that the airline would survive six months and few thought that it would last longer than a year. They still wanted to give it their best shot. 'The cabin crew thought easyJet was a good idea but we wouldn't have been that upset if it hadn't worked at the time,' said Philipa. 'There was a big feeling that everyone was making it up as we went along. The head of the cabin crew had a suggestion box which he encouraged us to use. There were suggestions for entertainment for passengers or things that we could sell on the carts.'

Apart from the jokes and on-board comedy acts, the flight crew's day followed a standard routine, which hasn't changed throughout the years. After reaching the airport an hour before the flight took off, the crew would assemble in the briefing room, where they were informed how many people would be flying with them that day and if they had to watch out for any particular passengers, such as celebrities or people with special needs. A safety briefing followed, providing a review of details such as the location of the fire extinguishers on-board.

Once the ground staff had given cabin crew their approval and the safety checks had been carried out on-board, the passengers were allowed to board the aircraft and sit wherever they wanted. There was less of a stampede than normally accompanies easyJet flights today. Next, passengers were shown a safety demonstration and the plane flew to the day's destination, hopefully arriving on time. Approximately thirty minutes after the last passenger left the aircraft, the whole process would start again with the next batch of passengers.

EasyJet threw small parties for cabin crew every time that a new group qualified to join the airline to ensure that staff morale remained high. Stelios often joined in the parties and had fun with his employees. He made sure, however, that he didn't reveal anything about his private life. Even at parties, all he talked about was airlines and business.

The flight attendants were mostly happy to work hard because of the healthy relationship they enjoyed with management. 'The really good thing was that you had the support of the management behind you,' said Philipa. 'You could make decisions on-board and know that you would be backed up by the bosses.'

Stelios made sure that strict rules and operational guidelines accompanied the laughter and games of easyJet's early days. He had strong ideas about how the airline should be run and expected everyone to adhere to them. Nor was he prepared to back down to anyone who challenged his ideas. 'Stelios was very tough on what he wanted,' according to Philipa. 'If Stelios wanted something done a certain way, then you would have to do it that way and not question it. You couldn't have a run-in with him. The head of the cabin crew at the time had a few arguments with him and was fired. There was a personality clash between the two of them. Stelios was very business-minded and strict. That said, none of what he asked for was unreasonable. He was a fair boss. Even though he was a bit over the top sometimes, he was popular with the cabin crew and came across as a genuinely nice guy.'

Not having to serve meals on-board freed up more time for the easyJet flight attendants to help passengers and get to know them. When there were any passengers, that is. It was still taking time for easyJet to get its message across. 'EasyJet didn't seem real to people as the whole concept of budget travel was so new,' said Philipa. 'The cabin crew individually did a lot of advertising. I used to go down to the pub and advertise easyJet myself and tell people to fly with them and reassure them that it was safe! I know that other cabin crew used to do the same. A lot of people learnt about easyJet through word-of-mouth.'

Gradually some business passengers started to realise the economic sense of buying a cheap ticket with the budget carrier. Executives even started to commute to work between London and Glasgow courtesy of the airline. One regular passenger used to take the 6 a.m. flight from Glasgow and be in his office in London by 9 a.m. He and the other passengers started to pay for block bookings of tickets. Flying with easyJet was cheaper than taking a flight with British Airways – and cheaper and much quicker than the train – and Luton was far less busy than London Heathrow, even if it was harder to reach for some people.

EasyJet strove to keep costs as low as possible so that it could continue offering low fares. One of its money-saving strategies was to adopt fast half-an-hour turnarounds of its aircraft between flights. Within thirty minutes, the crew had to ensure that the safety equipment was in place and each passenger seat had its safety card inserted in the back pocket.

The crew had to check the toilets, cupboards and under the seats. Then they had to clean up the cabin before the next passengers came on-board. It was hard work. But easyJet had paid hefty mortgages on its two planes. The only way to pay for the aircraft was to 'sweat the assets', as Stelios liked to say, by keeping them in the air. 'I love planes but, as Sir Freddie Laker said, they're only metal tubes for making money,' he once commented. 'You can only really fall in love with a boat.'

The airline made sure that on-board catering was kept to a minimum to cut back on costs. Drinks were coffee and tea served in plastic cups. The rumour within the airline was that Stelios had bought the cups himself at Tesco. Gone too were the traditional airline's plastic meals. Instead passengers were invited to buy flapjacks or sandwiches, the latter said to be made by an employee before each flight. Passengers were encouraged to bring their own food as well as alcohol on-board, which proved popular. The flight crew intervened if someone was drinking to excess.

Many passengers moaned about the lack of service and huffily pronounced that they weren't prepared to pay fifty pence for a small beaker of coffee. In response, flight attendants reminded them how cheap their ticket was. 'We were trained to communicate to passengers that we weren't putting any costs or money on the tickets for the price of china or meals,' said Philipa. 'We were instructed to tell them that easyJet wasn't cheap but affordable so if people complained, they should just compare their ticket price to the fare charged by BA.'

EasyJet also saved money by operating leased aircraft. The planes were old and the interiors shabby, adding to some passengers' fears about the plane's safety. Their fears were unfounded. The airline didn't make any cutbacks when it came to safety. EasyJet used the same equipment as that used by more traditional airlines and operated to high safety standards. The fledgling carrier was aware that an accident or safety mishap could destroy its reputation and then nobody would fly with it again. EasyJet had a good reference point. It only had to look at the US budget carrier ValuJet, which folded a matter of months after one of its planes plunged vertically into the swamps of the Everglades following a fire on-board on 11 May 1996. The crash destroyed the aircraft, all 105 passengers and five crew, as well as some US travellers' confidence in no-frills aviation. The Florida-based airline was subsequently accused of poor maintenance practices by the National Transportation Safety Board investigation.

Indirect support by famous passengers helped promote easyJet's name to the general public and assuage passengers' mistrust of the airline. The Scottish band Big Country, which was enjoying the height of its popularity at the time, flew to Scotland a few times with easyJet. The airline was quick to advertise the fact, naming one of its aircraft after the group. The pop star Boy George also flew with easyJet in the early days, as did the group Wet Wet Wet. The snooker player Alan McManus was less fortunate in his experience with the airline. He was snowed in at Glasgow airport when he was due to be playing in a snooker tournament in London.

McManus wasn't the only easyJet passenger, famous or not, to be stranded at an airport because of bad weather in the first couple of years. EasyJet's early Boeings weren't equipped with the most up-to-date radar control equipment and Luton's geographical position meant that the airport was often fog-bound.

But those who flew on easyJet's first flights were generally far more tolerant about any delay than passengers today. The novelty factor helped: easyJet was just so different and so cheap. But passengers were still shocked to find out that they wouldn't be given a free night's accommodation when a flight was cancelled. They were told instead that they would be automatically rebooked onto the following morning's flight for free. EasyJet informed passengers that it didn't consider accommodation its responsibility. The company message was that customers wouldn't receive free accommodation if they had been travelling by train, so why should they expect anything different with easyJet?

It wasn't long before passengers' tolerance of mishaps started to weaken as the novelty factor wore off. Tempers were flaring by the time 120 furious passengers landed in Edinburgh more than ten hours late a few days before Christmas in 1997. The plane was forced to turn back to Luton after the pilot couldn't retract the aircraft's nose-gear. Aircraft parts were flown in from Germany as engineers worked on the plane all day. The passengers were told an Airbus 2000 had been laid on to leave at 5 p.m.

Among the disgruntled passengers was Fiona Mulheron, from Bathgate, West Lothian. 'I'm having my family for a Christmas meal tonight, but because of the delay I won't be there when they arrive.' Susan Downie was also angry about the delay. 'I came up to Edinburgh for a holiday with my one-year-old son Craig. He should be in bed now, not being trotted around an airport.'

They were further angered when a luggage mishap caused more delay. 'We got on the plane and after forty minutes, they told us to get off again as there were too many pieces of luggage,' said Neil Blakesly, a Londoner who had planned to spend the weekend Christmas shopping with his Edinburgh girlfriend. 'It turned out to be a nonsense. I don't know why they hauled us off.'

Stelios managed to calm tempers and the bad press generated by the incident by promising to 'personally consider any reasonable claims for compensation' following the 'unacceptable delay'. It wasn't the last time, however, that easyJet would raise tempers and hit the headlines.

3. Going Dutch

EASYJET WELCOMED A new member to the team in March 1996, appointing Ray Webster as managing director. Stelios plucked the fifty-four-year-old Webster from New Zealand and asked him to invest in the start-up.

'This was several times the size of my mortgage to fork out on a business that was unproven,' Webster said at the time. 'It had load factors of about 30 per cent, two planes and £5 million of equity.' Still, it was better than sticking around down under, where the regulators had just forced Air New Zealand to ditch Webster's pioneering plans for a low-cost airline. Until then, he had spent over thirty years working for essentially the same company.

A carpenter's son, he described himself as an electronics buff with a low boredom threshold, who 'was building all sorts of things and blowing things up' as young as nine or ten. He did badly at school and couldn't wait to get out of his small coal-mining town. So he joined New Zealand's National Aircraft Corporation as an apprentice in 1964, largely because the post office and the air force wouldn't employ anyone who was colour-blind (a condition which made easyJet's trademark orange branding 'difficult to see – you spot it by association'). Within a few years he was winning all sorts of scholarships, and in his early thirties he became chief engineer for Air New Zealand before taking a year out to immerse himself in management courses at Stanford.

'Stanford over-delivered against expectations,' he said – a characteristic understatement for a year during which his marriage ended, he met his second wife Brigitte and 'gained a lot more confidence that I could do well outside my field'. ANZ kept him in California as the head of its Americas operation before calling him back to set up the ill-fated no-frills carrier.

Webster's face was lined with deep eye-bags and his measured New Zealand tones matched his relaxed work attire, normally comprising chinos, shirt and no tie. He owned a relatively modest house in Hampstead and his only personal luxury was a brace of Porsches.

EasyJet's focus now was on expansion. In January 1996, the carrier introduced flights from Luton to Aberdeen and started to assess which other routes to add to its network. The airline had started using its own Air Operating Certificate, meaning that it was recognised as a financially viable airline. What is more, easyJet now possessed two wholly owned Boeing aircraft. In April 1996, the airline used the new planes to start flying into Amsterdam, its first international destination; according to Stelios, 'It meets our criteria as a busy route with an overpriced fares structure.' EasyJet had to pay similar fees at Amsterdam and other airports as larger rivals, but planned to offer a cut-price service to Amsterdam with flights at less than half the £150 one-way economy class fare charged by British Airways.

EasyJet promoted the flights to Amsterdam by selling seats for 39 pence on the first day, much to the delight of the British flying public. Viewed by popular consensus as a 'Good Bloke', Stelios liked people to see him as both put-upon and playful. He also enjoyed annoying large multinationals and pulling off publicity stunts, as his next ploy proved. He printed coupons in easyJet's in-flight magazine addressed to the president of KLM, the national carrier of the Netherlands, complaining about the price of KLM flights to and from Amsterdam, then turned up with some easyJet employees at the KLM offices in Amstelveen, on the outskirts of Amsterdam, to present the coupons to Leo van Wijk, the president of KLM. They weren't granted an audience. But the incident did drum up lots of free publicity for easyJet on Dutch television and in the newspapers.

It wasn't the last time that KLM, Europe's fourth largest airline, would hear easyJet's name mentioned. EasyJet's one-way fare of 99 guilders was considerably lower than the return fare of 296 guilders that KLM had been charging between Amsterdam and London, and KLM was forced to reduce its fares dramatically to counter the threat. The no-frills carrier responded to the fare cuts by alleging that KLM was engaged in predatory pricing between London and Amsterdam.

EasyJet's predatory pricing case was significant. If the European Commission's competition arm decided that KLM had abused its position by operating its Amsterdam–London service below cost to force easyJet out of the market, then the Commission could fine KLM up to 10 per cent of the turnover earned on the route. An article from the Dutch press, which was discussed at the hearings, quoted from an alleged internal KLM memo calling for a determined tactical campaign to 'stop the growth and development of easyJet'. 'We didn't do anything which is not in line with EU legislation,' a KLM spokeswoman responded. In the end, a decision was never reached. EasyJet, now focusing on plans by British Airways to set up a no-frills airline, eventually dropped the complaint with the Commission and left KLM alone, at least for the time being.

The Amsterdam route marked a new era for easyJet. It was a prestigious new destination for the carrier and Amsterdam Schiphol, Europe's fourth largest airport, was a key transfer hub. The Amsterdam flights also attracted a new type of passenger, keen to capitalise on easyJet's cheap fares to spend a raucous weekend in the Dutch capital, getting drunk or smoking cannabis. Marijuana was still technically illegal in Amsterdam but the police tolerated coffee shops selling soft drugs, and business was booming. 'Enjoy your visit, have a fat one for me!' declared an easyJet passenger called Wadie on a web chatroom for marijuana users after a trip to Amsterdam. 'I'll be over in the next couple of weeks for some more! Thank the lord for easyJet!'

Of course, drunk, stoned or awkward passengers weren't exclusive to easyJet. But they formed the worst of the new breed of traveller who were lured on trips abroad by affordable fares. Claire Pakes, a twenty-two-year-old easyJet hostess, found the groups of lads on stag weekends the worst. 'They're all off together for the weekend and they are cooped up in a confined space surrounded by women waiting on them while consuming copious amounts of lager. It's never going to be an easy job for us, is it? They are often drunk before they even board the plane. Then we have to make sure all the lockers are shut and so you have to lean over passengers to check everything is secure. These types of guys always leave their lockers open and then make comments about your boobs or your bum. It's pretty predictable, but unfortunately you just have to do it.'

Fortunately, Claire never had to cope with proper abuse from any passengers, although some of her colleagues weren't so fortunate. 'I've heard of girls getting seriously groped but no one has ever gone that far with me. You just have to grit your teeth and smile nicely, which is the worst bit. Underneath, you seriously want to just punch one of them. A colleague of mine was kicked in the shin by a passenger because he got so annoyed with her. She had been having some problems with him since the start of the flight. After an hour, she started to ignore him a bit because he was being such a pain. Then as she was walking past, saying she would be right back to get him whatever he was demanding, he lurched awkwardly out of his seat and did a sort of rugby kick at her as she was walking past. She went down and the two drinks she was carrying went flying up in the air all over the other passengers. She just had to get up, smooth down her uniform and carry on as if nothing had happened. That's the lot of an air hostess, I'm afraid.'

In June 1996, five weeks after introducing flights to Amsterdam, easyJet added Nice to its network. To publicise the new route, Stelios invited the press to fly out with him and watch the Monaco Grand Prix from his flat in nearby Monte Carlo. This wasn't Stelios' sole bachelor pad. He also owned homes in St Katherine's Dock in London, and in Athens. His frequent business trips, however, meant that he slept mostly in hotels.

In the following months, easyJet added more international destinations within two hours' flying time of Luton, including flights from Luton to Geneva in December 1997. At the same time the company started to increase its number of aircraft. In July 1998, the airline placed an order for fifteen of Boeing's new next generation 737s, with a list price in excess of $500 million, to increase its fleet sixfold over the next five years. This was on top of an existing order for twelve Boeing 737-300s, which were due for delivery by 2000. EasyJet knew that a fleet of shiny new planes would enhance its safety reputation to potential customers. 'We're building Europe's leading low-cost airline with what will be one of the world's youngest fleets,' boasted Stelios.

Stelios was characteristically bullish about his ability to fill the new capacity as he expanded into Europe. But easyJet was not alone in attempting to win the lion's share of a new market that analysts believed could grow by 300 per cent over the next few years. Ryanair, which had by now converted itself into a no-frills carrier and the largest of the low-cost contenders, signed up for twenty-five new 737s with the option of another twenty, in a deal priced at more than $2 billion. Richard Branson had ambitious plans for his Virgin Express operation based at Brussels; and Debonair, easyJet's rival at Luton, was in talks to lease ten of Boeing's new 717 regional jets.

Debonair had started operations in June 1996 and linked Rome with Barcelona, Munich, Munchen-Gladbach and Copenhagen, and Madrid with Barcelona. The airline's fares were amazingly cheap. How about Munich to Rome for a mere Dm161 ($104) one-way, as against the regular air fare of Dm793? Or Copenhagen-Rome for Dkr920 ($155) compared with Dkr5,265?

Debonair's chairman was Franco Mancassala, whose twenty-seven-year airline career had begun with Luton-based Court Line Aviation and also included stints with Continental Airlines, World Airways and Mid Pacific Airlines. Mancassola fronted Debonair's own advertising campaigns, normally the preserve of used car salesmen and furniture magnates. Unusually, Mancassala's appearances were actually funny; showing Debonair's (real) finance director crouched at his feet in tears, begging his boss not to offer passengers such low fares.

Then British Airways entered the fray. In November 1996, Bob Ayling, British Airways' then chief executive, had invited Stelios for tea and discussed buying a stake in easyJet. 'He was very flattering,' Stelios recalled. 'He said, "I think you've cracked it."' Stelios took the older man's interest as external confirmation of what he was doing. Talks continued into the spring. Then BA abruptly announced that regulators wouldn't approve the deal. Shortly thereafter, in October 1997, when easyJet was starting to pose a serious threat, BA announced that it would launch an easyJet look-alike, Go Fly Airways, the following year.

Stelios was furious. As soon as he heard of BA's plans, Stelios brought an immediate writ 'to prevent BA illegally cross-subsidising its low-cost subsidiary', arguing, 'There is no point in waiting until you are out of business. Sue – and sue early.' The writ alleged that BA was guaranteeing the leases on Go's initial eight aircraft and that it was supporting other aspects of Go's business, including maintenance, insurance and advertising, and not accepting an adequate return on the £50 million it was investing in the project. It also said that Go benefited from the 'halo' or 'brand image' effect because customers would believe that a company associated with BA would have higher standards of reliability and safety. EasyJet pointed out that cross-subsidies by dominant companies were illegal under Article 86 of the European Community Treaty. 'We believe in fair competition and we asked BA to give an undertaking they would play fair, but they refused,' said Stelios.

BA denied doing anything unlawful, arguing that giving such advantages to a subsidiary was part of normal business for most companies and insisting that Go would be a standalone operation. A BA spokesman said: 'We established our subsidiary Go in response to the growing market for low-cost travel. We are confident the new airline will add to consumer choice and all of Go's operations will be lawful.' Stelios lost the battle. In May 1998, a High Court judge dismissed the injunction sought by easyJet against Go and easyJet was forced to accept that BA would go ahead with its low-cost ambitions.

Franco Mancassola, the flamboyant chairman of Debonair, was, like Stelios, suspicious about BA's motivation. 'Go is like a ten-year-old kid thrown into the ring with Mike Tyson,' he said. 'It should never be allowed to operate. It is a wolf in sheep's clothing, simply a way for BA to eliminate competition. BA can't do it themselves because they are too fat and they don't want to go to Weight Watchers.'

O'Leary, the baseball-capped chief executive of Ryanair, seemed more relaxed than Mancassola about the challenge presented by Go. 'BA has no idea how to run a low-fare airline,' he said dismissively. 'I know more about flying on Concorde than Bob Ayling does about running a low-cost airline and I've never flown on Concorde.' O'Leary predicted that Go would be a 'disaster' and would take passengers away from BA's mainline services.

'Look at Ryanair on London–Stockholm,' said O'Leary. 'Our midweek return fare is £99, while BA's is £500. BA screws you if you don't spend a Saturday night away. If Go were to start on that route, for example, it would have to pitch its pricing somewhere in the middle. Traffic would move from economy cabins to BA and SAS. There's no doubt that Go is going to cannibalise BA's economy passengers over London.'

It was a scene to make all bar a boxing promoter blush as two of the executives holding the key to the future of the European airline industry met for the first time at an industry event in March 1998. Stelios, normally a public relations dream – young, dynamic and always ready to take on and use the media – was strangely subdued as he joined the cream of Europe's airline industry in London to hear a speech by Karel Van Miert, the EU competition commissioner. Asked how easyJet was faring, all Stelios could manage was a barbed comment aimed at Barbara Cassani, Go's chief executive officer: 'Everything's fine apart from that woman over there.'

Cassani, a forty-one-year-old wisecracking American in a miniskirt, shook up the conservative, male-dominated airline industry. A master's graduate from Princeton University, she started out as a management consultant at Coopers and Lybrand (now PricewaterhouseCoopers) in Washington and moved to the company's London offices with her husband, Guy, a British investment banker. Soon after arriving in London, she answered a British Airways advertisement for a job in sales and marketing and thereafter rose swiftly through the airline's management ranks. She helped to buy the airline's Galileo computer reservation system, was part of a negotiating team for BA's long-running alliance talks with American Airlines and became the airline's first general manager in the US.

Cassani became a protégée of Bob Ayling, the airline's former CEO, and it was no surprise to BA employees when she was appointed as head of the airline's new no-frills subsidiary. Cassani said that Ayling told her: 'You've got £25 million – goodbye and good luck', recalling, 'And so there I was with a bagful of money in one hand and a bag of ideas in the other.' After retreating into the cotton wool confines of the BA corporate machine for a few months, Cassani quickly put together a team and secured eight aircraft for Go's launch in May 1998. She declined to divulge any more details about the new airline: 'I haven't even told my mother where Go will be operating to.'

She was determined to make Go work. One thing, however, that she hadn't counted on was a surprise appearance by easyJet's orange army on Go's inaugural flight from London Stansted to Rome in May 1998. Stelios and six of his employees showed up, dressed in orange boiler suits, clashing with Go's purple and green colour scheme. Before boarding at Stansted, Stelios declared: 'Go has been given permission by BA to lose £29 million and then close in three years, having put its rivals out of business.' He added: 'You have only to look at BA's track record to see how predatory they are.' Go denied the claims. 'The low-cost market is set to quadruple in the next five years and there is huge potential,' said Go sales and marketing director David Magliano.

Stelios and his team turned the spotlight away from Go and on to his own venture by handing out 150 letters promising free flights on easyJet. Cassani, travelling among the 147 passengers with her husband Guy and five-year-old daughter Lauren, found herself alone at the front of the plane while journalists piled into the back to interview the garrulous Greek. But she pointed out that Stelios's appearance in an orange boiler suit brought Go far more publicity than it otherwise would have earned, and asserted, 'People don't feel comfortable with the orange brashness of easyJet.'

After its dramatic launch day, Go started operations with twice-daily services from Stansted to Rome, Milan and Copenhagen, none of which was served by easyJet. It hoped to fly to six destinations by the end of its first year. Passengers could buy tickets up to one hour before take-off, with all fares set at £100 return.

Go adopted a more conventional approach than easyJet and was accordingly perceived as slightly more upmarket. The new airline believed in allocating seats rather than the first-come-first-served principle of easyJet, and dressed its flight stewards in proper shirts as opposed to the easyJet crew's polo shirts. Before long it was flying to a larger number of destinations, less frequently than easyJet and with a more fixed discount tariff structure. Food, such as bacon, lettuce and tomato sandwiches or a breakfast box comprising Cornflakes, a muffin and a cereal bar, was available on flights but as on easyJet, passengers had to pay extra for it. The airline also offered the world's first gift vouchers for flights.

In theory, there was plenty of room for growth in the sector. Fewer than 10 million European passengers flew on low-cost carriers in the late 1990s, representing a modest 5 per cent of the region's traffic. That compared with close to 30 per cent in the US, where the no-frills experiment had begun and which provided the inspiration for the new European airline entrepreneurs.

But making a success of the low-fares strategy was less easy. Debonair's ads showing the airline's financial director in tears proved to be a little close to the bone when Debonair missed revenue and profit targets, being put into administration in October 1999. The airline blamed competition from Go for its demise. Mancassola claimed Go was an 'artificial' low-cost airline because it had the wealth of British Airways behind it. 'I believe in competition and I admire easyJet,' he stated. 'What the company has achieved, it has earned. What is not fair is having a parent company that will benefit from the downfall of another airline.'

Industry experts put Debonair's failure down to an inappropriate strategy. The airline had offered low fares but had high costs: it flew to expensive airports; offered business class, which meant frills, and operated the thirsty BAe 146, which meant high fuel costs. To be successful, budget carriers needed low unit costs and high loads. EasyJet didn't break even until loads reached 70 per cent, and Debonair's loads were much lower. Unlike easyJet, which presented a clear no-frills message, Debonair seemed unsure of its own identity, attempting to appeal to both backpackers with low fares and to executive passengers by offering business class.

As Debonair faltered, easyJet was going from strength to strength. The airline used some of its new aircraft to expand its base in Glasgow, creating 150 new jobs and two new routes out of Glasgow, to Palma in Majorca and Geneva in Switzerland. The decision was seen as a vote of confidence in Scotland by the Luton-based airline. EasyJet was already operating daily flights to Glasgow, Edinburgh and Inverness, the latter traditionally expensive to fly to and very time-consuming to reach by train. And Glasgow to Luton services were running at a healthy 75 per cent capacity.

EasyJet then turned its expansion to Northern Ireland, introducing new flights between Luton and Belfast in September 1998 at a special promotional single fare of £9 plus tax of £10 for the first two weeks. The low fares were well received by Belfast residents. One incident, however, helped cool easyJet's popularity with some people in Northern Ireland. Passengers aboard a Belfast-bound easyJet plane were left freezing after a door seal gave way. Dozens of people put on coats and covered their eardrums as wind whistled through the plane. The plane's pilot was forced to do a quick U-turn and fly back to Luton.

Passenger Stephen Whiteman said, 'It was so noisy you couldn't hear a thing. And it was so cold people were putting their coats back on. It was very uncomfortable. They should call themselves Breezy Jet rather than easyJet.' Another passenger, John Earl, complained: 'My ear drums were throbbing. And when the pilot told us that he was returning to Luton I was delighted. When we got there, we ended up in a hangar where a guy with a toolbox spent an hour and a half fixing a seal on the passenger door. I'm nervous flying at the best of times so I was over the moon when we finally got into Belfast International. A lot of people were very annoyed because they were going to be late for business meetings. But the crew did apologise for the delay over and over again.'

EasyJet reassured passengers that there had been no risk to the plane or its passengers at any time during the alert. 'A slight leak in the seal was identified shortly after take-off and the captain was informed. The captain felt that because of the noise level inside the aircraft it was easier to return to Luton to have the problem corrected. This resulted in a 90-minute delay. The leak did not affect the cabin pressure and there was no risk whatsoever to passengers.'

Meanwhile, Go was making it clear that it wasn't afraid of competition. In August 1998, just three months after its launch, the BA subsidiary announced its first route in direct competition with easyJet, pitching its London to Edinburgh services at £70 return – just £2 more than easyJet's lowest fare on the same route. Then, in October 1998, Go introduced a £15 one-way fare on the same route. Stelios was outraged; EasyJet's lowest single fare to Edinburgh at that time was £29 from Luton.

Stelios decided to fly to the European Commission to make a complaint against Go. Never one to miss a public relations stunt, he took with him 150 friends and staff clad in orange boiler suits. The Boeing 737-300 carrying the orange army to Brussels advertised Stelios's message: 'Stop BA, stop Go,' it screamed in giant orange letters on the side of the plane. Stelios alleged that Go's £15 fare was a 'cheap trick' designed to crush the opposition. He claimed that the below-cost fare was subsidised by BA and amounted to unfair competition in breach of EU trade laws.

'I am sure BA/Go is losing a fortune with such prices,' said Stelios. 'I was forced to match that fare since easyJet will never be knowingly undersold, but the BA/Go fare is predatory. A dominant company like British Airways is prohibited by law from operating at a loss in order to eliminate competition.' Stelios admitted that easyJet couldn't afford to keep matching Go's low Edinburgh fare before plunging into 'heavy losses'. He said: 'Consumers must understand that this short-term bonanza of low fares to many destinations will end if we stop flying on the Edinburgh route. Go has the financial strength behind it to squeeze us out.'

BA denied the claims, saying the new rate was simply a promotional fare available for midweek travel until early December, and the European Commission took no action. But the intense rivalry between the two budget carriers provided British tabloids with colourful copy throughout the ensuing seasons. When Luton Airport closed for several days because of a dusting of snow, Go ran advertisements asking, 'Would you rather fly with a) the airline most likely to get you there on time, or b) the airline with a generous refund policy because they don't?' When Go was voted best low-cost airline, Cassani rented a billboard outside Luton Airport on which to proclaim victory – for a year.

The airline even resorted to taking out a full-page advert in the *Evening Standard* newspaper, reprinting press clippings about cancellations and delays at easyJet. In response, easyJet ran an ad listing the six accolades it had won over the past six months. The ad's headline ran: 'BA is wasting shareholders' cash to rubbish easyJet. If their own low-cost airline is so bloody brilliant why does easyJet win all the customer awards?' 'Stelios is a spirited competitor,' Go's sales director, Magliano, commented cheerfully. 'We enjoy our little spats.'

In the meantime, easyJet was working on a project that would help set it apart from other new low-cost operators: the

Internet. Stelios first became aware of the Internet in 1995, when he was setting up easyJet and the world wide web was commercially in its infancy. He learned that there was something called the global distribution system, a computer system where all travel agents log on and sell you tickets. However, in 1995, Stelios still thought that the Internet was something 'for nerds', he later admitted to the *Guardian* newspaper.

He started to change his mind when he began travelling to the US to see Boeing and noticed that the Internet was becoming more commercially available. In April 1997, easyJet decided to launch its own website, easyJet.com, to provide information about the airline. Like that of many businesses at the time, the easyJet website was little more than an invitation to phone the company.

But Stelios decided to experiment with the new tool. He instructed his team to put a separate number on the website and was startled to find so many people using it. As more and more people found easyJet's number online, he realised that here was a perfect business opportunity: instead of paying call-centre staff about £1 for each seat sold, passengers booking online reduced the marginal cost of distribution to almost zero. The airline started its transformation from a telephone business into a web business.

In April 1998, easyJet sold its first seat online at easyJet.com. Web bookings grew from zero to 26 per cent of business within a year. On the first day of trading during one promotion, 13,000 seats were sold, believed to be a record for the most commercial transactions carried out on the Internet in a twenty-four-hour period. By mid-1999, when its Internet sales represented 58 per cent of the total, easyJet became the first airline to make more sales on the Internet than through normal telephone reservations. Stelios was so pleased that he announced that whoever bought the one-millionth seat online would win a prize of unlimited free travel on easyJet for a year. The carrier reached the one-million-seat mark in October 1999. Five months later, in March 2000, easyJet reached two million seats, and it took only another three months to reach the three million mark. By 2001, online bookings regularly reached 80 per cent, the highest proportion of online sales for any airline in the world.

'The Internet is the kind of tool that becomes available to people once in a generation,' Stelios commented. 'The Internet has probably had a bigger effect on people's ability to fly than the jet engine. The jet engine was an improvement on the propeller, but what really made it a mass market was the ability to fly someone for £1. You can only do that with the Internet.' EasyJet pioneered the concept of offering a discount to Internet customers, offering £5 off for each leg of a journey, and the fuselage of each plane proudly proclaimed it to be 'The Web's Favourite Airline' – a claim that was designed to annoy BA, 'The World's Favourite Airline'.

An analysis by Schroder Salomon Smith Barney pronounced that easyJet's embrace of the Internet was 'already enhancing earnings, in the form of higher load factors, lower marketing costs, a leaner organisation structure and better management information'. According to the investment house, easyJet was becoming a paperless company with a powerful electronic infrastructure. The results were lower administration costs, better management information and more responsive decision-making. The major airlines were far behind easyJet, 'encumbered by historical travel agency relationships', the analysis stated.

EasyJet's decision to champion the Internet was, unsurprisingly, not appreciated by travel agents, including those in Stelios's homeland. Greek travel agents took offence at an easyJet advert which posed the question 'Who needs travel agents?', highlighting online booking for the airline's budget Athens–Luton service. The travel agents took easyJet to court in Athens, alleging that the airline's policy of issuing tickets directly to travellers violated fair play.

Representatives of easyJet pledged more than 800 tickets for people who turned up at court to support the company, and hundreds of people accordingly converged on the Athens court hearing in July 1998. The court decided to ban the ads for offending the integrity of travel agents, who insisted that easyJet's budget prices were misleading, offering no in-flight refreshments or refunds for cancellations. Stelios lost his case but – inevitably – gained more publicity.

The success of online ticket sales encouraged Stelios to set up a chain of Internet cafés called easyEverything, allowing travellers cheap and straightforward access to the web. Month after month, a new cavern packed with computer terminals would open in a big city: Amsterdam, Munich, New York. The rate of expansion proved so unsustainable that the value of easyEverything was written down by 99 per cent, forcing Stelios to make an emergency cash injection of £15 million.

The cafés, which charged £1 an hour for internet access, burnt through £40 million since the first outlet was opened in London during the dot.com boom. Stelios admitted that the chain had made a string of elementary retail mistakes, such as having its shops too widely dispersed geographically, and wasting money on expensive shopfronts. EasyEverything's lacklustre start took the sheen off Stelios's reputation as it became clear that his magic touch with easyJet wouldn't necessarily transfer to new ventures.

EasyJet's next publicity coup wasn't self-generated. In January 1999, the UK television channel ITV decided to air a reality TV series called *Airline*, based around the passengers and staff at easyJet. The airline was first approached about the possibility of filming during mid-1998 after an earlier series with Britannia Airways was discontinued; ITV staff had heard about Stelios's colourful publicity stunts and hoped that the airline's fresh approach would translate to screen. The first series on easyJet consisted of ten thirty-minute programmes, giving a 'warts and all' account of goings-on at easyJet's Luton operation. The viewing public watched irate late arrivals, overreacting staff and moaning C-list celebrities at the airport and witnessed Stelios personally go to Seattle to kick the tyres of the new Boeing planes that he had ordered.

It was a surprise hit. Soon 10 million people a week were tuning in to watch what was to become the most popular fly-on-the-wall documentary of all time. For several weeks, it was almost the third national soap opera, beaten in the ratings only by *Coronation Street* and *EastEnders*. The format never varied. Every week, a group of easyJet passengers went berserk before being subdued by staff with basilisk stares and excuses that verged on the brilliant. The cameras have been with easyJet almost constantly ever since. In 2003 *Airline* was ITV's most popular factual programme, with a total of 75 million viewers worldwide; it has been sold to countries including New Zealand, Australia and Japan.

One night's episode illustrated World Cup fever at Luton Airport. Disaster struck for one group of football fans with tickets for the semi-final between Brazil and Holland. Their plane developed a technical fault and they were desperately trying to change their flights. Frustration grew as kick-off time approached. The cameras then focused on Bruno Taylor. Bruno may have hitchhiked all around the world but getting out of Luton was proving to be his greatest challenge yet, as he had come away without his passport. Good old Mum came to the rescue, sending a courier to the airport with the vital document. The series made supervisor Leo Jones and broad Scouser Leanne Cheung favourites with the viewing public. It also helped reinforce the importance of arriving at the airport on time with a valid passport if you wanted to be allowed on to an easyJet flight; and though it occasionally showed the airline at less than its best, the publicity was a gift.

Meanwhile the company continued its domestic expansion. In January 1999, easyJet officially established Liverpool's Speke Airport as a hub airport, with aircraft and crews based in the north-west. The airline started four new scheduled services from Liverpool to Geneva, Barcelona, Belfast and Malaga. 'This is the beginning of the easyJet masterplan to turn Liverpool into an easyAirport,' said Stelios. 'The north-west has been neglected. People are fed up with having to travel to London airports or go via Manchester. Speke is a wonderful, uncongested airport and the routes we're offering will give people new holiday choices. Geneva will be for skiers, Barcelona for city breaks, Malaga for sun seekers and Belfast for people visiting friends and family.'

Keen to encourage short-break travel, easyJet started to plan overseas expansion alongside its burgeoning domestic operations. In April 1999, the airline rebranded a Swiss charter operation, TEA Basel AG, as 'easyJet Switzerland' and moved it from Basle to Geneva. EasyJet had bought a 40 per cent stake in the ailing Swiss carrier in March 1998 for three million Swiss francs. In June 1999, the company increased its stake in easyJet Switzerland to 49 per cent and acquired an option for the remaining 51 per cent. It set about making Geneva its third hub airport, planning services for easyJet Switzerland from Geneva to Nice, Amsterdam and Barcelona – the first easyJet services wholly outside the UK.

Stelios was about to celebrate easyJet's inaugural flight from Geneva to Barcelona on 29 July 1999 when word came through the captain that the Swiss authorities had withdrawn easyJet's commercial licence to fly the route after alleged objections by Swissair, the national carrier. Swissair, which didn't welcome easyJet's approach, claimed that national laws gave it a de facto monopoly over the Barcelona route. The decision lay with the Federal Office for Civil Aviation, an industry watchdog in Switzerland. EasyJet said it was prepared to go to court if FOCA ruled against them. The company had already sold 6,500 seats on the disputed route and vowed to fly via London if necessary. To the airline's fury, a spokesman for FOCA stated that as long as Swissair 'flies this route, it has the right to maintain an exclusive concession until 2008 at the latest or until the bilateral accords with the EU take effect'.

Rather than accept defeat, Stelios pulled off a masterstroke.

Announcing the bad news to passengers, he then explained: 'We can however still fly you to Barcelona as a private flight. So, I'm pleased to refund all your money in cash, and welcome you aboard the plane as my guests.' Never one to miss a trick, he then walked up and down the aisle with a bucket, saying: 'Collection for the pilot.' He managed to recoup 40 per cent of the fares in cash.

EasyJet went ahead with its plans to fly passengers from Geneva to Barcelona despite Swissair's objections, operating the flight as a tour operator rather than an airline, which entitled it to a different licence, and ran a free bus from Barcelona airport to the city centre to conform with tour operator requirements. Swissair insisted that the rival airline obey an obscure rule that the only way to operate flights on the Geneva–Barcelona route was to sell a package that included accommodation. So easyJet bought five tents and erected them at a campsite 60 miles outside Barcelona. 'We got them from Argos for £29.99 each,' Stelios announced proudly, explaining that anyone who booked a cheap flight to the Catalan capital from Geneva was welcome to camp out at his expense. Not surprisingly, only a few people took up his offer.

4. Turbulence over Luton

STELIOS CONTINUED TO lose no opportunity of getting his voice heard. He took out a full-page advert in *The Times* when catering employees at British Airways were about to go on strike. It read: 'Our catering staff will never vote for a strike . . . we don't have any!'

He placed another *Times* advert asking UK Chancellor Gordon Brown to review airport tax as he launched a campaign against the government's proposed changes to Air Passenger Duty – a tax on airline passengers introduced by the Conservative Party in 1994. 'The Tories doubled it to £10 on all flights, which is ridiculous if you're only paying £29 to fly to London,' Stelios complained. 'It should be proportional to the cost of the fare. That would reduce the tax for the low-budget individual traveller and increase it for the long-haul business traveller who is on an expense account and doesn't care anyway.' EasyJet's lobbying efforts proved successful. The government decided to reduce taxes on flights within Europe to £5.

More people continued to climb aboard easyJet's tangerine aircraft. EasyJet welcomed its 10 millionth passenger and in June 2000 celebrated the sale of 3 million seats online. Every Friday evening some 40 per cent of the viewing public tuned in to watch the fourth series of *Airline* on ITV, which attracted twice as many viewers as the new series of the US sitcom *Friends*.

EasyJet was determined to cater for its growing passenger numbers. In March 2000 the airline placed a firm order with Boeing for a further seventeen next-generation 737-700s. Deliveries were scheduled to begin in July 2001, increasing easyJet's fleet size to forty-four aircraft by 2004.

Meanwhile the airline's relationship with Luton Airport was growing sour. Immortalised by Lorraine Chase's 'No, Luton Airport' catchphrase, the airport was managed by a consortium of Barclays Private Equity and Airports Group International, and Luton's chief executive Graham Roberts wanted to raise take-off and landing charges from £1.60 to £8 per passenger when a five-year agreement with the airline ended in February 2001. The airport claimed that it needed to increase fees following an annual loss of £5 million, which it attributed to the end of EU duty-free sales and low landing fees. But easyJet said £40 million lavished on a new terminal was behind the loss. 'The airport has built an over-sized new terminal and seems to expect our passengers to pay for their mistake,' Stelios complained.

In June 2000, Stelios cut up his own Barclaycard and led a protest outside the Luton branch of Barclays Bank against the increase, which he described as 'absurd and greedy'. He stressed that easyJet was responsible for about 60 per cent of the 5 million passengers passing through Luton each year. 'Luton Airport was in decline before easyJet started operations in late 1995. The fact that it has turned £1.3 million profit into £330,000 in the past year and is on course for such big losses endorses everything I've said about the company and its management.'

EasyJet urged Deputy Prime Minister John Prescott to regulate fees at Luton to stop the airport 'ripping off' passengers. The airline took out full-page adverts in most of the national press, claiming that low-cost airline services would be under threat if Barclays were successful in raising landing charges. 'That is a huge increase which would wipe out our profits at Luton because we would not be able to pass the charge on to our passengers,' said easyJet PR spokesman Toby Nicol. EasyJet also enlisted passengers' support in an Internet campaign against the increase and threatened to take the case to the European Union.

Stelios and his staff even boycotted the royal opening of the airport's new terminal, snubbing the Queen. A spokesman for easyJet announced: 'We do not mean any disrespect to the Queen but we are protesting at the airport management being hell bent on a suicidal route to wrecking Luton Airport and returning it to the days of Lorraine Chase.' The airline threatened to reduce its Luton operations – even to pull out of Luton altogether – unless something was done about the take-off fees. A spokeswoman for the airport replied, 'If easyJet left Luton of course it would be a blow to the local economy and jobs in the area. But we can no longer keep up with the increasing number of passengers at Luton and at £40 million the new terminal is not expensive.'

EasyJet decided to cap its development at Luton in favour of expansion at other airports where it operated. EasyJet's flights from Geneva had already increased four-fold in the previous twelve months. It also signed a twenty-year deal at Liverpool Airport to base up to seven aircraft there from the following April. The airline was keen to develop Amsterdam Schiphol airport into its fourth European hub. Stelios wanted to operate flights to destinations already served from the UK and make use of the 'Open Skies' bilateral agreement, which allowed airlines to operate between countries they did not have their headquarters in. The company said it would start twice-daily services to Edinburgh and daily flights to Belfast and Nice from Amsterdam from 5 January 2001, on top of its existing flights between Amsterdam and Luton, Liverpool and Geneva.

Stelios had been eager to get established in the Netherlands for some time, having twice failed to acquire bankrupt charter carrier Air Holland. The airline was eventually snapped up in January 2000 by local investors. KLM, the Dutch operator, with its low-cost carrier, Buzz, was meanwhile cutting 2,700 jobs. To rub salt into KLM's wounds, Stelios said he intended easyJet to 'become the Dutch low-cost carrier'.

Hiccups inevitably accompanied easyJet's expansion. Like every airline, it experienced mishaps. More flights meant that more delays, incidents and cancellations plagued passengers, even as more punctual, problem-free flights took off each day. In May 2000, easyJet had to pay over £1 million in compensation after fog at Luton Airport delayed over sixty flights for longer than four hours. In June it paid out another £600,000 following an incident earlier in the year when snow closed Luton for twelve hours. Spokesman Toby Nicol took advantage of the situation to point out that compensation was a crucial part of easyJet's customer service contract.

Another public-relations problem awaited easyJet. In October 2000, charges of manslaughter and shipwreck were brought against Stelios in an Italian court following the explosion of the *Haven* oil tanker in April 1991. The charges had been dismissed twice in the lower courts, but a Genoa prosecutor filed an appeal with the Supreme Court alleging Stelios's responsibility for the disaster. At the time of the sinking, Stelios, then twenty-four, had been a director of the company that owned the ship, and as such could be pursued for manslaughter under Italian law.

Stelios dismissed the new appeal, pointing out that the earlier trials, which acquitted him, had placed the blame on human error, not on company negligence. 'In typical Italian fashion, however, they have gone after the wealthiest man they could find, and his son. It's a joke. This is a politically motivated attack – the prosecutor, having lost at the first and second degrees, has to be seen to be taking the case to the third and final degree. The only consequence for me is that I will have to pay more money to my lawyers.'

It was bad timing for easyJet: the trial took place just before the budget airline's planned £600 million flotation on the London stockmarket in November 2000, with Donaldson, Lufkin & Jenrette and UBS Warburg as joint co-ordinators. People still weren't sure whether Stelios was a proper businessman or just a playboy having a bit of fun on Dad's account. 'I think whether I am a proper businessman or not will be judged by the results. EasyJet will open its books in a few months and people will have to judge for themselves. As for me being a playboy, I don't have the time!' he laughed. 'Look, I'm not a suit, that's for sure. I enjoy starting companies, starting dreams. Maybe a proper businessman would have stayed in Greece in the family firm.'

Stelios divided his time between his home in Monaco, where he still had the requisite yacht, his family in Athens, the airline at Luton and easyGroup headquarters in Camden, north London, where he devised new companies to add to easyGroup, the umbrella organisation he had set up in 1998. His plan for his easyGroup companies was to follow the route he was taking with the airline and float them. Which is why he considered the flotation of easyJet as his biggest test to date. 'I don't know how I'll like running a public company, I've never done it,' he admitted. 'I'm adaptable and a fast learner but it is like asking me how I'd like being an astronaut. I just don't know.'

EasyJet appointed managing director Ray Webster as chief executive to help prepare it for the listing, while Stelios was to act as non-executive chairman. To the outside world, Stelios remained the public face of easyJet but Webster was the brains behind the operation. It was his customer yield management system, which he brought with him from Air New Zealand, that made easyJet tick. Yield management explains why the passenger sitting next to you has always paid less than you have. The key is to find the trade-off between selling discounted ticketing in order to fill up the plane completely, and selling full fare tickets and only filling up a portion of the plane.

EasyJet's yield management system was a complicated animal but worked on the basic principle that the later you booked the more you paid. EasyJet fares increased up to threefold as the plane filled up. The idea was that fares rose with demand – the antithesis of classical airline yield management. Webster finessed the technique and introduced a sophisticated system at the airline.

Webster helped easyJet motor towards its stockmarket lift-off at the same time as other airlines, including British Airways, were starting to suffer from a downturn in the industry amid heightened competition from their low-fares rivals. 'We're in a different business,' Stelios declared. 'It is a sign of the times that a company like BA, that in the past has made money from charging its customers a fortune, has discovered that the world has become more cost-conscious. The number of people prepared to pay £500 to £600 to fly to Europe is diminishing and at the same time they are stuck with high fixed costs. We've designed our business to have a very low cost base.'

EasyJet opened its books before its listing and showed the world that it was profitable and should be taken seriously. In the year to September 2000, the airline reported pre-tax profits of £22.1 million on sales of £263.7 million. This followed annual pre-tax profits of £1.3 million on sales of £139.8 million in 1999, and profits of £5.9 million on sales of £77 million in 1998.

EasyJet shares were formally admitted to the London Stock Exchange on 15 November 2000 at an offer price of 310p, in the middle of the 280p–340p target range. EasyJet spread its wings in early trading, ending its first day on the stockmarket with a price tag of £860 million. The shares, which closed the day's trading up 10 per cent at 341p, were almost six times oversubscribed.

The float raised £195 million, which the company planned to use to buy thirty-two new Boeing 737s as it expanded its European operations. 'The IPO is a significant milestone for easyJet and will allow us to maximise our growth potential by helping fund our planned new Boeing 737-700 purchases,' said Stelios. The airline's flamboyant founder and his family retained a 64 per cent chunk in the company, worth roughly £550 million, with Stelios's stake worth nearly £280 million.

The float enabled the company to reward its 1,400 executives and staff with share options worth about £90 million. Webster owned options giving him the right to buy 4.3 million shares at 182p each. Amir Eilon, a former Barclays and CSFB banker who had acted as easyGroup's in-house corporate finance adviser, had options to buy 3.2 million shares at the same price.

The flotation also boosted easyJet's confidence, and it declared that it could continue to expand at 25 per cent per year. Seat sales were continuing to grow strongly, with October proving to be a record month.

Of course, growth at easyJet, as at all airlines, continued to be accompanied by calamities, such as the one at the end of December 2000, when easyJet passengers were stranded by the freezing weather. Police were called to two airports as passengers staged furious protests. Liverpool's airport was closed for most of one day because of icy conditions and freezing fog, and easyJet staff were reduced to tears at Luton as the airline cancelled flights at both airports.

More than 200 people were forced to spend the night sleeping on the floor at Luton Airport, the scene of a sit-down protest by 100 passengers, and others took a whole two days to get from Belfast to Liverpool. Passengers flying from Glasgow also faced marathon journeys, with some taking fifty-six hours to complete what should have been a one-hour trip.

Passengers reported scenes of chaos and fury. Lucy

O'Neill, a technical manager for Tesco who was travelling from Luton to Belfast, said she should have flown at 7 p.m. on Friday but heard at 9.30 p.m. that her flight was cancelled. She said, 'One lady was flying to Barcelona to get married and was very upset because she couldn't get hold of her husband-to-be to tell him what was happening. One guy got very irate with one of the check-in girls. She just walked off in tears.' Karen Kemmett, from Brighton, who was forced to spend the night at Luton, said, 'The main problem was a complete lack of information. There was no concern, no cups of coffee, no nothing. A few people had had enough.'

Merseyside Police were called to Liverpool's airport when a forty-three-year-old man who had been waiting three days for an easyJet flight to Amsterdam started hurling abuse. Witness Matthew Marks, one of 450 passengers affected, said travellers were angry at poor communication from easyJet. 'A crowd of well over fifty gathered around one easyJet employee,' he said. 'He was trying to talk to the crowd but was constantly interrupted. The police intervened and hauled away one man who was particularly vocal but we could all understand his frustration.'

Problems with de-icing on easyJet aircraft were responsible for the most serious delays. EasyJet blamed a sub-contractor employed to de-ice its aircraft. 'Because they were not de-iced we could not fly and therefore had to cancel flights,' said a spokesman. 'We have said we will refund fares for anyone delayed over four hours and we will look at all claims for compensation.' Mike Goodman, easyJet's commercial director, said: 'This is very embarrassing; it's tragic during the holiday season and we apologise wholeheartedly. We have been let down badly by our de-icing supplier who has had problems with their fluid and machines. But we would not compromise safety.'

EasyJet never recorded a fatality or a crash. The carrier may have been stringent about cost-control but money was not an issue when it came to safety. Like other low-cost operators, however, easyJet was subject to delays, cancellations and mishaps which inevitably resulted in frustrated passengers.

The New Year saw relations with Luton put under further strain. In January 2001, Barclays sold its 65 per cent stake in Luton Airport to the airports operator TBI for £82 million. The deal raised TBI's holding in Luton to 90 per cent, strengthening its position as a regional airports operator. TBI funded the purchase with £50 million of new borrowings and £31.7 million from an underwritten share placing.

Negotiations between Luton and easyJet broke down and until August the airline had to accept the increase of passenger charges to £8. EasyJet said that the higher fees it was now being forced to pay would henceforth appear as a 'Barclays legacy charge' on passenger booking confirmations. Webster announced that easyJet would absorb half of the increase and pass on the other half, meaning passengers would pay an extra £4 per ticket. 'The Barclays legacy at London Luton is that it has negotiated an obscene return on its initial investment which will have to be carried by users of the airport,' he added. The carrier also warned that TBI might not get any easier a ride, pointing out that, as an existing shareholder in Luton, it had been party to all the negotiations over landing charges at the airport.

Keith Brooks, the chief executive of TBI, said he had some sympathy with easyJet but claimed that Barclays had 'called all the shots and made all the running'. He added that TBI had always enjoyed a good relationship with easyJet at Belfast Airport, which it also owned. 'EasyJet is looking for a long-term agreement and we want to help the growth of the airline so I would hope that in a few months we can come to a reasonable agreement,' Brooks said.

In March 2001, easyJet joined a consortium of UK airlines, called the 'The Airline Group', which was awarded the contract to run NATS, the UK's air traffic control system, under a public-private partnership for a thirty-year term. The group's other members were Airtours, Britannia, British Airways,

British Midland, JMC, Monarch and Virgin Atlantic.

The budget carrier continued to add routes to its network. In March, easyJet started operating scheduled flights between Geneva and Barcelona after ailing Swissair abandoned its services on the route. EasyJet must have felt some satisfaction in taking over the service from the carrier that had battled so hard to keep it away. In April 2001, easyJet announced the launch of five new services in the next few months: Amsterdam to Barcelona and Glasgow, Belfast to Edinburgh and Glasgow and London Gatwick to Nice, and started its Amsterdam to London Gatwick service. By July, easyJet had sold 10 million seats through its website.

In August, easyJet's attention was diverted back to the landing-fee row at Luton when the French group Vinci made a hostile £516 million bid, at 90p a share, for airports operator TBI. One of the conditions of the Vinci offer was that the Luton landing fees did not come down. The 'no reductions' clause was in the original cash bid and remained in the formal offer documents.

But easyJet was not prepared to back down and accept higher landing fees. The company vowed that it would not increase the number of its 737 aircraft at the airport, currently standing at eighteen, unless either prices came down or the access and airport infrastructure were improved. It was stalemate.

5. Crisis control

EASYJET'S CAREER AS a public company started badly, with losses of £10.3 million for its first six months, though industry analysts pointed out that the loss was to be expected since the airline traditionally made all its profits in the summer period when passenger volumes and yields were high. More encouragingly, first half revenues rose 43 per cent, while passenger numbers increased 31 per cent to 3.2 million, with 86 per cent of bookings made on the Internet.

Meanwhile, the major carriers were recording falling passenger numbers. The US economy was entering recession, and as transatlantic travel fell away the large carriers saw their margins being eroded. Airlines had grown accustomed to taking the easy way out, and many were fat and complacent after pampered decades of government control. Fragmented and financially fragile, the European aviation industry was reeling from rising fuel prices, an excess of seats and hefty costs, particularly for labour. Earlier in 2001, Germany's

Lufthansa had capitulated after a strike of just three days and awarded its pilots a 12 per cent pay raise. Airlines were acutely vulnerable to industrial action; even the threat of a strike encouraged passengers to switch allegiances to rival carriers. As Daniel Solon of leading London aviation consultants Avmark International pointed out, 'The cabin unions realise they have a grip on the windpipe of the industry.'

British Airways bade farewell to CEO Bob Ayling. In Ayling's place, the flag carrier welcomed Rod Eddington as its new chief executive; speculation arose that Eddington was brought in because his greater popularity with employees might make it easier for him to push through as many as 20,000 job cuts. Credited with revitalising the fortunes of domestic carrier Ansett Airlines, the second largest airline in his native Australia, Eddington had grown up in the countryside in Western Australia and was incredibly down to earth. A Rhodes scholar, he had married an air hostess at Cathay Pacific, where he was formerly managing director, and had two children. After running Ansett, in which Rupert Murdoch had a 50 per cent stake before selling to Air New Zealand, Eddington became a non-executive director on the board of Murdoch's News Corporation. He was expected to leave the airline industry and run Murdoch's Australian media operations but an offer to take the £500,000-a-year job at BA proved too hard to resist.

During his first twelve months as CEO at BA, Eddington got rid of BA's much-mocked ethnic tail fins, held and then broke off merger talks with KLM and suffered the aftermath of the Concorde crash in July 2000. Eddington had walked into a tough job. At the start of September 2001, the new CEO predicted an annual pre-tax loss of £65 million for the year ending March 2002, his first full year in charge, compared with a previously forecast full-year profit of £150 million.

Labour costs at the British flag carrier were rising as pilots demanded more money. It looked increasingly likely that BA would cut more jobs in 2001, having already shed 3,000 in

2000. It had already announced its intention to reduce its passenger-carrying capacity by 25 per cent by March 2003. Airline traffic volumes for BA's crucial long-haul business were nose-diving as Western economies deteriorated faster than expected and competition intensified. Profits from the long-haul business were simply no longer robust enough to cover the spiralling costs of its short-haul flights, which were losing customers in droves to the no-frills airlines such as easyJet.

'We are getting to a crossover point where the likes of BA will say "enough is enough",' Webster predicted. 'They will recognise we have deep pockets and they will concentrate on long-haul business and leave short-haul to us. I believe in the near future there will be two ways to travel over any distance in Europe: either high-speed train or low-cost airline.'

BA's new CEO worked hard at consolidating and rationalising the company's short-haul UK and European businesses, which had been losing BA £300 million a year. He cut BA's long-haul flights from Gatwick, transferring some to Heathrow, and reduced the number of companies using the BA brand. He also promised to fight back in the domestic and European short-haul market against easyJet and Ryanair, who by now were both larger than BA in terms of market capitalisation. Given that BA's cost base was three to four times higher than those of its no-frills rivals such as Ryanair, it seemed a quixotic quest.

Ryanair liked to compare itself with Walmart in the US: 'pile it high and sell it cheap', a philosophy that was making the company Europe's fastest-growing airline. Having carried 7.4 million passengers in the year to 31 March 2001, a rise of 35 per cent on the year before, Ryanair raised annual pre-tax profits by 44 per cent to £104.5 million on revenues up 32 per cent to £487 million. Ryanair's strong growth was accompanied by a stellar share performance. The airline was a darling of the City, with brokers showering it in 'buy' notes.

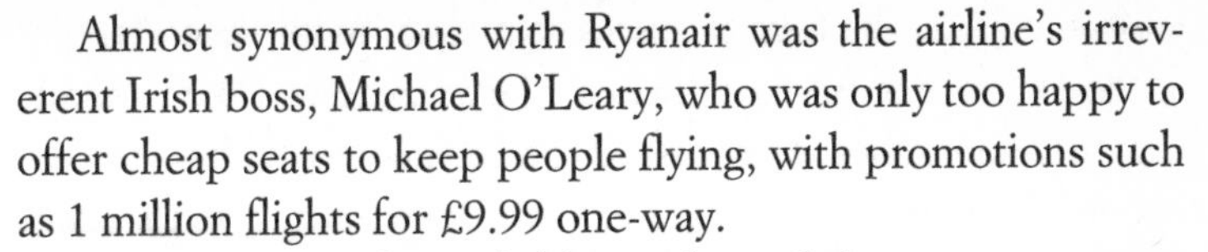

Almost synonymous with Ryanair was the airline's irreverent Irish boss, Michael O'Leary, who was only too happy to offer cheap seats to keep people flying, with promotions such as 1 million flights for £9.99 one-way.

O'Leary, one of six children whose father was an entrepreneurial type with a background in farming, rabbit-breeding and property, had trained as a tax consultant with KPMG in Dublin, where he met Tony Ryan, Ryanair's founder, and became his adviser. By 1990, when Ryanair was on the brink of going under, he agreed to become chief executive in return for a 25 per cent stake. Habitually dressed in old Levi's, a rugby shirt and a baseball cap, O'Leary transformed Ryanair from a money-losing carrier serving Ireland and Britain into the leader, alongside easyJet, of Europe's low-fare airlines. By emulating the same low cost, no-frills model pioneered by the US's Southwest Airlines, Ryanair offered fares as low as one-tenth of the price of the national carriers on intra-European routes.

Unlike easyJet, Ryanair didn't compete head-on with the national carriers or fly into major airports such as Amsterdam. Instead, the airline flew to secondary airports outside main cities, targeting the discount market, which the majors had long shunned in favour of the business-class traveller. A hop to Paris with Ryanair, for example, really meant a flight to Beauvais, 43 miles north of the city in Picardy, where the terminal looked like a bus depot stuck in the middle of farmland.

While easyJet had to pay standard airport fees at major airports, out-of-the-way terminals were so hungry for business that Ryanair could negotiate airport fees of as little as €1.50 per passenger and get marketing and training support for as long as twenty years. That was a fraction of the €15 to €20 per passenger charged by Europe's major hubs. Because there was so little congestion at these locations, Ryanair's planes were back in the air no more than twenty-five minutes after landing.

Far from fearing the recession, Ryanair and easyJet

embraced it as the best business opportunity for years, largely at the expense of BA and the other large carriers. Like Ryanair, easyJet maintained it was well positioned to withstand any economic slowdown, arguing that it would benefit from passengers trading down to cheaper carriers. 'We have been praying for a downturn for years,' said Webster. 'There is a cascade effect as people trade down from the traditional carriers to the new low-cost operators.'

The percentage of easyJet customers who had 'business travel characteristics' (they booked last minute and left and returned within the week) had increased to 55 per cent from 36 per cent a year previously. 'There is an increasing acceptance among business travellers of easyJet and if there is a recession then there could well be a further migration of these passengers,' Webster reported enthusiastically.

British Airways' no-frills arm, Go, was also enjoying success. Go ran services to twenty destinations from Stansted and in May 2001 opened a new hub at Bristol, offering flights to eight destinations with plans to fly over half a million passengers from the new base in the first year. Go also had smaller-scale operations in Glasgow and Edinburgh, and was aiming to grow total passenger numbers from 2.8 million in 2000 to 'closer to 4 million' for 2001. The company had already expanded its fleet from thirteen to fifteen aircraft in 2001 and hoped to increase this to seventeen by 2002.

Aviation analysts at Merrill Lynch expected Europe's burgeoning low-cost airline market to grow between 25 per cent and 35 per cent over the following five years, and easyJet was in a prime position in that market. 'EasyJet looks to be positioned to grow at least in line with its sub-sector peers, and we believe it could be a beneficiary of any consolidation opportunities within the sector going forward,' Merrill Lynch analysts said.

And then, in just one day, the world changed irrevocably. Millions of people saw the devastating pictures of planes

crashing into the World Trade Centre on 11 September 2001. The world was plunged into grief and fear.

Several European carriers had already been wobbling before 11 September, and now many airlines were left struggling to survive. Many people decided it was too dangerous to fly and rapidly cancelled their holiday plans. Businesses axed travel budgets. Big national carriers – Belgium's Sabena, Ireland's Aer Lingus, Spain's Iberia, Italy's Alitalia and Switzerland's Swissair – came under enormous financial pressure, some even teetering on the brink of insolvency as passengers were scared away from flying.

To counteract falling passenger volume, Europe's major airlines cut flights, grounded aircraft, raised fares, and sacked workers in their tens of thousands. Alitalia called the situation 'the worst crisis commercial airlines have faced since the end of World War II'. To meet it, Italy's national carrier announced cost-saving measures including the cutting of 2,500 jobs, or 12 per cent of the workforce. Aer Lingus dismissed almost a quarter of its 7,000 employees. Lufthansa cut catering from European flights and asked staff to accept a four-day working week, pay cuts and early retirement. The crisis may have had a silver lining for some; as Seamus Conlon, at the time managing director of Airtours Holidays, commented, 'Everything that the airlines had wanted to do for years suddenly became possible.'

Many airlines cut fares in a bid to encourage passengers back on to their planes. From mid-October British Airways offered 5 million tickets to twenty-one European destinations at bargain prices, with 500,000 tickets to cities such as Amsterdam, Paris, Berlin, Brussels, Barcelona and Madrid at £69, and an additional 'children go free' deal. Despite the promotion BA announced a 73 per cent fall in profits in the six months to September 30 and stepped up its ongoing jobs cull, announcing 7,200 job losses and a 9 per cent cut in capacity, while executives accepted pay cuts. The carrier reported an 11.6 per cent drop in passenger numbers for September, including a 32.1 per cent reduction on routes to the US. BA's passenger numbers fell by 24.7 per cent in October, and by November the flag carrier was losing £2 million a day.

The terrorist attacks precipitated a massive shake-out in the industry as airlines battled for survival. Ansett Airlines of Australia went bust within a few hours of the disaster in New York. Swissair, already on the brink before the attacks, owing to an ill-judged spending spree buying stakes in some of Europe's worst-performing airlines such as Belgium's Sabena and Air Lib of France, grounded its fleet on 2 October 2001 and filed for protection from creditors. Swissair's collapse helped bring down the ailing Belgian national carrier Sabena.

Europe's major aviation industry was experiencing a financial crisis that bore 'no relation to anything we have ever seen', declared Karl-Heinz Neumeister, head of the European Aviation Association in Brussels. The AEA predicted full-year losses of $8.9 billion, far more than the industry's previous largest annual loss of $2.4 billion after the Gulf War. Between 11 September and 4 November, North Atlantic air traffic fell by 35 per cent and European traffic by 10 per cent for major European airlines.

Industry experts predicted that many of the continent's money-losing flag carriers were headed towards bankruptcy, mergers or take-overs. BA's Eddington believed that Europe's fourteen national airlines would be replaced by just three main airlines grouped around Europe's largest carriers – British Airways, Air France and Lufthansa.

But as other European airlines cut thousands of jobs and dramatically scaled back services amid escalating losses, one sector of the airline industry continued to boom. Not only did 11 September fail to have any adverse effect on low-cost airlines, paradoxically it actually helped their business. People were queuing to travel on low-cost carriers such as easyJet, Ryanair and Buzz, which were recording unprecedented heavy bookings. Low-cost airlines traditionally did better during slow-downs; ten years previously, US discount airline Southwest

Airlines had seen its business increase four-fold immediately after the Gulf War.

While major European flagships such as Air France and Lufthansa saw double-digit declines in their business after the terrorist attacks, easyJet's bookings recovered to their pre-11 September levels within a few days, after falling by 26 per cent on the morning after the terrorist attacks. The carrier flew 680,383 passengers in September, 150,000 more than in the previous year. In October and November, when most European airlines were watching their traffic disappear, easyJet's traffic rose 32.5 per cent and 39 per cent respectively year-on-year.

The number of tickets easyJet sold over the Internet also increased. During November, 90.1 per cent of sales were made online, up on November 2000's figure of 79.4 per cent. The update came just days after British Airways reported a 17.8 per cent slump in passenger traffic during November, which it attributed to 'challenging' trading conditions.

One of easyJet's key strengths was that it didn't fly to the US. 'Our competitors suffered more because they fly the Atlantic,' said Stelios. 'I am almost embarrassed to admit we have benefited from the events of September 11.' Another advantage was that its costs were half those of leading European carriers, allowing it to offer rock-bottom fares. In the weeks after the attacks, easyJet slashed 150,000 seat prices by up to 60 per cent, with flights from London to Glasgow and Belfast for £12.50.

It seemed that people were willing to accept the additional risks of flying, provided it was with a budget airline such as easyJet or Ryanair. Part of the explanation was the assessment that terrorists were less likely to attack an airline with a name such as easyJet than a flag-waving carrier such as American Airlines or British Airways. People also reasoned that it was unlikely that a terrorist would blow up a plane that flew from Stansted Airport to Malaga or Tenerife.

There also seemed to be a widespread willingness to accept

a higher risk of death in return for lower prices. Money is regularly traded for risk when people decide not to buy a smoke alarm, a bicycle helmet or the safest car available. 'After the terrible tragedy we cut our prices even lower and seats on our planes sold like hot cakes,' Webster said. 'If the price is right people will accept your offer.' Michael O'Leary, chief executive of Ryanair, which was offering flights for just £1, echoed Webster's views in an interview with the *Sunday Telegraph* newspaper: 'Drop your prices and you'll be amazed how demand comes back!'

Stelios declared that easyJet was proof of public confidence in the economy. He praised shoppers for taking to the high street to help arrest an economic downturn after the attacks: 'The worst move to make at the moment is to give up. If you sit around waiting for a recession, it will find you. I'm taking a more positive approach. Business may not be as easy as it was but there's still a profit to be made.'

Indeed, easyJet's maiden set of results as a plc proved that the tragedy had done little to dent the airline's fortunes. In October 2001, easyJet announced that full-year pre-tax profits were up by 81 per cent to £40 million, well above even the highest forecasts of £37 million, on revenues of £356.9 million. The airline carried 7.1 million passengers in the twelve months to September 30, up 27 per cent on the previous year. The full-year load factor, or proportion of seats filled, increased by 2.2 per cent to 83 per cent. By now, easyJet was operating thirty-five routes out of seventeen airports. 'September 11 proved something that we have always been very confident of, namely that in a recession the low-cost model is a lot more resilient than traditional airlines,' said Webster.

By the end of October 2001, easyJet's share price had doubled in a single year relative to the average share price of the European aviation sector. EasyJet said that while traditional airlines had suffered from the slump in demand and disruption caused by the hijackings, it saw a chance to expand faster than it had expected. Stelios commented, 'I believe that easyJet is well placed to take advantage of the changing market conditions and the continued strong sentiment towards low-cost airlines. I am cautiously optimistic and believe that out of every crisis there is opportunity.'

The carrier predicted that as rivals merged or reduced services, then landing slots, aircraft and even cheaper pilots would become available. The company started to draw up growth plans with the aim of taking over vacant slots and services being abandoned by national airlines such as British Airways.

Webster flew to Brussels in October to demand the right to take over spare capacity at Gatwick Airport and make the airport its main base. EasyJet managers thought that a move to Gatwick would allow easyJet to tap into a bigger and wealthier market. Webster aimed to make easyJet's Gatwick operation two to three times bigger than that at Luton by around 2005, and said easyJet was also in talks with Paris Orly, Brussels and Zurich airports to gain control of take-off and landing slots vacated by airlines that were cutting capacity.

Webster's demands put easyJet on a collision course with BA, who wanted the Commission to relax its 'use-it-or-lose-it' rule, which forced airlines to give up any slot not used for 80 per cent of the time. BA felt it should be waived until passenger numbers rose back to normal levels, while easyJet argued that while transatlantic routes should be safeguarded, such a move within Europe would amount to an unfair state subsidy. Webster believed BA was trying to hold on to the slots to stop low-cost airlines taking them over. 'They know they have no future in continuing to develop European operations,' he said. 'Any airline that chooses not to fly a route should return its slots and they should be reallocated.'

At the end of October, with £244 million in the bank, easyJet announced it was planning to expand. It had ordered twenty-five new planes from Boeing, and wanted more. Webster said easyJet would put down a deposit on thirty Boeing 737s. At cost, the aircraft would set easyJet back as much as £20 million. But Stelios insisted that the new planes were necessary to boost easyJet's fleet and let it expand into airports such as Gatwick. Webster also said that the airline was looking to hire additional staff to cope with the company's growth plans. The aircraft announcement came just weeks after BA chairman Lord Marshall admitted that he was seeking to wriggle out of aircraft contracts with Boeing in a bid to reduce costs.

EasyJet moved to bolster its financial position. A year after its flotation, it announced plans to raise more than £90 million to exploit the turmoil afflicting rival airlines. The extra money would help fund expansion of the easyJet fleet, create new routes in the short-haul market and take over routes abandoned by other airlines.

Stelios also revealed that he wanted to sell some of his holding to raise as much as £67 million to support his other ventures. He needed the proceeds from his share sale to recapitalise the struggling easyEverything Internet cafés venture and launch more businesses under the 'easy' brand. After Internet cafés, rental cars and a credit card, he was 'looking at cinemas'. He said that the share sale would allow him to retain a significant stake, while freeing cash to invest in other ventures. 'After six years building this company up, I now wish to monetise some of my investment to invest in my new ventures,' he announced, 'although I will still retain a very significant investment in easyJet and have no present intention to sell any more shares.'

Stelios was in an unusual position: he was both benefiting and suffering from Europe's economic downturn. His London-based easyInternetcafé chain, which he hoped to make the McDonald's of web access, had burned through $58 million in two years. Faced with price-sensitive customers and spiralling expenses, the founder had to dig into his own pockets for $22 million to keep twenty outlets open in twelve European cities and New York. He sacked the company's CEO and closed stores in Rotterdam and Antwerp to preserve cash.

The planned share sale was the first time Stelios had taken cash out of easyJet. He denied that his proposed sale betrayed a lack of confidence. 'Of course not,' he said. 'It is only 7 per cent of the family's holding and I have no other income from the business except for capital gains. Every shareholder would prefer me to do it this way alongside the results than surprise them.' He added, 'Remember I come from a rich family. I do not need to sell easyJet shares to fund my lifestyle.'

In November, easyJet issued 26 million new shares and Stelios and his family sold 13 million. The combined share deals left Stelios with a holding in easyJet of 27–29 per cent and his family with 30.9 per cent. UBS Warburg and Credit Suisse First Boston sold the placing and open offer of 26 million shares on a three-for-forty basis at a price of 375p a share. Webster announced that the rights issue was 4.5 times over-subscribed; it raised £93.3 million for easy Jet.

'I am delighted at the success of this fund raising which will enable us to accelerate the expansion of our services to Europe's flying public,' Stelios said. 'To have succeeded in raising new money of this level is very encouraging in today's market.'

EasyJet also announced that it had resolved its long-running dispute with Luton Airport's owner TBI over landing charges, with a twenty-year agreement keeping easyJet charges at existing levels (£5.50 per passenger and 50p for baggage, an amount easyJet had previously said was excessive), which could be reduced if passenger numbers grew, compared with the airport's standard tariff of £8 per passenger. At the time, 2.1 million of the airline's passengers used the airport.

EasyJet now had an incentive to grow at Luton rather than moving its extra business to Gatwick, as threatened. Webster added: 'This announcement gives us certainty over our operations from London Luton Airport.'

Normality in aviation seemed barely possible in late 2001. Two months and a day after 11 September, just as the wounds were starting to heal, the world learned that American Airlines flight 587 had crashed on take-off from New York's Kennedy airport. The crash killed 260 on-board the Airbus A300 and five people on the ground. Even though terrorism was rapidly ruled out, the accident piled on the agony for Europe's major airlines, and many introduced fuel or insurance surcharges to compensate for rising oil prices and higher industry costs.

EasyJet continued to bypass the industry's turbulence; between 24 September and 12 December, easyJet's shares soared by 49 per cent. Stelios encouraged people back to flying, pronouncing, 'You can't save souls in empty churches.' He was blunt about why easyJet had prospered since 11 September: 'It affected Americans flying to Europe, so our competitors, especially BA, suffered a lot more than we did. The Europeans are more familiar with terrorism, and went back to flying much faster. So we could accelerate our growth while BA had to start retrenching.'

The terrorist attacks made it unpleasantly obvious that in security terms the airline industry had become a soft target, and airlines throughout the world increased their vigilance, with tighter security and better policing at airports and on planes. British pilots agreed to reinforced steel cockpit doors, extra searches on crews and passengers, and restrictions on sharp implements. Pilots were told that not even their spouses could join them in the cockpit. Plans to deploy undercover armed guards on British planes sparked fierce debate. The Israeli airline El Al had carried armed marshals on all its flights for more than thirty years, and Lufthansa also used guards on some flights. EasyJet made no attempt to follow their example; Stelios argued that guns on planes could fall into the hands of would-be hijackers and put the lives of passengers at risk.

People continued to be scared away from flying. In an attempt to relax nervous passengers, easyJet hired drag queen May McFetridge, alias comic John Linehan, to provide in-flight entertainment on its flights from Belfast to Glasgow and Edinburgh. Dressed in an orange and green kilt, green Dr

Marten boots, a sporran with poodle hair, waistcoat and blouse and a Scottish 'Jimmy' hat, the comedian handed out sweets and told bad jokes (one example was: 'If you are going to be sick throw up in the bag in front of you, whether you know her or not'). The tactic proved popular with most passengers, but not all; one Scottish businessman complained that he couldn't concentrate on his preparation for an important meeting.

In general, people continued to perceive the budget carriers as unlikely targets for any terrorist attack. Until that is, twenty-nine-year-old Kerim Chatty was caught trying to board a Ryanair flight from Vasteras in Sweden to Stansted with a pistol in his hand luggage. Half Tunisian and half Swedish, Chatty was an experienced pilot who – like nine of the 11 September hijackers – had undergone training in the US. The CIA believed that Chatty had planned to hijack a Ryanair Boeing 737 and fly it into a US embassy in Europe – probably that in London.

Chatty, who had previous assault and weapons convictions, told investigators he found the gun in a borrowed car a few weeks before his arrest. He said he put it in his bag and forgot about it when he left for the airport to fly to an Islamic conference in Birmingham. The district court in Vasteras said Chatty's explanation could not be dismissed, and prosecutor Thomas Haeggstroem dropped hijacking charges because of lack of evidence. Instead, Chatty was jailed for four months for weapons violation.

Then a reporter from Scotland's *Daily Record* newspaper used a fake identity card in the name of Hani Hanjour, who crashed an airliner into the Pentagon on 11 September, to travel on flights with both easyJet and Ryanair. No one at either of the airlines challenged him over his false identity.

EasyJet was resolute about adopting a zero-tolerance approach when it came to security measures; short shrift was given to even the most obvious of jokes. In October, Malcolm and Betty Ashworth, both in their late sixties, were checking in at Liverpool John Lennon airport when they were asked if they had any dangerous items. Mr Ashworth turned to his wife and jokingly inquired: 'Have you got your pistol, dear?' The couple were escorted away for a thorough baggage search; although no offending items were found, they were not allowed to board their easyJet flight to Belfast.

EasyJet's policy even extended to children. An easyJet pilot turned away a group of thirty ten- and eleven-year-old schoolgirls on their way from Belfast to a netball tournament in Liverpool because they were a 'security risk'. The pilot refused to allow them to board the plane because he claimed that the four teachers accompanying them weren't enough to look after the children, leaving the girls in tears. The pupils from Rockport School in Craigavad, Co Down, had to take a ferry and an eight-hour coach journey instead, though easyJet later apologised and refunded the cost of their outward flight.

The carrier was determined to enforce its security policy that passengers, even on domestic flights, had to carry a valid form of photographic ID, namely a passport or national identity card, with visas when applicable. Age made no difference; lack of the correct ID meant that Scottish fourteen-year-old Jamie McGovern was not allowed to fly to Liverpool for trials with Everton football club, while ninety-four-year-old Elsie Brigg from Liverpool missed the family reunion her daughter had planned for months after easyJet staff refused to accept her bus pass as identification. Her daughter Jacqueline Gee complained that easyJet staff had made her 'feel like a gun-wielding maniac'.

One person tried to take advantage of the heightened sense of security. Alan Burton, who lived in the flight path of Liverpool's airport, became so frustrated with the noise of planes flying overhead that he called the airport in the early hours of the morning twice in three days, telling staff there were bombs on two easyJet flights to Belfast. Each time Special Branch officers became involved. Burton was jailed for twelve months at Liverpool crown court after pleading guilty to two charges of making hoax bomb calls.

Meanwhile, easyJet was busy planning its expansion into the French market. The airline applied to Cohor, the body which distributed take-off and landing slots at Paris Orly Airport, for 20,000 of the 35,000 slots that had become available following the collapse of AOM and Air Liberté, France's second largest airline.

Air Liberté, which together with its sister, long-haul and charter carrier AOM, employed 5,200 staff, had been struggling to overcome losses for years. Until May 2000 it was owned by British Airways, but after failing to turn it round, BA booked a big loss and sold it for £50 million to Swissair, which held 49 per cent, and its 51 per cent sleeping partner Taitbout Antibes, controlled by Paris-quoted Marine Wendel. Losses mounted to £500,000 a day and had helped plunge Swissair into loss too, causing Air Liberté executive chairman Marc Rochet to file his company's insolvency in June 2001.

EasyJet saw great potential for its low-cost model in the French market, which had no domestic equivalent. 'Paris and London have a similar passenger base, but the difference is four low-cost carriers serve London,' said easyJet spokesman Toby Nicol. 'How many serve Paris?'

EasyJet aimed to become the first low-cost carrier operating out of France, and to use Paris Orly as its second major European operating base after Luton. The airline wanted to base ten Boeing 737-700 and 737-300 short-haul aircraft at Orly, reroute some of its existing cheap flights from Luton and Liverpool and provide cheap, high-frequency flights to European cities such as Nice, Barcelona, Madrid and Geneva. It projected building up a 2.5 million per year passenger base from Orly 'very quickly'.

In response to easyJet's French ambitions, O'Leary was planning to expand Ryanair's presence at Beauvais Airport, outside Paris, to compete head-to-head with its no-frills rival in the French market. There were no slot restrictions at Beauvais, so Ryanair's presence there was limited only by its willingness to invest. Like easyJet, Ryanair was increasing the size of its fleet and had plans to open other bases in continental Europe. The Irish airline began flights from Brussels Charleroi airport, its first base outside the UK and Ireland, in March 2001.

Ryanair had also thrown down the gauntlet to Lufthansa, mainland Europe's biggest flag carrier, announcing its plans to make Frankfurt-Hahn a hub airport. Ryanair already flew a handful of flights from Hahn and planned to ramp up its operations at the German airport to offer more than thirty flights a day from February 2002. O'Leary claimed he could undercut Lufthansa's fares by as much as 75 per cent. Ryanair was already engaged in a bruising price war with Go on routes between Ireland and Scotland, with both airlines offering tickets for as little as £9.99 for a return flight between Dublin and Edinburgh.

However, easyJet's French aspirations were met with resistance from the outset. The French authorities refused to provide take-off and landing slots on the grounds that the airport was full. Webster hoped the prospect of 300 new jobs at Orly, at a time when Air Liberté was poised to shed 1,400, might tip the balance, and he flew over to Paris to lobby the French Transport Ministry officials. In the meantime, easyJet offered employment to potentially displaced employees at AOM/Air Liberté, in the event that the regional carrier failed to secure the appropriate financial backing it needed to survive. AOM/Air Liberté were continuing to operate in what amounted to the equivalent of US Chapter 11 bankruptcy, while its employees participated in sporadic strikes. But the beleaguered carrier's employees refused easyJet's offer and pressed for a solution to protect all jobs.

Management at the carrier clearly liked the concept of introducing low-cost flights into France. In the event Jean-Charles Corbet, the former pilots' union leader, backed by

Canadian bank CIBC, bought Air Liberté and AOM for a token sum and attempted to turn them into a low-cost carrier named Air Lib. Corbet planned France's first low-cost internal flights from Paris to Nice, Toulouse, Toulon, Perpignan and Lourdes, adding Marseilles, Nimes, Bordeaux and Montpellier later, with one-way fares as low as £20. Unfortunately, the high fuel burn of its aircraft and stubborn union resistance to more flexible working and low-cost business practices left the new chief executive officer with low fares but high costs.

Air Lib was watched closely by easyJet, Ryanair, Go and Virgin Express, all of whom had expressed interest in expanding their development in France, especially Paris. Only Buzz flew at low prices from anywhere in Britain to Paris, with Ryanair using Beauvais Airport north-west of Paris for flights from Dublin. Air Lib wasn't about to help easyJet fulfil its ambitions, however. The new carrier had agreed to hand back 35,000 of the 75,000 slots it controlled at Orly Airport, following the French authorities' request for it to abandon 40,000 of the slots. But then Air Lib changed its mind about the number of slots it was willing to relinquish, giving back only 12,000 instead.

EasyJet, which was still hoping to gain 20,000 of the slots given up by Air Lib, was outraged. 'It is scandalous that Air Lib has not fulfilled the terms of its restructuring,' said Webster. 'It is a piece of blatant anti-competitive protectionism. This company should at least have the decency to abandon those slots it knows it cannot use.' In the end, Cohor awarded the bulk of the available slots to Air Algeria, Iberia and Air Malta. EasyJet's Swiss arm, easyJet Switzerland, was given a few slots from Paris to Zurich and Geneva, but easyJet was no nearer to fulfilling its French ambitions.

But the company was still able to expand elsewhere. Webster felt that the airline's strong post-11 September performance strengthened its position at airports. 'Four to five years ago, airports treated the low-cost sector as a very risky experiment. I think we have now created enough good experience in airports around Europe that the word is that the low-cost business is a good business. It's viable. Every major airport nowadays contacts us and says, "Can we talk?"'

The carrier continued to develop its presence at London Gatwick by announcing four new routes (to Edinburgh, Malaga, Majorca and Zurich) in December 2001, making easyJet the second largest scheduled airline at the airport after British Airways. By the end of the year, easyJet was flying thirty-five routes between seventeen airports.

Webster was already looking ahead. 'I've always stressed as intrinsic to the airline that the trick is not making it profitable today, it's making it profitable when it is very large. If you want to get from roughly thirty aircraft now to three hundred aircraft, you've got to make sure the things you do are repeatable. You can't get there by just taking opportunistic moves when one comes up. Opportunities, whether it be cheap airports or cheap planes, are not predictable enough in their availability. If you want to grow 25 per cent a year for as far as you can see into the future, you have to make sure you have a business that can continue to retain the same business model . . . By picking major airports and brand-new planes we build what we call a cookie cutter. Having every passenger buying exactly the same seat on exactly the same plane is an example of how we apply the concept of simplicity. You move complexity, you move costs.'

Meanwhile, O'Leary estimated that Ryanair's business would double to 15 million passengers by 2003, and double again by 2008, making Ryanair Europe's number one international airline. In November, Ryanair reported a 39 per cent surge in interim profits to £55 million. The tragic events of 2001 may have left many European airlines in a tailspin but Ryanair and easyJet were soaring even higher.

6. Going, going, gone

EASYJET'S ARCH-RIVAL GO was also growing in leaps and bounds. Just as Go had been beginning to perform successfully in November 2000, Ayling's successor, Rod Eddington, surprised Cassani by deciding to offload it. Eddington didn't want to wait to find out whether Go's promised profits would arrive the following year, after estimated losses of about £25 million in the previous two. Eddington thought Go was cannibalising British Airway's customer base, nipping away at its parent's undercarriage with fares of £39 return to Munich and £49 to Rome. 'It's not a business segment we're in,' said Eddington; though the joke ran in aviation circles that Eddington should have sold the rest of British Airways and kept Go.

EasyJet already had its eyes set on its rival, and for a while, there was talk that the orange airline would take over Go, thus eradicating a powerful competitor and increasing its size and strength. But it wasn't easyJet's turn yet. In June 2001, after months of negotiations, BA let Go go for £110 million to a management buyout team. The management team then sold it on to their financial backers, the private equity group 3i, retaining a 22 per cent stake. Go was now a rival to BA. But a BA spokeswoman maintained that the airline had made the right move: 'We believe we got the timing right and that we got an excellent return of some 400 per cent on an initial investment of £25 million.'

Chief executive Barbara Cassani hurried home to play Monopoly with her two children after completing the deal. 'I wasn't able to spend a lot of time with them while we were putting the deal together,' she admitted. Cassani relished running the airline and was clearly proud of it. Moreover, she was determined to quash speculation that Go had only survived until then because of BA's financial support. She planned to open one new base a year for the following three years, buy new aircraft and set up operations on the continent on her own terms. 'Now we can grow,' she exulted. We want to double in size every couple of years. That was never possible under BA.'

Charismatic, a stylish dresser and a witty conversationalist, Cassani was a public relations dream. She combined an informal approach with a steely determination and a hard-nosed American business style. Go employees loved her easy-going, approachable manner. She became known for hosting dinners at a pizza restaurant near Stansted, where she gave cabin crew and back-office staff lessons in share ownership. She told one interviewer: 'All of a sudden you see a light come on in their eyes – and the first thing they say is, "Is there a catch?" And I say, "Yes there is a catch. The catch is they aren't going to be worth this unless we do something."' Diners were always restricted to two courses only; their boss liked to remind them they were working for a low-cost airline. Like Stelios, Cassani wasn't afraid to muck in with the troops – she was once an air hostess for the day, making coffee and cleaning seats with the rest of the cabin crew. In 2002, she was named Veuve Clicquot's businesswoman of the year.

Expansion was rapid. In March 2002, Go increased its passenger numbers to 428,999 from 358,626 passengers in February and 319,000 in January. It was now the UK's third-largest airline. Go flew on thirty-eight routes within the UK and mainland Europe, with a fleet of twenty-four 737-300s and another three aircraft due to be delivered by June 2002. Go's load factor was an impressive 76.5 per cent, and some 83 per cent of its ticket sales were sold via the Internet. It announced a four-fold increase in pre-tax profits to £17 million for the year ending 31 March 2002. Full-year sales rose 46 per cent to £233.7 million and passenger numbers increased 55 per cent to 4.3 million. Cassani was understandably proud of her achievements and planned to float the airline in the next two years; she was confident that Go could repeat easyJet's success and raise close to £1 billion on the stockmarket.

And then the bombshell was dropped: easyJet was in talks to take over Go. Cassani was outraged, but easyJet had had the takeover in mind for years. Unlike Ryanair, Go followed near-identical business models to easyJet and targeted the same passengers. Taking over Go would annihilate easyJet's fiercest opponent and at a stroke make easyJet Europe's largest low-cost airline.

Unsurprisingly, Cassani was fiercely opposed to easyJet taking over what she called her 'third baby'. She told staff she was 'extremely disappointed' that Go might no longer be an independent company. Her ambitions to float Go now lay in tatters. Cassani claimed that her management was '100 per cent' behind her opposition to the transaction. But easyJet was confident not only of 3i's support but of that of Go's management – which would be essential as easyJet integrated the two companies. Go's senior management accounted for the bulk of the 18.5 per cent staff equity holding in the company; the twenty-seven top managers at Go would become millionaires when easyJet bought the airline, sharing about £60 million. Cassani, who owned 4 per cent of the company, would gain about £16 million from the deal. Ironically, easyJet also had to pay £42 million to Barclays Private Equity in return for its 11.2 per cent of Go, only two years after Stelios had cut up his Barclaycard as part of easyJet's dispute with the Barclay Group about its hike in landing fees at Luton Airport.

Cassani also became embroiled in a personal row with Stelios, who claimed to have offered her the role of Webster's deputy at the enlarged airline with a promise of taking over when Webster retired. 'There can only be one chief executive in a business,' Stelios said. Cassani insisted she had never been offered a role in a merged airline. In an extraordinary move, she issued a formal statement saying that she had 'never been offered a role', did not want one and would quit if the deal went ahead. Stelios countered by saying that he had offered her the number two job over dinner in a private room at Mark's club in London's Mayfair the previous year.

Stelios branded her version of events as libellous. 'She is calling me a liar and she is calling my chief executive a liar,' he said, rubbing salt in the wound by insisting that Cassani was allowing 'emotion and ego' to cloud her judgement. He added that Cassani would not be allowed to stand in the way of a deal, pointing out, 'No company is ever a one-man or one-woman show.' Ryanair's O'Leary suggested that Cassani should 'shut up, take the money, be very happy that she's one of the very few people who have made a lot of money out of aviation'.

Cassani's anger wasn't just directed at Stelios. She was also furious with Go's majority shareholder 3i for agreeing to sell to easyJet and cash in so quickly. The venture capitalist had been down a similar flight path before, when it sold British Caledonian to BA in the mid-1980s. The company made a living by buying low and selling high. In an emotive message to her 900-strong workforce, Cassani said, 'When we bought Go from BA they indicated to me that they would wait for a flotation to get their money out, but they felt that the potential offer was just too good.'

Cassani's wrath wasn't sufficient to hold back the deal.

EasyJet got the green light from its shareholders and from competition regulators for the merger to go ahead. The first flights by the enlarged easyJet were due to take off the following March. Cassani called the deal 'a tremendous compliment to all of us at Go' and added that she was 'particularly pleased that everyone at Go will share in the rewards from our success'.

In August 2002, easyJet and Go completed the merger deal to create Europe's number one low-cost airline. Stelios called the takeover 'one of the most exciting developments' in the airline's history, and Webster added that the group wanted to create an airline that could 'capitalise on any opportunity in Europe'.

Cassani continued her fighting talk even after the conclusion of the takeover, claiming that Go was a better company than easyJet. Webster conceded that Go often provided a better service. 'There are certain things that Go does better,' he admitted. 'It is better at looking after customers both on board and in its after sales service. We want to bring these things forward into the easyJet model.' Douglas Johnson, a policy adviser at the Air Transport Users' Council, concurred. 'We got a lot of feedback suggesting that Go was the best of the low-cost carriers. We hope that some of the things that made it successful will be carried over into the merged airline.'

Cassani urged her staff to take the 'Go spirit' with them to carry out a reverse culture takeover. The deal had split the Go management team. Four leading executives, including chief financial officer Andrew Cowen, left the airline. EasyJet persuaded three other senior directors to stay on with the use of 'golden handcuffs', namely chief operating officer Ed Winter, sales and marketing director David Magliano, and director of customer services Dominic Paul. The takeover made Winter, a former British Airways manager who had been Cassani's right-hand man at Go, an instant multimillionaire. He became the new chief operating officer of the enlarged easyJet, provididing day-to-day leadership of the airline while Webster focused on easyJet's longer-term strategic development.

The two companies continued to operate in parallel while easyJet worked out the best way of proceeding with the practicalities of the merger. Go launched a promotion after the takeover was announced, offering flights between its base at Stansted and Belfast for £5. Go moved to reassure its passengers who were calling its booking line that their tickets would not be affected by easyJet's deal. No routes were to be dropped in the short term – not even those to Nice, Barcelona and Malaga, where both airlines flew.

The widely admired Go brand was set to disappear by early 2003, and the name would start to be erased from 1 December, when the sales staff would start selling all tickets under the easyJet banner. All cabin crew were to wear easyJet's uniform, and all the old Go aircraft were repainted in easyJet's trademark orange. Webster said that easyJet's most urgent task was to decide on the location of the combined company headquarters, as easyJet considered moving from Luton to Go's base at Stansted Airport in Essex, 30 miles away. In the end, easyJet decided to stay in Luton. It hoped Go staff based at Stansted would want to relocate to Luton.

EasyJet financed the £374 million acquisition partly by raising £276.7 million through a rights issue. Credit Suisse First Boston acted as the sponsor and financial advisor to easyJet and was the sole book runner in placing the rights, underwriting the issue alongside UBS Warburg and Schroder Salomon Smith Barney. EasyJet financed the rest of the deal out of its own capacious pocket. The company was financially stable: it reported pre-tax profits of £1 million in the half-year ending 31 March 2002 compared with a loss of £103 million a year earlier. Revenues rose 36 per cent to £194 million pounds during the six-month period. EasyJet shareholders had to pay £9.5 million in advisory fees relating to the acquisition and £5.5 million relating to the rights issue, and existing shareholders were offered four new shares for every eleven held at a price of 265p.

The takeover enabled easyJet immediately to reach a size it

might otherwise have taken several years to achieve, not to mention giving it another London base at Stansted. 'Buying Go will produce a 100 per cent step-change in growth by bringing expansion more quickly and smoothly,' said Webster. The purchase put blue sky between the combined airline and European rivals such as Buzz and Virgin Express, and made it even larger than Ryanair. The purchase increased easyJet's fleet to fifty-four aircraft from thirty, compared with Ryanair's forty-four planes, and almost doubled its routes to eighty-one from forty-five, compared with Ryanair's seventy-six routes. EasyJet and Go together flew more than 12 million passengers during the twelve months ending in March 2002, compared to 11 million passengers on Ryanair. The enlarged company had a turnover of almost £490 million – £210 million more than its Irish rival.

But O'Leary maintained that he wasn't concerned by the takeover, adding that it would probably be good for Ryanair if the three main low-fares airlines were reduced to two. Ryanair said it had no interest in muscling in on the talks. '[Go's] fares are about 50 per cent higher than ours and their costs are about 60 per cent higher,' said O'Leary. 'We spend our time trying to drive down costs, forget it.'

Stelios said that the planned acquisition would 'contribute significantly to our objective of becoming Europe's leading low-cost airline by strengthening our position in important target markets and providing a larger, stronger platform from which to exploit growth opportunities profitably'. The real point of easyJet's deal seemed to be to outfox the competition. Increasingly, that didn't mean Ryanair, which was growing by offering super-cheap fares to ever more out-of-the-way destinations. EasyJet and Go, by contrast, took the more expensive option of flying to major airports in places where people already wanted to go. Taking over Go meant taking out one of the players.

The Consumers' Association worried that easyJet's purchase of Go might lead to a fare increase for passengers. 'The downside is that we will see less competition on the routes where the two carriers currently overlap,' the association said. EasyJet and Go had competed fiercely on busy domestic routes, from London to Edinburgh, Glasgow and Belfast and on routes to holiday destinations such as Malaga. But Webster told BBC radio that the combination with Go would not mean an increase in fares. 'This is an opportunity to keep prices low,' he said. 'That is the beauty of our model. We need low fares to stimulate the market that we are developing.' Stelios likewise dismissed warnings of raised fares, arguing that because of its increased size the easyJet/Go combination would be able to make savings on purchases of fuel, insurance and aircraft.

Go was not easyJet's only takeover target. At the same time as its acquisition of the former BA subsidiary, easyJet announced that it had acquired an option to buy Deutsche BA, the German subsidiary of British Airways. Deutsche BA operated 130 flights per day on seven German internal routes with a fleet of sixteen 737-300s. In the last financial year it had had a turnover of £212.5 million and carried 3.5 million passengers. Deutsche BA had embarked on a no-frills strategy earlier in 2002, cutting fares to €39 on its domestic network. Other low-cost measures included launching a €48 million cost-cutting drive through September 2003, charging for on-board services and promoting Internet ticket sales. But it hadn't worked; the carrier hadn't made a profit since it was set up in 1992, though it didn't reveal the extent of its losses.

The agreement with DBA gave easyJet the option to acquire 100 per cent of the chronically unprofitable German airline at any time up to 3 July 2003. In the interim, BA would retain full control of Germany's second-largest airline but easyJet would place three managers with Deutsche BA, contribute £3 million towards capital expenditure and pay BA £366,000 per month. BA estimated the deal to be worth between £18.3 million and £28 million.

Observers were concerned that the bigger easyJet became, the more it would change to become like a conventional airline and thus lose its point. Size meant complexity, and one of the reasons easyJet had been such a success was that it had kept its operations simple and cheap. London aviation consultants Avmark International noted that easyJet was straying from the low-cost business model it originally embraced, that of Southwest Airlines in the US, which championed organic growth, and pointed out that Go and Deutsche BA had both been started by British Airways and had different business cultures.

Analysts were even more concerned about easyJet's proposed takeover of Deutsche BA than its purchase of Go, and several investment houses downgraded easyJet's stock to 'underperform'. Lehman Brothers commented: 'We believe the market is over-estimating the profitability of future growth and that the management has under-estimated the structural differences in the German market and the task at Deutsche BA.'

Jürgen Weber, chairman of Lufthansa, said he could not see how easyJet would manage to turn around unprofitable Deutsche BA and claimed he was unfazed by the prospect of easyJet's entry into his home market. Weber emphasised that budget airlines catered to a different customer base from Lufthansa, Germany's flagship airline. 'The tasks ahead for easyJet are enormous: the integration of three companies – Go, Deutsche BA and easyJet – into one firm has to be established first. According to our estimates, the acquisition of Deutsche BA by easyJet does not create a more competitive environment.' BA itself said that selling Deutsche BA was a step towards improving the performance of its European short-haul business.

Webster characterised the deal as a quick way for easyJet to establish itself in Germany. EasyJet would follow in the footsteps of Ryanair, which had established a base at Frankfurt/Hahn – its second in continental Europe – in February 2002.

A combined easyJet/Deutsche BA would immediately be propelled into pole position in the German market, with significant opportunities for growth, declared Webster. Time would tell.

7. Stelios quits

EASYJET WAS PROSPERING. Its sales were buoyant, its share price was at an all-time high and it was taking over its greatest rival. Which, as far as Stelios was concerned, meant that it was time for him to leave. In April 2002, in a statement to the London Stock Exchange, he announced that he was going to give up the chairmanship of easyJet. The statement startled investors and fans of the airline alike. EasyJet without Stelios? Surely that was like jam without bread? Virgin without Branson?

EasyJet's impromptu press conference held later that day was, true to form, a no-frills affair. Reporters who made the trek to the airline's bright-orange headquarters at Luton Airport to hear about Stelios's resignation first-hand had to pay 80 pence each for their plastic cup of coffee.

Stelios told a gathering of surprised reporters that he was to be replaced by Sir Colin Chandler, the chairman of Rolls-Royce subsidiary Vickers Defence Systems and deputy chairman of engineering group Smiths. Chandler, a City veteran and part of the blue-chip establishment, turned up at the press conference in a tie that was swiftly dispensed with before the photo shoot. EasyJet banned ties except on the flight deck, a rule that applied equally to senior management.

Stelios told the media that he had a low boredom threshold and had lost interest in what he called 'the tedious business of chairing a major plc'. He maintained that he wasn't cut out to be a corporation man. 'I like taking risks,' the easyJet founder explained. 'And taking uncalculated risks is the privilege of the entrepreneur, not a chairman. You have to recognise your strengths and weaknesses early in life. It is all about finding what you are good at. In my case it is starting a company, coming up with ideas and turning dreams into reality.'

To outsiders, Stelios's decision to give up control of the business might have seemed strange, but it was typical of the thirty-five-year-old millionaire, who didn't believe in standing still. 'For me, this is like growing up – easyJet is not a baby any more,' said Stelios. 'I like having a dream and making it a reality, but I prefer other people to run the companies once they are set up. When people ask me what my favourite business is, I say the next one.'

By leaving, Stelios was also bowing to pressure from City investors, who did not like him being a major shareholder as well as chairman. Institutional investors feared that Stelios had been running the airline as his personal fiefdom and worried that other investors' interests were not being properly represented. 'The City likes to have its cake and eat it,' Stelios complained. 'They need you there to drive the business when it is growing but once it gets successful they turn around and say they want someone else to chair the company.'

London-based Pensions Investment Research Consultants, the shareholder voting advisor and corporate governance consultants, had issued a circular in March 2002, just prior to Stelios's announcement, recommending that clients block Stelios's re-election to the board, as well as that of his appointed non-executives. Boardroom best practice, enshrined in the Cadbury and Greenbury codes, dictated that all non-executives were to be independent of the company. Stelios had also infuriated institutional investors by attempting to change the articles of association to give the controlling shareholder (namely himself) the right to appoint the chairman and two non-executive directors in perpetuity.

Representatives from the Co-operative Insurance Company (CIS), which owned 17,205 shares out of easyJet's total of 292 million, turned up at easyJet's annual general meeting to rage about the board structure and the total absence of an environmental impact policy.

Christopher Hirst, CIS's chief investment manager, said that while a company such as easyJet might have delivered good shareholder value, the concern was about sustaining that performance. 'Proper corporate governance is needed to ensure that the right structure is in place in case things go wrong,' Hirst said. 'CIS has major concerns about the way easyJet is run. The corporate governance failings are so severe, we felt we had no option [but to vote against accepting the report in the accounts].'

EasyJet's other leading institutional investors included Standard Life, Britannic Asset Management, Fidelity of the US and Wellington Management. Shareholders were also keen to have a more experienced company chairman at the helm as easyJet expanded rapidly and headed for a possible place in the FTSE100. Stelios admitted that his colourful personal style might not be what the company needed most as it reached adulthood. 'It is a sign of maturity in a young company to have a chairman who is independent from the controlling shareholders,' he agreed.

Stelios denied being driven out of his chairman's role but said that he agreed with investors' complaints that he had too much control over the business. 'I have taken their views on board and I have decided this is best for us. I am doing it voluntarily. Nobody has forced me to do this. It is part of natural evolution. Starting a company requires different skills to those needed to chair a plc and I consider my strengths are in the former. I am a serial entrepreneur. The history of the City is littered with entrepreneurs who held on to their creations for too long, failing to recognise the changing needs of the company, its business and its shareholders.'

Asked if he might follow Stelios's example and take a back seat at the airline, Ryanair boss O'Leary glowered, 'There are very few examples of where I would follow Stelios in anything. He's Greek and I'm Irish. The Greeks will never outdo the Irish in anything. We'll even outdo them in drinking.' At least O'Leary had something nice to say about Stelios. 'He's the son of a billionaire,' proffered O'Leary. 'He could have been a rich tosser but at least he did something and set up an airline.'

Understandably, some outsiders were apprehensive about Stelios's move. Stelios had turned a £5 million cheque from his father into a business worth £1.5 billion with his drive and vision. A well-known personality, he was generally popular, depending on whether you had just enjoyed a cheap flight to Amsterdam or had suffered a delay at Luton Airport. He still got complaints addressed to him personally, even if the days when he had time to answer them personally had long gone.

But Stelios was aware of the danger of just one man being behind a company. 'The problem with very personal businesses is they are not saleable,' he said. 'If you build a whole business around your own personality, it can't grow. At some stage you must step back and say, "This business has to deal with its customers through its departments rather than through its founder."'

Stelios's decision to leave easyJet also meant that he could spend more time in the easyGroup headquarters in The Rotunda, a converted piano factory in Chalk Farm, London. He intended to carry on as chairman of the other companies within the easy empire and declared that his intention was to rebalance his portfolio between 'cash, listed equities, unlisted companies and risky start-ups'.

Stelio's car rental business, easyRentacar, was on track for a stockmarket flotation at the end of 2004. It had been a bumpy ride. The sales pitch for easyRentacar was impressive. With prices from £19 a day for a Mercedes A-class car in cities such as London or Glasgow, it sounded like a steal. But the final bill with all the extras was often a shock. There was a £15 'preparation and cleaning fee' for the first day's rental, mandatory insurance charges that varied depending on the customer's driving record, and a penalty of £100 for returning the car late. Moreover, the daily mileage limit was a mere 75 miles, then 20 pence for each extra mile.

Ever one to change the rules, Stelios had also decided at the launch of easyRentacar to recover the cost of damage in a different way from usual. Passengers returned rented vehicles in what they insisted was immaculate condition and later discovered that their accounts had been debited because of alleged damage, such as a scratched hubcap, even though the damage had been noted by the rental office before they collected the car. Stelios ended up with what he himself admitted was a huge customer backlash and a sizeable embarrassment, including at least two appearances on the BBC's *Watchdog* and damage to the easy brand.

Meanwhile, Stelios was working on a new bright-orange business called easyCinema. Stelios planned to offer prices as low as 20 pence for those who bought a ticket a month or two in advance, with higher prices for last-minute or peak-time bookings. EasyGroup held talks with estate agents to find a suitable location. The site turned out to be at what Stelios dubbed the 'centre of the entertainment world', otherwise known as Milton Keynes. Cinema buffs could forget Hollywood for true glamour and catch a bus up the M1 to the bright-orange box with ten screens. They might have to wait to see the latest hits: the big studios would not let him show their new movies.

Another one of Stelios's brainwaves was easyDorm, a chain of hostels providing cheap accommodation. Rooms were nine times bigger than a phone box and made from fibreglass. The little box's soft furnishings were in the company's familiar lurid orange, which no doubt didn't aid a restful night's sleep. Guests had to clean up after themselves or else pay a fee. But at least the rooms cost as little as £5 a night, if booked in advance.

Stelios was on a mission to prove wrong the sceptics who taunted that he was just 'lucky first time' with easyJet. 'Film distributors say, for instance, that I cannot change the cinema industry,' he said. 'Everyone thinks their industry is different, more difficult than the others are. But I will come along and tear up the rule book.'

He planned to use easyJet as the bank account for all the nascent easy businesses. Stelios did not receive a salary from any of his companies, nor any dividends, so he relied on occasional share sales to raise fresh funds. 'I have made clear on several occasions in the past,' he explained, 'I have no other source of income from easyJet other than disposal of shares and as I engage in new ventures, I may need to liquidate some of my stock from time to time. As I have said before, I need to sell my past to finance my future.'

Stelios said he intended to remain a 'significant' shareholder in the airline for a very long time. 'I have no present intention to sell any easyJet shares in the near future,' he said. His stake was diluted from 27.4 per cent after easyJet's rights issue to finance the Go deal. His brother and sister owned a further 24.4 per cent.

When Stelios announced his resignation as easyJet chairman in April 2002, he said that he would be standing down in early 2003. But after the speedy takeover of Go, he brought the date forward and said that he would quit the post in November 2002, when easyJet released its full-year results.

Not everything was going smoothly at the airline. After completing the takeover of Go on 1 August 2002, easyJet expanded by 60 per cent, ballooning overnight to a network of eighty-one European routes. While easyJet enjoyed the fame associated with its new ranking as Europe's largest low-cost airline, employees were left struggling to cope with the increased workload and the inevitable collision of cultures that followed a merger. EasyJet admitted that it was 'stretched to the limit' in the two weeks following the acquisition of its former rival.

EasyJet's pilots were among those who had to work the hardest following the merger and they consequently complained the loudest. Growing numbers of pilots at the company called for industrial action, claiming that easyJet was paying them less than their peers were receiving at Go. An easyJet spokesman said that while its pay scales were lower than starting salaries at Go, the overall package was almost identical when pension contributions, food and other elements were considered. On average, easyJet paid captains base salaries of £60,000 and first officers £38,000. Pilots also benefited from a bonus scheme and a share option programme. Pay at Ryanair was higher; the Irish airline had just agreed a five-year pay deal with its pilots which would see their annual salaries rise to more than £82,600.

A number of easyJet pilots in the British Airline Pilots' Association called for a strike vote if the company failed to improve its offered pay increase of 2.3 per cent for captains and 1.3 per cent for first officers, at a time when the management had enjoyed a collective £10 million bonus following the Go acquisition. The pay offer was rejected overwhelmingly by postal ballot and Balpa demanded an urgent meeting with Webster to discuss pay and pressures on the airline's staff.

EasyJet had recently employed more pilots after going on a recruitment drive in 2001 and offering pilots 'golden hellos' worth up to £30,000, believed to be the first scheme of its kind in the industry. The company needed to recruit over 250 pilots to fly the new planes it had on order for its fleet, due to reach forty-four aircraft by mid-2004. The new enlarged airline employed about 750 pilots and 1,000 cabin crew. But that still wasn't enough to cope with the surge in passenger numbers.

Almost as soon as the Go acquisition took place, nineteen flights had to be cancelled because easyJet did not have enough staff or extra aircraft when two planes developed technical problems. Thousands of passengers suffered delays and many abandoned their journeys.

EasyJet's troubles reflected wider problems in the budget airline industry. Many customers of no-frills companies such as easyJet, Ryanair and Buzz had come to expect delays, wayward baggage and bad service as part and parcel of a bargain flight. Ryanair's customer service department – consisting of five staff – said only one in 1,000 passengers complained. But with 1 million passengers a month, that was still 12,000 complaints a year. Despite the best efforts of those involved, delays at the two main no-frills airports – Luton and Stansted – were also the worst of all UK airports, exacerbated by shortages in air-traffic controllers and by increased security checks.

EasyJet admitted that it was struggling and warned that it needed to cut flights to regain control over its schedule and ease the severe pressure on its pilots and cabin crew. As part of its restructuring, it planned to end all Go flights from Belfast to Glasgow and Edinburgh and contacted the 9,882 affected passengers to offer them alternative easyJet flights where available. The cancellation of the Belfast flights raised questions over easyJet's ability to cope with other services it had taken over from Go.

A bungled new rota system added to easyJet's problems and pushed many of its pilots to the point of resignation. The rostering system, introduced in June, forced easyJet to cancel twenty-eight flights in July. The airline said it tried to cancel flights that hadn't been heavily booked. EasyJet said that air-traffic control delays, building projects at Luton Airport and bad thunderstorms worsened the situation. Almost 10,000 people had their flights cancelled in August and many more suffered delays. The new rostering system was splitting up crews, meaning that a re-fuelled plane and a pilot could be waiting at Luton Airport while the cabin crew was stuck in Barcelona or at another easyJet destination.

'EasyJet pilots complain a lot about the roster pattern,' explained one pilot who moved over to easyJet from Go after the takeover. 'The Go pattern used to be very stable. Since the merger, pilots operate a system of three early shifts and three late shifts, meaning that they will get up three times at 5 a.m. and then work late three times until, say, midnight. Obviously adjusting your body clock like that makes you very tired.' An easyJet spokesman said: 'We thought that the new rostering system would be more efficient and better. It proved to be anything but that. Hands up, we got it wrong.'

Morale sank among easyJet pilots. One pilot, who moved over to easyJet after the merger with Go and didn't want to be named, complained of a poorer working atmosphere following the takeover: 'Go had a lot more company pride than easyJet. It may be a result of easyJet being a larger company now following the merger. There was a lot of ill feeling and loss of morale after the merger as Go employees felt patriotic towards Go.'

Employees also missed the team spirit they had enjoyed at Go. 'Cassani was very popular and had all the staff on-board working as a team and pulling together,' the pilot continued. 'With easyJet management you just do as you're told. Webster keeps himself in the background and is not so close to the day-to-day running of the company. He is more interested in keeping the shareholders happy.' Former Go pilots also griped about the ending of Go's travel scheme, whereby staff could fly to any destination for £25 return including taxes. 'EasyJet, meanwhile, doesn't really believe in staff travel,' the pilot complained. 'It does have a scheme but its fares are often higher than the standard ones advertised for passengers!'

On a day-to-day basis, the pilots' workload didn't change when they moved over to easyJet, the pilot said. 'Both airlines are pretty similar in the way that they try to get the most productivity out of their employees. As far as I can see, airlines are low cost by getting the highest staff productivity for the least money. I subsidise the passengers' air fares by accepting lower pay.'

It wasn't just the pilots who were feeling the strain brought on by easyJet's rapid expansion. EasyJet cabin crew were also toiling hard. Michael, one cabin crew member, commented: 'EasyJet is expanding so much. It's getting bigger and bigger every day. But it's getting too much and is expecting too much from its staff in terms of long working hours and the amount of work you have to do in those hours. Some days are short. I have to report to work at 6 a.m. and can fly for example to Rome and be back home by 1 p.m. On the other hand, if there's a flight delay or an emergency then I may not get back until 7 p.m. Or some days I might do a double shift, for example from East Midlands to Venice and back and then to Prague and back, which is a very long day.'

Some pilots feared that the pressure placed on flight crew might lead to mistakes or even prompt an accident. One pilot said: 'I have repeatedly told managers the situation has become dangerous but their only concern is profits. They have pushed staff to the limits and now we are seeing the consequences. It would be terrible if it took a crash to force them to rein back on this breakneck expansion.'

An easyJet spokesman said: 'I'm alarmed if one of our pilots is saying those things. We have worked our pilots incredibly hard and made great demands on them in the past two months. We are negotiating with them over pay and they have rejected our first offer.' EasyJet decided to try to improve working conditions and dispel pilot unrest, and planned to return to its old rostering system. Eventually the airline won an alleviation from Civil Aviation Authority rules to change the rostering pattern to five early working shifts for pilots followed by five late shifts, which meant that pilots needed to readjust their body clocks less between shifts.

Fears over pilot safety at easyJet and at its fellow no-frills carriers escalated again when an air-traffic controller who feared a crash in the skies above London raised his concerns in a safety report to the Confidential Human Factors Incident Reporting Programme, which was then published in *The Times*. He claimed that pilots in the no-frills sector, which thrived on keeping its planes in the air longer than traditional carriers, were so desperate to avoid delays that they were putting passengers at risk.

The air-traffic controller said that pilots ignored instructions from ground control to allow them to meet tight deadlines. He alleged that pilots sometimes approached landings too fast and had to abandon the manoeuvre because they were too close to the aircraft in front. Pilots also ignored longer flight paths to cut down on noise disturbance and instead took shorter routes over nearby houses, he claimed; they frequently challenged the order in which jets took off and landed, and gave 'overly aggressive responses' to air-traffic control. '[This] is occurring with increasing frequency and, in my judgement, is due in part to the aggressively commercial ethos that exists within some airline companies,' the air-traffic controller stated in the report.

A spokesman for easyJet said it was a common misconception that shortcuts were taken by budget airlines. 'Low-cost airlines become more effective by squeezing the time on the ground. It's got nothing to do with air-traffic controllers; it's [about] effective baggage handlers and getting people on and off the aircraft.'

No-frills aircraft typically travelled four return journeys to Europe in a day, double the number of a typical British Airways jet. Planes and people worked much harder than on traditional airlines. In particular, the turnaround time – from the moment the pilot of the inbound aircraft applied the parking brake at the gate to the start of the push-back at departure – was typically scheduled to take only twenty-five minutes at easyJet and at other budget airlines. If the arrival was delayed, there was no slack to help make up time.

Budget airlines quashed speculation that their pilots cut

corners to keep to tight schedules. A spokesman for easyJet said: 'We would refute any allegations that our pilots are disobeying air-traffic controllers' orders. Safety is absolutely paramount and all our pilots conform to very high standards of training and supervision.'

But a letter by Stelios to the *Financial Times* in June 2002 served only to re-stoke the fire. Stelios argued in the letter that those low-cost airlines who used old aircraft were unwise to do so because their reputations would not survive in the event of a crash. 'Combine a low-cost airline with old aircraft and the odds of your reputation surviving an accident are against you,' he argued. 'Old aircraft flatter profits in the short term and, in my opinion, have more to do with management's attitude to the risk of damage to reputation as a result of an accident involving an old aircraft than to the long-term business model.'

Stelios mentioned Ryanair in his letter. The Irish-registered airline operated some of the oldest aircraft in Britain at the time, with twenty Boeing 737-200s dating back to the early 1980s. EasyJet, meanwhile, swore by a young fleet – the average age of its planes was 4.6 years. But if Stelios hoped to make the City think twice about Ryanair, his rambling letter raised more doubts about himself. One analyst declared: 'Stelios has lost the plot. It doesn't matter how old aircraft are – it's whether they are maintained properly. Stelios has broken the golden rule in airlines – you never hit out at rivals over safety because you never know when it might happen to you. The letter smacks of desperation.'

Nor did Ryanair take the blows lying down, stating that it adhered to the 'highest standards of international safety'. 'What surprised me was that he would put his name to such nonsense,' cried O'Leary. 'It would seem that those of us who offer the lowest air fares just get on with it, and those who do not, write whinging letters to newspapers.' Ryanair marketing director Tim Jeans added: 'We don't cut corners while the aircraft is airborne. Turnaround times are tighter but safety and security are an absolute priority and there is nothing we would do to compromise that.'

Even as it struggled to assimilate Go's flights to its network, easyJet kept up the rapid pace of its own expansion, announcing in August that it would introduce new routes from Liverpool to cities including Prague, Milan and Rome. More than 2 million passengers a year were using Liverpool's newly rebranded John Lennon Airport and the airport had just upgraded terminal facilities that would lift annual capacity to more than 3 million passengers. Two-thirds of passengers using the airport flew with easyJet. 'EasyJet has had a massive impact on the airport; it has been phenomenal,' said Robin Tudor, the airport's corporate affairs manager. 'EasyJet has been a godsend to Liverpool John Lennon Airport,' agreed Mike Doran, a spokesman for Liverpool City Council. 'The airport has risen from the ashes on the back of easyJet.'

EasyJet's new flights met with huge popularity in the north-west. Indeed, easyJet had to rip up posters advertising £17.50 fares for its new services from Liverpool to Paris as it ran out of tickets following a landslide of applications. Other regions also benefited from easyJet's expansion drive. The airline recruited thirty-three new cabin crew and based two aircraft permanently at Belfast International Airport, marking its most significant expansion in Belfast. EasyJet said it planned to introduce seven daily flights to Liverpool and six to London Luton for the summer, bringing its total daily flights to and from Belfast to forty-two. This was a seven-fold increase on its flights from Belfast in just three-and-a-half years, making easyJet's Northern Ireland's largest airline.

Citing research carried out by Ulster Marketing Surveys, easyJet claimed that seven out of ten of Northern Ireland's frequent flyers flew with easyJet on business, as cost-conscious companies recommended that employees use low-cost airlines whenever possible. An increasing number of company heads, directors and senior managers said that easyJet above any other airline was their main business carrier to Great Britain.

EasyJet announced that it planned to set up a base in Newcastle in October, the airline's fourth regional base in the UK, creating more than 100 jobs. Go had run a regular service to Newcastle from London Stansted and easyJet promised to unveil a network of routes from Newcastle in December 2002, including flights to Barcelona, Alicante, Paris and Nice. EasyJet planned to base two aircraft on Tyneside, rising to four in 2004. The airline aimed to carry about 750,000 passengers to and from Newcastle in the first twelve months from the start of the base operation.

Nor had the no-frills carrier forgotten Scotland. It also planned to offer up to three flights a day from Glasgow and Edinburgh to Malaga, Barcelona, Nice, Geneva and Paris as part of an expansion of its Scottish services from Glasgow and Edinburgh. One question remained, however: would easyJet have enough aircraft to fly all of its potential new passengers?

8. Airbus soars off the runway

IN OCTOBER 2002 Stelios unveiled plans to enter the big league by massively expanding his fleet. EasyJet already had sixty-four planes in its fleet following the merger with Go and a further twenty-three new Boeing aircraft on order. Stelios decided that it wasn't enough. He announced that he wanted to buy eighty-five new aircraft and then revised his target to an even more ambitious order of 120. To fulfil his ambitions, Stelios opened negotiations with Boeing Co. and Airbus Industrie.

In the middle of what was thought to be the biggest recession in airline history, easyJet was planning to buck the trend with a multi-million-pound deal. People initially scratched their heads, wondering why Stelios should want to buy new planes when a number of airlines such as Lufthansa were trying to cut capacity and sell off their planes secondhand. But Webster defended the move: 'Given the current state of parts of the global aviation industry, this is potentially a very good time to be addressing our long-term aircraft needs.' The new planes were needed to support easyJet's targeted growth rates, he continued. 'We have already committed to grow aircraft capacity by approximately 25 per cent a year until 2004 and need to secure delivery positions beyond that date.'

EasyJet wasn't interested in acquiring secondhand aircraft. 'We like new planes,' said Webster. 'They require less maintenance overnight and are crucial to reliability and therefore short turnaround times and high aircraft utilisation.'

With transatlantic air travel crippled since 11 September 2001 and orders being cancelled worldwide, Seattle-based Boeing and Toulouse-based Airbus were both desperate to win the easyJet contract. EasyJet was aware that a shopping list for aircraft with a total in triple figures might prompt the salespeople to reveal unheard-of discounts. Competition between the world's two largest plane makers was fierce. France's Airbus was starting to win market share from Boeing and threaten the US company's position as the world's largest aircraft manufacturer. Earlier in 2002, Airbus had won the hard-fought competition to supply new jets to Air New Zealand, previously an all-Boeing customer. Boeing alleged that Airbus had sliced prices on its planes so viciously to win market share that Boeing had lost some key sales rather than match its rival's hefty and unreasonable discounts.

The low-fare market had become one of the airline industry's only bright spots. The European carriers, seeking to expand service, were taking advantage of the situation to get unusually steep discounts for new planes. Ryanair had already made the most of the industry slump, announcing in January that it would buy 100 Boeing 737-800 aircraft in the following eight years and taking options on fifty more planes.

EasyJet had also operated an all-Boeing fleet. Its preferred aircraft type had always been the Boeing 737 series, which it kept on adding to its fleet to accommodate its burgeoning network. In July 1998, easyJet had ordered fifteen brand-new 737-700s, followed in March 2000 by an order for seventeen more. Now Stelios was thinking of a change. The Airbus A319 had originally had 145 seats, compared to the 149 offered by the Boeing 737-700 aircraft, which had made the Boeing marginally more profitable for easyJet. But now the A319 would have 150 seats, with the possibility of increasing to 156, which, Webster announced, made it a viable competitive alternative.

The announcement sent shockwaves throughout the industry. The low-cost model was built on a handful of simple principles. One of them was that no-frills carriers only operated one type of aircraft: it saved on crew costs and training, not to mention spares. The doyen of the industry, Southwest Airlines, swore by its all-Boeing fleet. Two types of aircraft required two types of parts and two types of engineers. Only two years previously, in 2000, Stelios had announced, 'part of the process of keeping costs down is keeping the business very simple. You should only have one kind of aircraft, which in our case happens to be the same as Southwest's – the Boeing 737 – and that aircraft sets the limits of your range.'

Stelios had clearly changed his tune. Of course, price paid an essential role in his new thinking. Stelios knew that the dearth of airline orders might make Airbus sink its prices to unknown levels to secure the deal, which would cancel out the additional costs of operating a mixed fleet. And competition for Boeing surely couldn't hurt?

Boeing almost won the contract outright. In November 2001, easyJet received an unsolicited offer from Boeing which Alain Mulally, Boeing Commercial Airlines President, termed the 'deal of the century'. But Airbus heard of the offer and was quick to respond. Chris Buckley, Airbus's senior vice president Europe and the key point of contact for the aircraft negotiations with easyJet, emailed Webster at the end of November, stating that he could almost guarantee that easyJet would benefit from running a real competition with Airbus and Boeing to improve Boeing's offer.

One Friday evening in December, Buckley was relaxing at home when he received an unexpected telephone call from Stelios, who was in the middle of a meeting with the members of the easyJet board. Stelios put Buckley on speakerphone and on the spot, asking him to explain why easyJet should run a competition with Airbus. Buckley told them, 'Let's see what Airbus can come up with,' and encouraged easyJet not to sign a deal with Boeing immediately.

His persuasion worked. In January 2002, easyJet started a detailed evaluation process of both Boeing's 737-700 and Airbus's A319 – painfully detailed from Buckley's point of view, as the easyJet management pored over every aspect of Airbus's performance. And then, on a Friday evening in October 2002, several months after easyJet's initial call, Webster called Buckley and told him, 'I want you over tomorrow.' Buckley immediately cancelled his plans for the weekend, hopeful that victory was in sight.

The next morning a small team of easyJet executives, including Stelios, met Airbus executives at a hotel on Marylebone Road in central London and worked throughout the weekend to try and thrash out a deal. They reached a compromise on Sunday night. After months of playing off the world's biggest aircraft makers against each other, easyJet had finally made its decision. The airline held a press conference on the following morning, Monday 14 October, to announce its new aircraft order to the world. Stelios told journalists that easyJet was going for a deal with Airbus, thereby breaking Boeing's stranglehold on the European low-cost airline market. The industry was stunned.

Stelios became emotional during the press conference as he talked about Boeing and how it had repeatedly offered a lower price than its original one. Stelios had met Boeing's Mulally before Christmas. 'He said this is the deal of the century, so take it. It wasn't. He undercut himself again and again. Why should I believe him again?'

EasyJet placed an order with Airbus for 120 A319 aircraft,

plus ten-year price-protected options for 120 more A319 planes as well as the possibility of larger-sized Airbus A320s and A321s. The contract would see the no-frills airline take delivery of two A319 planes every month for five years as of August 2003. The A319 planes would be introduced at easyJet's Geneva hub, operating under the airline's Swiss air operator licence, but would eventually interchange with existing Boeings on all routes.

The order would almost treble easyJet's size from 9,500 seats to nearly 25,000 seats by 2007, but easyJet insisted that it could maintain the growth. 'By 2007, we will overtake Alitalia, Iberia and SAS and we will remain fractionally bigger than Ryanair,' the company explained. 'We're planning on compound growth of 25 per cent per year for seven years.'

Nobody was vulgar enough to talk about the price of easyJet's aircraft order, but given the state of the industry at the time, with the Arizona desert full of the white tails of parked aircraft that airlines no longer needed, easyJet was guaranteed a good deal. The A319 had a notional sticker price of $50 million, but, by buying in bulk, Stelios was thought to have picked up 120 for $20 million apiece – $5 million less than Boeing was asking for its 737 aircraft. 'The Airbus deal will give us a cost per seat which is 10 per cent lower than the last Boeing deal,' said Stelios. 'Now how often do you get 10 per cent off your cost base by doing just one transaction?'

The immediate costs of around £70 million to secure the order and down payments for the first aircraft were to be borne by easyJet's £400 million cash pile, which was swollen by two cash calls from the stockmarket over the previous year. The airline had to stump up 1 per cent or at least £20 million to secure the deal, then 30 per cent of the value of the ten or so aircraft it expected to have delivered within the following two years – at least another £50 million, with the balance payable on delivery. Longer-term deliveries could be bought outright (depending on the company's cashflow), mortgaged, or sold and leased back with third-party leasing companies.

The Airbus deal remained subject to shareholder approval, but since Stelios and his family owned 48 per cent of the business, shareholder consent seemed a foregone conclusion. Stelios said that he would personally spend a lot of time over the ensuing weeks talking to shareholders to explain the 'benefits of the deal'.

In New York, Boeing's shares fell more than 3 per cent to $31 on receipt of the news. Boeing said that it had 'fought aggressively' but added that it would not 'sell our aircraft at a price that is considerably less than the value of the product', hinting that Airbus had done exactly that. Noel Forgeard, Airbus chief executive, hit back, saying: 'This is a cash-positive transaction for us. At no point will this be cash out of our pocket in spite of the costs initially to help easyJet.'

The fact that Forgeard felt obliged to defend himself against the charge was possibly indicative of the state of the aircraft industry in 2002. Airbus and Boeing knew that there would be far fewer orders in 2002 because of the industry downturn, which made the easyJet competition all the more crucial for the two aircraft makers. The order subsequently gave Airbus an entrée into the profitable low-frills market and helped the manufacturer secure as many as nine consecutive wins against Boeing's 737 with low-cost carriers around the world; it also safeguarded as many as 10,000 jobs at Airbus plants in Broughton, Flintshire, where wings for the planes were made, and in Filton, South Gloucestershire, where key components were manufactured.

But the share price didn't react so positively to the news. Shares in European Aeronautic Defence and Space Company NV, the owner of 80 per cent of Airbus, fell by 4.4 per cent in Paris to €9.70 amid investor concern that Airbus might have agreed to too big a price reduction to secure the biggest order of the year. Investors were worried that Airbus was also taking a risk by underwriting the training costs when the new planes arrived.

Airbus was to provide 'extensive support' to ensure that

crew training and new maintenance regimes did not add to easyJet's costs. As part of the deal, easyJet had made Airbus guarantee that the introduction of the planes would not be more expensive than Boeing's 737-700 planes in the first two years. One industry executive, who did not want to be named, speculated that the easyJet deal might come back to haunt Airbus. 'One consequence of this deal is that Airbus is helping easyJet in further reducing its costs to compete with Airbus's best customers in Europe: British Airways, Air France and Lufthansa. And they are all having a tough time fighting the low-cost carriers in domestic Europe. Clearly these three carriers paid too much for their A319s when they ordered them years ago. We may see a round of negotiations between Airbus and these network carriers to bring their already negotiated prices more in line with the deeply discounted prices at easyJet.'

EasyJet's shares also fell after the Airbus announcement, dropping by nearly 5 per cent to 251¼p. Share prices had nearly halved since March amid fears that easyJet was growing too rapidly and that the airline would find it difficult to integrate Go. Investors were worried by the fact that easyJet would become the first large low-cost carrier in Europe to fly a mixed fleet, and concerned about the rate of easyJet's planned expansion. Dominic Edridge, an airline analyst at Commerzbank, said: 'Taking two aeroplanes a month is a challenge for any airline – the concern is where they can be deployed profitably.'

Stelios and easyJet had broken the mould before, so it was unwise to bet against them now, but there was no disguising the risk that Stelios was taking. After all, easyJet had only just begun to consume Go and it was already eyeing up its next course, Deutsche BA. It had less than a year to digest them before it began the task of integrating a brand-new aircraft into the fleet. Webster was highly rated and for good reason but observers worried that this would stretch even his managerial capacity.

Stelios admitted the decision might unsettle the City: 'I was faced with the dilemma of either following the conventional wisdom in the market place in order to keep shareholders happy in the short term or doing what's right for shareholders in the long run,' he explained. 'We decided to do what's right. We refused to overpay in order to improve the stock price in the short term. It should be an offence to misuse that level of corporate resources. At the end of the day, "low-cost" companies remain "low-cost" by not wasting money. Sticking to old-fashioned fads like "low-cost airlines only fly Boeing" does not reduce costs. The last thing we want is to be held hostage by one supplier.'

The airline argued that it would achieve 'substantial savings' by ordering the Airbus planes. 'About four years ago, as a small airline we bought fifteen B737-700s with no competition,' said Stelios. 'Today, buying 120 aircraft in a competitive market, we can now purchase aircraft at approximately 30 per cent below the prices, adjusted for inflation, we achieved then.' Stelios also cited 'the great success JetBlue has experienced with the Airbus product in the US'; the US low-cost airline JetBlue was able to achieve faster turnaround times because of the aircraft's wider aisles.

EasyJet and Airbus now had forty-five days of exclusive talks to finalise the deal, one of the most significant seen at Airbus. It was tough work. Buckley admitted that there were times when he shouted at Webster and other members of the easyJet team, as their thoroughness frustrated him. 'I'm not a most detailed person and I would shout out of sheer exasperation. Ray and the team were very focused on the deal and interested in all kinds of details.' But by the end of the year, everything was sorted out and all easyJet had to do was to wait for the planes to arrive.

Meanwhile, Stelios had successfully delegated himself out of a job on 26 November 2002, the day of the airline's annual results. Fellow entrepreneur Sir Richard Branson gave him a surprise farewell, presenting him with a model plane and paying tribute to his friend's achievements as the pioneer of budget airlines, adding that easyJet was 'by far the best' in the short-haul market out of the UK: 'Millions of people who could not afford to travel before are now travelling and he has done it with great style and panache.' Asked about Stelios's departure, Branson said: 'Easy come. Easy go. I cannot believe he is ever going to let go.'

Stelios revealed that he had the right to return as chairman at any time, as long as his stake in the company stayed above 10 per cent. But he added: 'I have no intention to meddle in the management and I do not expect to be chairman again. I will have my hands full with other easyGroup activities, but will continue to watch from afar with a close and fond interest.' Stelios's replacement, Colin Chandler, clarified that Stelios would return as chairman only 'if something goes badly wrong'.

The airline announced that for the year to 30 September, pre-tax profits had rocketed 78 per cent to £71.6 million, beating the analyst forecasts for £57 million to £66 million. Revenues for the period surged 55 per cent to £552 million, and the number of passengers increased 59.5 per cent on a year earlier to 11.4 million, helped by eleven new aircraft and a two-month contribution from the twenty-seven planes in the Go fleet. EasyJet also said it had overcome problems integrating Go, which was generating enough cash to pay for its major aircraft order with Airbus without easyJet having to seek fresh funds from the equity market. Stripping out Go from easyJet's annual figures, revenues had still risen 36 per cent to £486 million, with passenger numbers up 43 per cent at £10.2 million and operating profits 49 per cent stronger at £57 million. 'This is the last set of results that I will announce as the company's chairman and I couldn't have hoped for a better send-off,' Stelios said.

There was some negative news, however. The airline said the average fare paid by the customer had fallen 4 per cent from £48 to £46, while costs per available seat kilometre declined 1.3 per cent to 4.46 pence. EasyJet did not provide numbers for the second half of the year but Gert Zonneveld, analyst at West LB Panmure, estimated that easyJet's fares fell 7.5 per cent in the period. Other analysts said that the drop was closer to 9 per cent. Zonneveld commented, 'The shares have had a very good run, rising from 240 pence since early October. This is by no means a profit warning but these companies are not cheap. If anything goes wrong, you will immediately see people taking profits.'

The news of the results pushed easyJet shares, which had made a partial recovery in the last couple of months, down 14 per cent to 337p as a result of City concern that increased competition could put pressure on the group. One analyst, who declined to be named, said: 'The worry is that if current growth targets look too optimistic, it will savage the share price further. While easyJet has said that it doesn't need to return to the stockmarket in the next year, it has said that it may have to alter that. A steep share price fall jeopardises the confidence the City has in the group.'

Webster insisted that the airline remained well placed to prosper although it faced uncertainties, including the threat of war in the Middle East and fears of a consumer spending slowdown. 'Notwithstanding the uncertainties, market demand continues to be strong, but at lower average fares.'

EasyJet's employees would no doubt miss Stelios's presence at work. Staff had always felt a buzz from working for the jolly Greek giant. Stelios was dynamic, full of energy and liked to have a laugh in the office. One of the cabin crew said: 'He's totally down to earth and friendly. We all call him Stel Boy or Steli Babes. None of the girls would dare make a pass at him, even though we all want to. With that much money I'm sure that most of the guys would too!'

Stelios didn't take himself too seriously and that was part of the 'no-frills' ethic he had built into the company. He occupied the same space as everyone else in the open-plan office. No one had a private office and there weren't any

secretaries. Instead, people were encouraged to book their own travel on the Internet, take care of their own administration and run a paperless office. Document control scanned everything in, and documents were filed and forwarded to staff via email. Everyone organised their own email, correspondence and filing on the network.

One of Stelios's achievements at easyJet was instilling an 'orange culture' of being 'up for it', 'passionate' and 'sharp'. The 'orange culture' remained in place after his departure. Every Friday, the staff continued to socialise with each other at easyJet's weekly barbecue, even if 'Stel Boy' was no longer taking his turn at flipping hamburgers.

Stelios also succeeded in cultivating an attitude of friendliness among staff, which continued after he left. EasyJet attracted eager young cabin crew, some of whom seemed more akin to Butlins' Redcoats entertainers or local radio DJs in the way that they joked and jested with passengers. On a flight from Zurich to London, passengers were treated to the following announcement: 'We hope you have enjoyed your flight with us. If you have, thank you for choosing easyJet. If not, then thank you for choosing Ryanair.'

EasyJet prided itself in not employing 'trolley dollies'. Take for example, Pauline Mors, who didn't start work as an air hostess until she was forty-five, an age at which most airlines were retiring their flight attendants. The company believed that the life skills of mature workers far outweighed the youthful good looks favoured by their competitors, and used Pauline in a high-profile campaign against ageism. The carrier valued those with team working skills above those that knew how to apply make-up correctly. Crew needed an exceptional sense of humour and a 'get stuck in' attitude towards work and customers.

Pilots also needed to work hard yet remain jolly. 'You are reminded that smoking is not allowed on the plane,' quipped one pilot on an easyJet flight from Liverpool to Palma. 'Anyone found doing so will be asked to leave the aircraft.'

And you just knew that it had to be easyJet when you heard that pilots from an airline had posed for a nude charity calendar. The Christmas calendar featured photographs of nine naked male pilots from Nottingham East Midlands Airport on the flight deck and on the runway. They planned to donate the money from the calendar to Britain's National Society for Epilepsy.

9. Continental drift

AIR LIB, FRANCE'S second-largest airline, stopped flying in February 2003, stranding thousands of passengers. Air Lib was weighed down by €100 million of debt, most of which was owed to the French government. A Dutch company, ICMA, offered to re-float the airline but withdrew its offer after the French government declined to persuade Airbus to provide thirty new A319 aircraft, on credit, at bargain prices.

Many of Air Lib's 3,200 employees blocked access to roads to Orly Airport, near Paris, accusing the government of throwing them out of work. There were angry scenes at airports in Corsica, the French West Indies and several French regional cities as passengers found Air Lib check-in desks deserted, meaning they couldn't exchange or cash in their tickets. Jean-Charles Corbet, the airline's president, called on French President Jacques Chirac to intervene. But government officials made it clear that they believed hopes of saving Air

Lib and the fifteen-year-old dream of creating a second French airline to rival Air France were over.

EasyJet and its rival cut-price airlines waited patiently for the Air Lib saga to end, hungrily eyeing the extinct airline's take-off and landing slots at Paris Orly and Charles de Gaulle. EasyJet hoped to gain 20,000 slots a year at Orly, which would allow it to fly to London, French provincial cities and other capitals. The airline already operated services from Charles de Gaulle to Liverpool, London Luton and Nice, as well as flights from Orly to Nice.

Webster, who had bought easyJet's flock of white planes from Airbus around the same time as Air Lib was going under, had a blunt message for the French government: 'We bought your bloody aircraft, now give us somewhere to land them.' But his comments were in vain. The French government preferred to avoid further competition for state-owned Air France, and handed over most of the slots to Air France.

The French officials' decision frustrated easyJet but it decided to make the most of the meagre slots it had secured, announcing in April 2003 the launch of services from Paris Orly to Barcelona, Marseilles, Milan Linate, Nice and Toulouse. People were attracted by the airline's low fares, said Elodie Gythiel, in charge of marketing for easyJet in France: 'The French people like small players and have been pissed off by Air France before, either because of high fares or delays or other bad experiences. We have established a strong position as a consumer champion.'

Anne Dusoleil was one of the many French passengers who regularly used easyJet, largely to travel for her job in marketing at materials maker Saint Gobain. Dusoleil was growing accustomed to the easyJet way of doing things on her frequent business trips with the airline. 'I normally fly with easyJet on business but a lot of families travel with the airline too. Having all those children running around and shouting in the plane is not very relaxing so you can't really work on-board. Then again, the fares are cheap and travelling with easyJet helps my company cut travel costs so you can't really complain,' she commented. 'The downside of travelling with easyJet is the absolute chaos before passengers board the plane. The hostesses call out the numbers on our boarding passes for people to get on to the bus but nobody takes any notice at all. We French people can be so disorganised. And then the resulting chaos and people who try to jump the queue annoy those passengers who are trying to queue properly.'

Flights from the UK to Paris were among the most popular in easyJet's network. Passengers in Britain enjoyed being able to hop on a plane and spend a romantic weekend in the French city for a reasonable price. As with all airlines, however, not every flight ran smoothly and sometimes customers' expectations were thwarted.

Howard Elliot-Jones from North Wales was particularly unimpressed following his easyJet flight from Liverpool to Paris Charles de Gaulle. The commercial property developer wanted to whisk his wife away for a romantic, relaxing few days to celebrate her thirtieth birthday. The result was anything but. Arriving at Charles de Gaulle, the couple waited for their suitcase to appear, eager for their holiday to commence. But an hour later it had still failed to turn up. EasyJet staff quickly reassured the two passengers, telling them that they would be compensated if the suitcase were lost and handing them a form to fill in.

Over the next few days, the couple continuously phoned the airport to try and find out if their suitcase had been located. 'I can't speak French so it was all difficult, really,' remembered Elliot-Jones. 'I never seemed to speak to the same person on the phone and was constantly re-routed around an automatic voicemail system. Each time we finally got through to someone we were told that my luggage hadn't turned up. It was really frustrating. The holiday was awful. EasyJet basically ruined what was a very special occasion. I didn't have anything to change into so I had to wander around Paris in the same clothes I had travelled in. What is more, I didn't have my glasses as they had been in my suitcase. As I can't wear my contact lenses for long, I couldn't see the sights, never mind the restaurant menu in front of me. What was even more worrying was that my tablets were in my bag. I have to take Tenormin, high-blood-pressure tablets, and it was worrying to be without them, particularly as the situation was making me more and more stressed.'

As soon as they returned to Liverpool, the couple informed easyJet what had happened. Elliot-Jones waited for an apology and compensation. Instead, all he received was a standard letter headed 'Without Prejudice', meaning that the airline's comments couldn't be admissible as evidence in a court of law. 'The letter wound me up as soon as I saw it,' said Elliot-Jones. 'It was very matter-of-fact and unapologetic. EasyJet told us bluntly that it could give us £25 in compensation and asked us to sign yet another form. I was outraged by the paltry amount offered. I had about £750 worth of possessions in the suitcase, including glasses worth £300, new clothes that I had bought specially for the trip, as well as my best shirt and pair of trousers.' Elliot-Jones became even more outraged after he had spoken to an easyJet employee. 'What was worse was the attitude of the woman when I rang her up. She basically didn't give a damn and was completely unbending in her attitude. She just muttered standard responses.'

Three days later Elliot-Jones received a call from Liverpool Airport telling him that they had identified a piece of luggage as his. He was outraged to learn that the only reason it had been traced was because of the discovery of some letters addressed to him inside. 'There was absolutely no correlation between my complaint and anything being done to find the suitcase,' he fumed. 'In my opinion, what easyJet clearly offers is a cheap flight with nothing on top. What annoyed me about the whole thing, apart from messing up our holiday, was that there was no apology and absolutely no consideration shown at all. I fly nowadays with British Airways. They treat you a lot better.'

In response, easyJet referred to the terms and conditions listed on its Internet site, which stated: 'You are strongly advised to take out your own insurance to cover the value of your baggage and its contents, particularly if you are carrying important or valuable items. Claims are dealt with up to the airline's limit of liability based on the weight of the items concerned.'

Now that it had established a foothold in the French market, easyJet turned its attentions towards Germany. The country was the largest domestic air market in Europe but traditionally had been poorly served by low-cost airlines. EasyJet wasn't the only company that was eager to bring cheap airline seats to Germany. The number of planes operating on the 'pile 'em high, sell 'em cheap' principle in Germany was expected to reach eighty-six by the end of 2003, compared with just seven at the end of 2001. German charter airlines, including TUI AG (whose budget arm was Hapag-Lloyd Express) and Air Berlin (which ran the no-frills City Shuttle), were making moves into the budget sector to offset weakness in their core business. In TUI's opinion, there was only room for three budget players in the German market, indicating that there was disappointment ahead for some.

Lufthansa, the national carrier, had slashed fares to compete with domestic low-cost carriers such as Germania Express, offering round-trip fares including taxes as low as €88 as of early 2003. Lufthansa had also chased Ryanair through the courts after the Irish airline set up in Germany, offering flights to London Stansted, Glasgow, Dublin, Shannon, Charleroi, Girona-Barcelona, Milan, Pisa and Oslo. Lufthansa challenged Ryanair over its description of its German base, 120 kilometres (70 miles) from Frankfurt, as 'Frankfurt-Hahn'. In July 2003, a German court blocked Ryanair from using 'Dusseldorf' for an airport near the German–Dutch border, 70 kilometres (42 miles) from the city.

Meanwhile, Ryanair was considering whether to shut down

its operations at Belgium's Charleroi Airport after discovering that the European Commision was set to rule against it in a key competition probe over illegal state aid. Much of Ryanair's business model was based on negotiating payments from under-used airports and regional public bodies in recognition of the economic boost the airline generated. Some of Ryanair's competitors complained that these payments, when made by public entities, amounted to state aid that distorted competition. The EU challenge over Charleroi was not the first such problem for the airline. In September 2002, Ryanair was forced to suspend services to Strasbourg in eastern France after a French court barred local authorities from subsidising its advertising. Ryanair moved services to Baden-Baden, about an hour away over the border in Germany.

Despite its legal setbacks, Ryanair was booming. In November 2003, it unveiled record interim profits of €175.5 million and vowed to keep cutting fares to drive passenger numbers higher. The airline claimed it would be Europe's largest airline within eight years. Indeed, Ryanair had once again pipped easyJet to the position of Europe's largest low-cost carrier after buying unprofitable Dutch carrier Buzz from KLM Royal Dutch Airlines for €23.9 million in February 2003.

Even amid strengthening competition from the likes of Ryanair, easyJet was determined to establish itself as the biggest low-cost carrier in Germany. Taking over Deutsche BA as planned would provide easyJet with seven of the eleven crucial internal routes and hundreds of German crew and pilots in one swoop. The airline continued to pay €600,000 per month to hold its exclusive option to buy the British Airways subsidiary, as well contributing €5 million towards the cost of converting it into a low-cost operation. An integration group, comprising executives from both airlines, met once or twice a week to discuss strategy and progress.

EasyJet was aware that the acquisition would require a substantial restructuring of the German airline. While Go had complementary business models, culture and routes to easyJet, the Deutsche BA deal required its buyers to transform an airline which was over-manned, operated in a complex and hostile labour market and had a high cost base. Unlike easyJet, Deutsche BA concentrated on attracting business travellers, who paid higher fares. It filled around 65 per cent of available seats, compared with easyJet's targeted load factor of 85 per cent.

As a first step in its restructuring, easyJet aimed to put more seats in Deutsche BA's planes. Other key changes that easyJet wanted to implement included increasing the number of hours flown by Deutsche BA aircraft and changing over to easyJet's own distribution and yield management system. Deutsche BA was encouraged to abandon its traditional airline contracts with suppliers and to simplify all of its operations and systems, with the aim of selling 100 per cent of its tickets over the Internet within a year. It was an ambitious target. Deutsche BA only sold between 5 per cent and 10 per cent of its tickets online, as companies in Germany still tended to use travel agents.

That wasn't the only difference that easyJet encountered. EasyJet was eager to learn about the German political and business environment to work out how a British company could become successful in Germany. But it didn't count on how difficult it would be to change working practices for Deutsche BA's 800 staff, including introducing performance-related pay for 200 pilots. Every minor change required consultation with unions and workers' councils. The initial reaction from DBA middle management to the takeover had been one of fear – fear of losing their jobs through the merger process and fear of changes within the company. Only three Deutsche BA executives had known about the planned merger before Stelios made his announcemen to Deutsche BA employeest in an aircraft hangar.

Even those employees who welcomed the merger were daunted by the changes needed to make the transition from a traditional German airline into a British low-cost one. Webster and some of the key easyJet players took part in road shows, showing German employees how easyJet's so-called 'orange culture' worked and encouraging staff to exchange ideas. But easyJet's open culture simply didn't translate. Many German workers were simply left feeling uncomfortable by practices that were commonplace in the UK. German employees gasped in horror when they saw how little space easyJet employees were allocated in the easyLand headquarters. Accustomed to large, individual offices, they were appalled at the prospect of having to work in close vicinity with each other in the same room. There were laws against it, they told easyJet. Deutsche BA pilots put up even greater resistance to easyJet's plans. In February 2003, easyJet was forced to halt negotiations with the German pilots' union after failing to persuade pilots to adopt easyJet's salary structure.

The deal now stood on shaky ground. It was unlikely that easyJet would exercise its option unless the pilots agreed to the terms on offer. They did not. Eventually easyJet threw in the towel, announcing in March 2003 that it would not take up its option to buy the German carrier.

EasyJet's decision threw Deutsche BA's future into doubt. The German airline had been losing up to £25 million a year for the past ten years. British Airways insiders admitted that it had 'burnt a pretty big hole in our pockets', and it was now losing even more than it was before the easyJet purchase was signed. But with over 800 employees, the airline was too expensive for British Airways to shut down. British Airways said it would continue to develop DBA as a no-frills carrier. However, it admitted that it would be open to offers.

EasyJet's withdrawal shocked Deutsche BA managers, who had been convinced up until the last minute that easyJet would exercise its option. After all, the integration team had worked diligently to implement easyJet's proposed changes. Webster himself had spent weeks in Germany, working hard on the project. But easyJet, just like British Airways, simply failed to understand how Germany worked, said sources close to the negotiations. 'Everybody told us it was going to be difficult in Germany but there is nothing like getting first-hand experience,' Webster admitted. 'It is disappointing that we have had to make this decision. However, we always made it clear that we would not compromise the easyJet business model.'

EasyJet blamed its decision on Germany's unbending labour laws. Webster declared that the airline had been forced to recognise that German bureaucratic processes were incompatible with the needs of businesses today and a changing aviation market. 'Despite months of exceptionally hard work . . . there have been two insurmountable hurdles,' Webster explained. 'Firstly, the rigidity of German labour laws has made it impossible to get acceptance of easyJet conditions of employment from key staff groups, despite numerous attempts and different approaches.' Secondly, Webster said, the situation was exacerbated by 'a substantial deterioration in the financial performance of all airlines in the German market', including Deutsche BA. 'This is in large part due to the specific characteristics of the German market and in particular the highly aggressive pricing policies of Lufthansa.' Lufthansa declined to comment about the allegations of anti-competitive behaviour.

Sources close to the negotiations said that the real reason behind easyJet's decision was that it had simply taken on too much. The airline was already working hard to integrate Go into its business. By March the combined airlines were flying entirely under the easyJet brand. All cabin crew now wore easyJet's orange uniform and the on-board easyJet kiosk had been rolled out across the whole network. On top of that, easyJet's first Airbus 319 was set to go into service in Geneva in October 2003. Webster said that the decision to abandon its deal with Deutsche BA would not affect easyJet's deal with Airbus. 'We reaffirm that the order for 120 Airbus A319 aircraft has always excluded any aircraft needed in relation to the DBA option and we remain committed to organic growth of 25 per cent per annum,' he said.

Dropping the Deutsche BA deal meant that, on one hand, easyJet had removed a major investor uncertainty. On the other hand, easyJet's German presence remained limited to a Munich–London route. EasyJet was determined to develop flights out of Germany to connect the dots of its existing network. In November 2003, the airline announced plans to establish a new base in Berlin. EasyJet was to base six planes and operate flights to eleven destinations from Schönefeld Airport, about 20 kilometres (12 miles) from central Berlin. The first of the flights, to Luton, was due to start on 1 May 2004, with the rest – including flights to Paris, Copenhagen, Athens and Barcelona – to follow by the end of June. The introduction of the new services was expected to create about 300 to 400 jobs in Berlin.

EasyJet succeeded in attracting pilots by offering higher pay than many of its competitors, according to Michael Hahn, an easyJet pilot based at Berlin Schönefeld. Other budget operators already flying out of Berlin included Ryanair, Air Berlin, Germania, Lufthansa-affiliate Germanwings and travel giant TUI's Hapag-Lloyd Express. Only half of the pilots working at the Berlin airport were German, said Hahn. 'No German would leave Lufthansa to join easyJet as Lufthansa pays good money and it is still in the German's head that you either fly with Lufthansa or take the train.'

Bart Schöpflin, who worked for a bank in Frankfurt, summarised the German attitude. 'Sorry, I'm a convinced Lufthansa man. There is no way that I would choose easyJet for corporate trips. You can't buy flexible tickets with easyJet and I need that in case a meeting finishes later than planned. I also need to be able to fly at peak times and I'm not aware that easyJet offers those flights. Basically I don't care how much it costs when I go on corporate trips so I take the most convenient flight and that is usually with one of the larger airlines. Also I can then earn Air Miles, which I can't with easyJet.'

By moving into Schönefeld, easyJet had secured access to Germany. German passengers gradually learned to value the cheap tickets offered by the likes of easyJet, even if that meant not flying with Lufthansa. But flight attendants' lack of language skills sometimes caused problems with passengers; far from all of the cabin crew could speak German. One German passenger hit a member of the easyJet cabin crew during a flight to Cologne, as she failed to understand that she couldn't use her large holdall as a footrest but needed to stow it away in the overhead locker.

'I explained to her that for safety reasons, I would have to take her bag and put it away,' said one flight attendant, also called Michael. 'She replied to me in German, which I can't understand. I wondered if she couldn't understand what I was saying either so I used hand movements to explain the situation. But she was very adamant and refused to give me her bag. We play a German demo-tape before take-off which explains that you have to stow away large bags. It didn't make any difference. The woman's voice started to get very high and I could tell that she wasn't happy. By this time, all of the 148 passengers on-board were looking at me and I just wished that I could be beamed up. I was so embarrassed.

'I tried to get her bag off her again but she hit me on the arm and continued shouting. The woman was clearly being very abusive, even though I couldn't understand what she was saying. I told her that she would have to leave the aircraft as part of an emergency procedure as she was being so abusive. Eventually she moved her bag and the man who was sitting behind her apologised to me on behalf of the German people for the woman's behaviour.'

Problems with low-cost airlines weren't always what one might expect. Sometimes it was the older passengers who were the most demanding, Michael explained. 'The winter period is particularly difficult as the passengers tend to be more mature people with higher expectations. Some people who fly think that they're flying with British Airways. When I tell them that we don't have the extras such as blankets and pillows that they want, they go absolutely barmy and shout at me. People take it out at me and I'm often told things such as, "You don't get this with BA." But you can't win them all. It is a tough challenge trying to educate people that you can get cheap deals on easyJet and you can do different things, such as bring your own food on-board, but at the end of the day, it is not BA.'

Of course, there were good sides to the job, added Michael. He particularly enjoyed working on flights during the summer months, when lots of young couples escaped on romantic breaks, and introducing new passengers to the joys of flying. 'I've had lots of passengers on-board who have never flown before. There was a woman yesterday who was flying for the first time and she was very nervous. I try to be down to earth and to talk people like that out of their nerves. I told her to try and spot her house when we were taking off. It is a good tactic to calm down passengers as they can concentrate on something else. Some get scared if the plane is a bit wobbly during take-off or during turbulence. I try to be a bit cheeky to make them feel better, telling them that wouldn't their car be a bit wobbly if it had 150 people in it.

'My Mum is not a good flier. She is probably typical of people her age who think that easyJet planes are going to be fifty years old and that the tickets are too cheap and therefore wonders what is wrong with the airline. I went out to Spain with her on easyJet. She was dreading landing back in the UK but ended up pronouncing her landing the best one she has ever had and that was during a snowstorm! Nowadays my Mum flies with easyJet all the time. She travels up to Edinburgh for £25 return to go shopping for the day with her friends. After all, it is only a thirty-five-minute flight from East Midlands.'

Michael said he enjoyed seeing the many celebrities who travelled with easyJet, including Barbara Windsor, Delia Smith and various football players. Some of his passengers were distinctly less well heeled, however. 'Yesterday was funny. I had two women on-board who were in their late forties but dressed as if they were twenty-five years old, wearing cropped tops, which unfortunately showed off their caesarean scars. They were carrying their shopping bags from the shop New Look and trying to act as if they were young and posh but it just wasn't working. They asked for a glass of Chardonnay at 6.30 a.m. Well, we only carry one brand of white wine and one brand of red wine on-board and certainly don't stock Chardonnay. It was obvious that they just wanted to go away for a few days and pretend they had a really glamorous life and simply feel a bit special. They managed to get a cheap ticket with easyJet and could carry out their fantasy. They probably couldn't have afforded that otherwise.'

10. Honeymoon over?

STELIOS'S DEPARTURE MARKED the end of a winning streak for easyJet. In early 2003, the US and UK were preparing to go to war in Iraq. The conflict could hardly have come at a worse time for the industry, as airlines struggled to cope with terrorism fears and the weak economy. The International Air Transport Association expected international passenger travel to drop by 15 to 20 per cent during the war. As well as fuelling passengers' fears of flying and denting consumer confidence, war in the Middle East would also push up fuel costs as the price of crude oil soared; with the added factor of a strike in Venezuela that had choked off the country's oil exports, oil prices had soared above $30 a barrel in January 2003.

In January 2003, easyJet announced that it would slip back into the red for the first half of its financial year, September to March, and that annual growth would fall back from 40 to 25 per cent. EasyJet insisted that the announcement was not a profit warning but illustrated that the company was 'trading as normal'. The airline traditionally posted a loss in the first half, which did not include the key summer months. In the previous year the company had managed a £1 million profit, but easyJet insisted that the previous year's result had been 'exceptional'. 'EasyJet was helped last year by very mild weather and the fact that Easter fell in the first half,' said a spokeswoman. 'Also, post September 11, we dropped prices last year to excite the market and many people were flying short-haul. Furthermore we have had a high level of disruption this year such as bad weather and air traffic control problems, which mean we have had to suspend flights and compensate passengers.'

Concerns about easyJet's welfare escalated in February when the airline warned that average ticket prices in the first half would be lower than previously expected. In a circular to shareholders, the company declared that its average fares in the four months to January were 6 per cent lower than the same period last year, as it cut prices to boost passenger numbers while also having a much greater seat capacity to fill. In a thinly veiled profits alert, the no-frills airline said that it was not at all certain about the outcome for its full financial year: 'Although current forward bookings are robust, the overall profile of the last quarter's revenue, and hence the full-year outcome, will not become apparent for at least several months.' The warning sent easyJet shares tumbling down 34 pence to 208p, a dramatic fall from the airline's high that year of 504p.

EasyJet's interim results were as bad as predicted. In May, the company reported a pre-tax loss of £48 million for the six-month period ending 31 March 2003 – its greatest-ever interim loss. The loss included £18 million of charges for integrating Go and the company also spent £9.2 million on its aborted attempt to buy Deutsche BA. Stripping out one-time costs and goodwill charges of £8.9 million, largely from the Go acquisition, easyJet's underlying losses were £24.4 million.

However, first-half revenues increased 92 per cent to £373 million – a 25 per cent increase on the combined revenue of easyJet and Go the previous year.

To compound the bad results, Webster announced that fifty middle management jobs would be shed at the firm's head office in Luton, as part of easyJet's restructuring following the acquisition of Go. The job cuts came on top of 116 job losses resulting from the closure of the Go call centre at Stansted, announced in March. EasyJet insisted that the integration of Go was making better progress than expected. Although the airline ran up integration costs of £5.6 million in the first half, Webster said that the combined company had been able to make significant cost savings. But investors couldn't yet breathe a sign of relief. The outlook remained 'challenging', added the CEO, warning that profits for the year to September were dependent on the summer months.

Analysts stated that easyJet was suffering from the old problem of trying to expand too fast. EasyJet's purchase of Go brought it lots of extra seats to fill, while Iraq war fears and the economic downturn hit demand. The airline was quickly learning that greater scale meant greater complexity and resulted in declining margins and falling return on capital. This was particularly the case when an acquisition with different systems and methods of operation needed to be integrated, but it was even more so for easyJet as it moved from one centre of operations to multiple hubs in different countries with different types of planes. Managing growth is always difficult – managing growth with added complexity, growing competition and a worldwide slump in demand was even tougher.

While passenger numbers were up by 40 per cent to 9.3 million, the average fare paid by passengers was 10.7 per cent lower than in the same period a year earlier at £37.45. EasyJet dismissed claims that this was the result of competition from Ryanair, which had itself reported an 8 per cent year-on-year fall in fare revenue to the end of December. Webster argued that O'Leary's incessant attacks on easyJet were designed to distract attention from his own carrier's underlying problems. 'I think a lot of the profit growth at Ryanair is coming from Ireland while the new routes he is launching, particularly since taking over Buzz, are unprofitable,' said Webster.

Ryanair had launched a new phase in the air fares war in April 2003, attacking easyJet for being more like a flag carrier than a low-cost airline. The Dublin-based carrier ran a series of adverts poking fun at easyJet and disputing its claim to offer the lowest fares available on the routes it operated. One advert depicted Saddam Hussein's former Information Minister, Mohammed Saeed al-Sahaf, who had been dubbed 'Comical Ali', as easyJet's new head of information. Other advertisements described easyJet's claim as 'a load of bullocks' and one of the 'four greatest lies told by man'.

Ryanair's decision to attack easyJet, rather than British Airways or Lufthansa, marked a distinct shift in strategy, particularly as easyJet only competed with Ryanair on six of its 125 destinations. O'Leary said that criticising high-fare airlines such as BA had become a 'bit like kicking a dead sheep', and that Ryanair's objective was now to 'reposition' easyJet in the minds of air travellers. 'We want to eliminate the idea that easyJet is somehow a low-cost airline,' O'Leary declared. 'It isn't. Its average fares are 70 per cent higher than ours. There is only one low-fares airline in Europe and that is Ryanair.'

It was clear that Europe's no-frills market was disaggregating. At one end of the spectrum, there was a genuinely low-cost, low-fares operator in the shape of Ryanair, and at the other end a host of wannabes such as bmibaby. EasyJet, with its higher cost structure because of its mixed fleet and preference for principal airports, fitted somewhere in the middle, appealing to those who wanted a cheaper fare than BA rather than the lowest one going.

EasyJet responded that it had always been careful not to claim that it offered the lowest fares available and added that flying with Ryanair was like a geography lesson: 'They go to places you can't spell and have never heard of, and certainly don't bear any resemblance to the destination advertised,' said an easyJet spokesman. 'And by the time you have paid for a taxi to take you into the city centre it would probably have been cheaper to fly with British Airways, let alone easyJet!'

Webster stressed that easyJet operated a different business model from Ryanair's. 'Comparing ourselves to Ryanair is irrelevant,' he argued. 'We are trying to be the cheap operator between airports that people really want to use. If you are flying to Beauvais [where Ryanair lands], it is not Paris. My wife is Parisian and if you mention Beauvais she says it is the country.' Ryanair's voluble boss retorted that the majority of easyJet's traffic involved Luton, Liverpool, Belfast and the East Midlands, which were hardly sought-after locations. 'EasyJet is not low cost and it is not low fare. It is much more like BA because it charges high fares and it loses money. Case closed.'

It was somewhat disingenuous of easyJet to talk about inappropriate ads. The orange airline was known for its colourful adverts, including one inviting passengers to 'discover weapons of mass distraction' above a picture of a woman's breasts in a bikini top and the promise 'lowest fares to the sun'. A total of 186 people contacted the Advertising Standards Authority in summer 2003 to label the newspaper advert 'offensive and demeaning to women' and 'trivialising the war in Iraq'. The ASA rejected the complaints. EasyJet said the advert was the latest in a series designed to be 'topical, humorous and irreverent' and dismissed accusations it was either sexist or demeaning to women.

The ASA also rejected a complaint by Charles Ingram, who was convicted in April 2003 of using deception – via the coded coughs of an accomplice in the audience – to win the top prize on quiz show *Who Wants to Be A Millionaire?* EasyJet ran a newspaper ad soon after the verdict with the headline 'Need a cheap getaway?' above a photograph of Charles Ingram with his wife Diana and the words 'No Major fraud required'.

EasyJet's shares received another hammering in August, when Stelios sold a further £19 million of shares in easyJet to fund four new ventures: pizza delivery, minibus services, and budget hotels and cruises. The sale of 8 million easyJet shares, equivalent to just over 2 per cent of the stock, reduced Stelios's holding to 18.8 per cent. EasyJet shares fell 7 per cent to 241p on the news.

Stelios seemed keen to apply the principle of yield management to absolutely anything, whether it was the shiny new Airbuses soaring ahead or cheese and tomato pizzas in cardboard boxes. James Rothnie, spokesman for easyGroup, decribed easyPizza as a 'classic easyGroup concept', allowing people to buy a pizza for as little as £1 at traditionally quiet times like afternoons. Next was easyBus, which would transport passengers not to glamorous destinations such as Paris or Nice but between Hendon in north-west London and Milton Keynes for as little as £1. Another of Stelios's brainwaves was easyCruise: Mediterranean cruise ships on which passengers would have to clean their own cabins and supply their own bedding and toiletries in return for a fare of as little as £29 per night. Forget lavish banquets and white-jacketed stewards; the bright orange-painted cabins wouldn't even have windows. Rooms in easyHotel were only nine times the size of a phone box and guests had to bring their own sheets and toiletries. EasyMobile, meanwhile, planned to offer the lowest tariffs for voice calls and text messaging in the UK.

Stelios conceded that extending the easy brand into other markets was anything but easy. 'I think the mistake I made is I thought it would be easier. In the early days with easyJet, I worked very hard in the unglamorous surroundings of Luton. I now realise that you have to do the same with every business.'

The outspoken entrepreneur blamed the 'catastrophic failure' of managers for £120 million of losses incurred over the previous four years at his easyGroup companies, which excluded publicly owned easyJet. 'The explanation does not lie in the branding strategy,' Stelios maintained. 'It lies in a catastrophic failure of cost control by the managers I chose to run these companies.' And possibly a lack of enthusiasm among consumers for being shuttled up to Milton Keynes in an easyBus to watch a little-known film in the weathered, squat home of easyCinema? At least Stelios appeared to be becoming more cautious, rejecting proposals for an easy-branded undertaker service (with orange coffins?) and a cosmetic surgery service he dubbed easyBoob.

Under an agreement, none of the easy companies were permitted to compete directly with one another. Nor could easyJet set up non-core subsidiaries that generated more than 25 per cent of its total revenue. None of which had stopped easyJet from forming a partnership with Europcar – an easyCar rival.

Stelios argued it was 'slightly simplistic' to focus on easyGroup's accumulated losses. 'It is a bit meaningless. I am a venture capitalist. I invest money in the hope to get it back and more in a few years. I think in decades not years.' He warned that there would be more share sales to come, insisting, 'As I have been consistently saying for a while, from time to time, I will be selling a bit of my past to finance my future'; though in the previous autumn, standing down as chairman of easyJet, he had proclaimed that he had no present intention to sell any easyJet shares in the near future.

The departure of a company's founder, even when he had already put in place a highly competent successor such as Webster, was normally a sign for a company's shares to fall – and once the dust had settled easyJet was no exception. Analysts said that whatever the merits of eliminating a competitor, the Go purchase had also provided a convenient cover for Stelios to sell a significant slice of his shares at a price he would have been hard pushed to get if the institutions had not been excited by the deal. By persistently selling off his past to finance his future, as he put it, Stelios was doing his original and most successful creation no favours at all. Stelios was entirely open in stating that he intended progressively to flog off his shares in easyJet in order to fund his various other easyGroup ventures. Nonetheless, each time it happened, it came as a surprise and knocked the share price, which was still languishing close to its Iraq-war lows.

The umbilical cord with easyJet's founder hadn't been completely cut. Stelios's presence was everywhere to be seen in easyJet's Portakabin-style headquarters, from a framed photo of him to the 'thank you Stelios' poster in reception. But Webster maintained that Stelios didn't intervene in the day-to-day management of the airline. The chief executive briefed the airline's founder after every set of results and Webster and Stelios caught up twice a year at a meeting of the easy companies. That was it. Stelios concurred: 'If they decide tomorrow to fly business class, I'd give them my negative thoughts. But if you ask me to name the routes easyJet flies, I couldn't.'

Webster had no intention of fundamentally straying from Stelios's original strategy but some things had changed since the founder's departure. For one, competition was getting tougher. Low interest rates, a glut of secondhand aircraft and the example of the successful market leaders had lured hopeful start-ups into the market. By mid-2003, there were at least thirty-four no-frills carriers in Europe and seven 'coming soon'. It was hard to keep up with the no-frills scene. Aside from everyday names such as easyJet, Ryanair, bmibaby, Virgin Express, Germanwings and Hapag-Lloyd Express, you could find Basiq Air (Amsterdam), Snalskjutsen (Sweden), SkyEurope (Bratislava, Slovakia), Volareweb (Milan/Venice), Evolavia (Ancona), Jetmagic (Cork) and Air Catalunya (Barcelona).

The reach of European no-frills airline networks had mushroomed. It was easier to count the countries European low-cost airlines didn't serve than those they did. The Baltic states weren't yet served by any carrier that could be realistically defined as no-frills and neither were the more remote Eastern European countries like Belarus, Ukraine, Moldova or

Bulgaria. But outside this handful of nations, there were few exceptions. In central Europe, Poland and Hungary and Slovakia had their own low-cost airlines. Prague was a perennially popular destination for budget carriers from Germany, Scandinavia and the UK. And at least three no-frills airlines were now flying to cities on the Dalmatian coast of Croatia, as well as to Serbia, Bosnia and Herzegovina and FYR Macedonia.

In Western Europe, Luxembourg was unique in being the only EU country yet to play host to a no-frills service – though the private regional airline VLM usually provided a better deal on low-fare flights to London than any competitor. Independent travellers could increasingly find low-cost flights to elsewhere on the continent in every country, from Iceland in the far north-west to Georgia in the south-east, including the most unlikely regions – Denmark to Kosovo, anyone? A growing trend pioneered by Air Berlin and Snowflake was to provide cheap connections from Europe to destinations in North Africa, such as Egypt and Morocco, as well as to eastern Mediterranean countries like Turkey and Lebanon.

Meanwhile, the low-cost boom continued in the UK, which played host to more no-frills carriers than any other country in Western Europe. Coventry Airport greeted Thomson Fly, a new low-cost airline run by TUI, the same German parent company that operated Hapag-Lloyd Express. Full-service airlines had added to the competition by creating their own no-frills clones – Britain's British Midland had set up bmibaby and Scandinavia's SAS had established Snowflake Airlines. Other full-service airlines added to the competition by matching many no-frills fares, especially for late booking, with one-way prices and no Sunday-stay requirement.

While British Airways and the other large established airlines could partially ignore easyJet when it flew from Luton to a handful of destinations, they were inclined to compete more vigorously as easyJet got larger. Martin George, marketing and commercial director of British Airways, said that BA had no intention of relinquishing short-haul routes to no-frills carriers: 'Some may retreat but we're fighting to make money on short-haul.' As the cost of jet fuel soared, some network carriers tried to compensate by raising ticket prices, only to give up within days. Budget airlines controlled pricing in the market and the larger airlines were being forced to respond. Passengers were being offered more choice and better prices.

Competition wasn't the only thing easyJet had to worry about. The airline also needed to find new routes and landing slots. It had to fill sixteen additional aircraft in its fleet in 2004 and twenty-three more planes in the following year. Ryanair, meanwhile, had about 100 Boeings on order whose seats it needed to fill. Keith McMullan of Aviation Economics calculated that each of these aircraft would have to carry 250,000 passengers a year to earn their keep. It was a tough target to meet. In 2003, easyJet carried 21.1 million passengers, while in the year ending March 2004, Ryanair carried 23.1 million passengers. In order to fill up all the new planes, already arriving in the airlines' fleets at the rate of one every fortnight until the end of 2008, easyJet and Ryanair needed between them to attract 52 million new passengers – more than double their current numbers.

Webster revealed that he had short-listed half a dozen airports for talks about expanding the airline's network of 105 routes between thirty-eight airports. He wanted to pick one or two of the short-listed airports to launch new services the following summer. The problem was that most of the bases operated by easyJet and Ryanair were in Ireland or Britain. The London airports were dominated by low-cost traffic, with the sector's share at almost 40 per cent, against only 12 per cent in Paris and less than 20 per cent in Frankfurt's airports. EasyJet and Ryanair held a measly 7 per cent of intra-European flights at Paris Charles de Gaulle, Orly and Beauvais combined. EasyJet complained about discrimination at Charles de Gaulle, where it paid the same landing fees as Air France but was relegated to Terminal Three, a bus ride away from the main airport. Unless the two airlines could gain greater access to airports in France or Germany and so tap new markets, both would struggle to maintain their growth and would have to continue their bitter price war. They were making some progress, but it was an uphill struggle.

Industry analyst Chris Tarry of research consultancy CTAIRA commented: 'Ryanair and easyJet are very much of a UK phenomenon and here the full-service carriers BA and bmi British Midland have fought back hard. It is also a market dominated by the M25 factor, where passengers are prepared to pay a little extra for a full-service flight or one that doesn't go from Stansted. Add the collapse in corporate spending and fall in consumer confidence and discretionary spending, and you see the problem. You could say the honeymoon is over.'

In February 2004, Stelios decided to go on a 'little shopping spree'. He came home with more than just a few groceries. Over the course of a few days, Stelios made commitments to buy a cruise ship capable of carrying 250 people for easyCruise, a twenty-five-room hotel in London for easyHotel, and a fleet of Mercedes buses for easyBus. As ever, easyJet provided the cash for Stelios's shopping excursions. He sold 4 million shares, or 1 per cent in the airline, to fund his purchases, bringing his stake in easyJet down to 16.57 per cent, or 66,076 million shares. But the Greek multimillionaire also underlined his ongoing commitment to the easyJet business. 'I have not sold out of easyJet, nor do I intend to sell out. I remain a great believer in the scalability and sustainability of the business model I developed.'

Some observers wondered if Stelios's foray into such a bewildering and unprofitable assortment of businesses was having a damaging effect even on easyJet itself. John Williamson, a director of brand consultancy Wolff Olins, commented, 'Stelios does not live the brand in the way that Branson or Michael O'Leary at Ryanair does. The "easy" brand is worth less now than four years ago.'

Overall, these were trying time for Stelios. Two years previously, in 2002, easyJet had been worth more than £2 billion, Stelios had a host of expanding businesses and more ideas than he had time to implement, and the future had seemed lurid orange. Since then, Stelios had been obliged to restructure his easyCar auto rentals business, which had lost £20 million, in order to save it from oblivion. Stelios also had been forced to rescue easyInternetcafé, which had lost about £90 million, with a multi-million-pound handout and he was still fighting a cartel of film studios that were refusing to let him screen new releases at his low-cost easyCinema.

EasyJet was also suffering. It wasn't that long since no-frills airlines had been cruising above the clouds of a brutal industry shakeout, boasting soaring sales and profits. The low-cost pioneers had been able to flourish simply by feeding off the soft underbelly of the established full-service airlines. It had been pitifully easy to undercut them. Times had changed, and budget carriers were increasingly being forced to compete against each other to sustain the breakneck pace of growth.

Low-cost carriers that had already gone under included Duo, which flew from Birmingham and Edinburgh, Irish airline Jet Greet, Cork-based JetMagic and Luton-based Now, which collapsed before its first flight, backing up the aviation industry's historic statistic that 97 per cent of all start-ups eventually failed. Airline expert Chris Tarry said it was 'inevitable' that more European airlines would go under as carriers fought to the death for bookings. EasyJet's German network of twenty-five routes was suffering from particularly strong competition. EasyJet had opened bases in Berlin and Dortmund to increase its routes and planned to raise capacity by 50 per cent in the winter, adding three aircraft, new routes and more frequent flights to existing destinations. With the UK market relatively mature, executives knew that future low-cost expansion would take place on the continent. That was why hanging on in Europe's most populous and central state was so important. 'Germany is the real battleground,' said

Chris Avery, an airline analyst at JP Morgan. 'The UK and Ireland broadly have the same penetration of low-cost carriers as in the US. So the rest of Europe is where the easy growth is. France is pretty much closed, so everyone has gone to Germany.'

EasyJet's arrival was causing consternation among the German start-ups, including Air Berlin, Germania Express, Hapag-Lloyd Express and Lufthansa-affiliate Germanwings, all of which were soundly based and operated routes to the UK. 'It is an emotional issue for us,' said Andreas Bierwirth, the deputy managing director of Germanwings. 'We will protect our market and we will protect our routes, especially London Gatwick to Cologne, to the last drop of blood in our bodies.'

Major carriers such as British Airways and Air France were an added concern for the budget carriers. Chris Tarry said easyJet was being hit by an aggressive response from so-called 'full-service' airlines like British Airways, after these slashed their fares in Europe. If you fancied a Riviera vacation, easyJet could fly you from Paris to Nice for as little as €84 but then Air France, which at first pooh-poohed easyJet's arrival at Paris Orly airport, had cut its Paris–Nice fare to just over €100. A BA round trip from London to Paris cost as little as €119 – more than the €62 easyJet charged for mid-week travel during off-peak hours but roughly comparable to easyJet fares at other times.

Many Europeans still preferred to fly old-line carriers even if it cost a little bit more, said Tarry: 'It turns out that Europeans are not so price-sensitive that a few euros on a ticket will make a difference.' Moreover, the old-timers were also continuing to adopt some of the discounters' innovations, such as easier online booking and the elimination of some stay-over restrictions. And passengers flying with the likes of British Airways could luxuriate in 'frills' such as frequent flier miles and a free meal on-board. The discounters continued to choose price as their chosen weapon and retaliated with even lower fares than the established airlines. After Aer Lingus started selling one-way Dublin to London tickets for €14.50, Ryanair dropped its fare to €13 as part of an average 11 per cent fare cut.

By April 2004, Ryanair chief executive O'Leary was Armageddon-like in his predictions of what was in store as the price war continued. 'I see a ferocious bloodbath among no-frills carriers. There will be tremendous competition, with the mother and father of all fare wars. We expect the coming year to be tough and the winter to be particularly difficult.'

His comments came as the Irish company announced profits were down 14 per cent. The squeeze on margins prompted Ryanair to axe three of its French routes, Reims, Clermont-Ferrand and Brest. There was more bad news. In February 2004, the European Commission had ordered Ryanair to repay €4 million in discounts it had obtained from Brussels Charleroi Airport – a ruling that took direct aim at the Irish airline's strategy of securing cheap landing fees at under-utilised regional airports.

The Dublin-based airline warned investors that it expected its revenue per passenger to plunge by as much as 20 per cent in the three months to September, the second quarter of its financial year, as it fought to increase market share. Ryanair reminded investors that it remained hugely more profitable in terms of operating margin than even the best of the full-service airlines. In an attempt to boost revenues while keeping fares low, the airline said that it intended to introduce in-flight entertainment on all of its flights but customers would have to pay for the privilege at an introductory price of €7 per flight. The company also worked on plans to ban large luggage.

Ferocious pricing from competitors was also hurting easyJet, which in May 2004 announced a loss before tax and goodwill of £18.5 million in the six months ending March, approximately what analysts expected but an improvement on its loss of £24.4 million in the same period a year earlier. Turnover was up by 18 per cent at £439 million as the number of passengers rose 16 per cent to 10.8 million. 'We are currently seeing unprofitable and unrealistic pricing by airlines across the European industry, seeking to grow or maintain their market share,' said Webster. 'The substantial oversupply of seats, especially in the London market, is unsustainable.'

The airline adjusted its outlook for the full year from 'cautiously optimistic' to 'cautious' because of what it termed an 'increasingly competitive marketplace'. There were further premonitions of doom. EasyJet said it expected its average fares to fall in 2004 from £42 to £38. The profit warning – just as the normally lucrative summer season got into full swing – shocked the City. That, plus disappointing trading over Easter and the collapse over the previous weekend of Duo, sent that day's shares in easyJet plunging a stomach-churning 25 per cent, or 73p, to 219p. More than £275 million was wiped off the budget airline's value and Stelios saw £49 million wiped off his shares.

Even worse, in June, easyJet came back to the City with another profit warning, announcing that profits might only just top last year's £52 million. This was well below market expectations. Even with recent profit forecast downgrades after the interim results, analysts had been pencilling in profits as high as £80 million. The airline claimed it was continuing to face pressure from unprofitable and unrealistic pricing in an increasingly competitive market. High fuel prices, thanks to an unstable Middle East, added to the problems. Airline fuel had risen by 10 per cent in the first three months of the year and the cost of oil had hit a high of $42.30 a barrel. The International Air Transport Association estimated that the fuel crisis could cost the global airline industry as much as $1 billion a month in extra costs.

'While demand for low-cost travel remains strong, the forward pricing environment is exceptionally competitive,' said easyJet in the trading update. Webster also served notice that there would be some 'bloody noses' among its rival low-cost operators as the fares war intensified. 'There is going to be a lot of blood on the floor and it is not going to be O'Leary's or mine. We are not going to sit on our hands as other airlines come along and try to take our market but nor are we going to open up the war chest and go out and pick a fight.'

The colourful words were more typical of one of O'Leary's ebullient outbursts than of the quietly spoken, reserved New Zealander. But if Webster thought that his macho comments might win favour with the City, he was wrong. EasyJet shares nosedived by another 37 pence to 163p on Webster's warning. In under a month, easyJet had issued two profit warnings and shares had crashed by a total of almost 50 per cent. The company was now valued at £629 million compared with £2 billion in November 2000, and some observers saw it as vulnerable to takeover.

Webster admitted that the airline had made a mistake in not being specific a month previously in its guidance but denied that it had been punished by the markets as a result. 'I wouldn't call it punishment; I would call it a correction,' he said defiantly, adding, 'Overall I was surprised at the reaction. We felt we had a good first half; we met our expectations so we certainly weren't anticipating the reaction the market gave back to us. One can only assume their expectations were much higher than ours.'

But City investors didn't like getting caught on the hop. 'EasyJet's second warning in a month dents the credibility of the management led by Ray Webster,' the *Financial Times* pronounced. 'The management's operational expertise is highly regarded but the warning suggests a cultural flaw of over-optimism and a lack of understanding of the stock-market.' Analysts and investors were angry. One shareholder said: 'The whole management process comes under suspicion when things like this happen.' Another investor said he felt that Webster would be viewed as 'damaged goods' for a while, adding that the worsening market conditions had been 'signposted' by O'Leary months ago. 'Mr Webster appears to have been caught out on what is really going on in the market,' the shareholder commented tersely.

These were stinging rebukes for somebody who for nine years or so, along with Stelios, had delivered spectacular growth in revenues, profits and passenger numbers. There were calls for executive heads to roll. 'I think the market is punishing poor investor relations,' said Stelios. 'I've spoken to the company and know that it is doing something about it. You measure investor relations by how well or otherwise the market receives bad news, and twice in the last month the stock plummeted by more than 15 to 20 per cent in one day. That cannot be good investor relations, no matter how bad the news is.'

Stelios also told the airline that it must cut costs. EasyJet announced plans to axe unprofitable routes and lose at least six planes, nearly a tenth of its fleet – the first time that the company had ordered such cutbacks. The airline said that it would stick to its new aircraft delivery schedule for its 120 new Airbus planes, despite the growing fears among analysts that there were too many planes in Europe and too few passengers. EasyJet itself also raised questions over what it would do with the eighty-two new planes Airbus was due to deliver over the following three years. The Luton-based airline was still expecting the market to expand by 20 per cent in 2004 but its predictions of a 25 per cent expansion in 2005 were looking over-optimistic. 'Capacity deployment for financial year 2005 is currently under review,' the airline said in a statement.

Webster organised a series of meetings with big investors in the UK, continental Europe and the US to try to calm anger over what was undeniably a serious communications failure from the cockpit. At these meetings, he re-emphasised that despite the current fuel price problems and increasing competitiveness in airline prices, easyJet should be able to report pre-tax profits that would exceed the £52 million it made in the previous year. The airline had already acquired the financial strength, size and breadth of network to see it through the turbulence, and, as Webster pointed out, it had a balance sheet that was flush with cash.

Webster reckoned that only two low-cost carriers, perhaps three at a push, would survive long-term in Europe – one of which would be easyJet and the other Ryanair. He recognised that the two had a mutual self-interest in not going head to head. 'Ryanair and easyJet will find a way of co-existing,' he promised. 'The important thing to recognise is that both of us are disciplined by the capital markets. If we ignore that and start depleting shareholders' funds we will get some pretty clear signals from investors.'

The chief executive's words helped calm angry investors but the damage was already done. The City's love affair with low-cost airlines had cooled. Stelios was watching his and his family's combined 41 per cent stake shrink in value by the day and analysts speculated that he would like nothing better than to take his airline private again and prove how wrong the City was to ease him out in the first place. The one question was whether he could raise the finance, given that Stelios's easyGroup businesses had yet to make substantial profits. With the shares now significantly lower than they had been when floated four years ago, the company would be a steal on its current valuation of £575 million, though any bid was likely to be pitched around at least £650 million. Chris Avery, transport analyst at JP Morgan, referred to recent reports that Stelios had received offers for his original shipping business, Stelmar Shipping, adding: 'If consummated, this might fund both start-ups and give Stelios the cash to take easyJet private again at a sensible price, perhaps returning to the stockmarket in a few years' time when the business model would be more mature.'

Webster dismissed the reports, saying that a buy-out 'is not on my radar screen'. He added that Stelios was a supportive shareholder who took a close interest in the running of the business and had his own representative on the board, making him an insider. A month later Stelios backed up Webster's statement, announcing in a letter to shareholders that taking the airline private 'would be something of an extreme measure' and that he had 'no current plan' to do so, though he admitted that he could change his mind if shares fell further or if he lost confidence in the board. At the same time, it was revealed that OMI, an oil shipping company, had withdrawn its £352 million takeover offer for Stelmar. The news didn't help; easyJet's shares slumped to a record low, falling 6½p to 143½p as investors stripped out any takeover premium from their valuations of the airline.

EasyJet did little to soothe fears in the City when it put out a trading statement in July saying there had been no improvement in the market since the previous month's unexpected profit warning. EasyJet carried 2.24 million passengers in June, putting it within spitting distance of the 2.27 million that Ryanair handled in the same month, with easyJet's aircraft flying at 84 per cent of capacity against Ryanair's 87 per cent. The planes were full but the fares were falling.

11. A grim winter

HARD TIMES LAY ahead for easyJet. In a bid to prepare for tougher times, the airline planned to increase the size of its fleet by just 16 per cent in 2005, instead of the 24 per cent previously planned, and retire about eighteen of its older Boeings 737s to ease over-capacity problems – six more than it had planned. Even so, analysts raised concerns that plans to slow the rapid growth rate of its fleet would not come into effect for another twelve months. Shares in the budget airline plunged even lower in September 2004, as easyJet admitted that there was 'continuing volatility in fuel prices' and that yields – average revenue per passenger – would remain under pressure in 2005. The company's stock slumped to 128p, less than half its flotation price four years previously.

Nine years had passed since easyJet's inaugural flight from Luton to Glasgow, when Stelios had pledged to bring flying to the masses. A lot had changed since that first orange Boeing 737 left the tarmac. Running easyJet was not so easy anymore.

With oil prices a hair's breadth away from $50 a barrel, margins were coming under pressure on all fronts.

The wider picture for the no-frills sector continued to look bleak. There were too many players, many of which were under-capitalised. Pressure on prices, relentless cost-cutting and selective route closures meant more players were going to the wall. The German outfit V-Bird was laid to rest, following the fate of others such as Now and Air Planet. The Danish operator Sterling had put itself up for sale. Virgin Express, meanwhile, had responded to the competitive threat by getting into bed with SN Brussels, which itself emerged out of the remnants of bankrupt Belgian carrier Sabena and its regional affiliate, Delta Air Transport, at the end of 2001. Then there was Hop – backed by Kit Malthouse, the deputy leader of Westminster council, and Tony Camacho, the former Buzz airline chief executive – which flopped before it even got off the ground after the financiers got cold feet.

There was little doubt that Ryanair and easyJet, two of the best-capitalised players in the sector, would survive. But for a while, the pickings would be thinner. The next duel that broke out between the pair concerned hand baggage. Ryanair raised its cabin baggage allowance to 10kg from 7kg. A week later, easyJet responded by abandoning the weight limit altogether. The only constraint was volume: your bag had to fit the 55cm by 40cm by 20cm maximum dimension, which corresponded to 22 litres. If you took a container of those dimensions full to the brim with lead weights, it would amount to 250kg. And if this generous allowance was insufficient for your needs, easyJet also allowed you to bring a laptop on board in addition. EasyJet hoped that the check-in process should be smoother and faster as a result of the eased restrictions although the boarding process could be slower as passengers tried to find places to stash their newly expanded baggage allowance.

Ryanair was testing the spartan spirit of its passengers by dispensing with its planes' window blinds, reclining seats,

Velcro-anchored headrest covers and the seat pockets where customers normally found a safety notice and free magazines. The required safety notice became a mere sticker on the back of each seat. EasyJet, meanwhile, was considering the introduction of a frequent flier programme. Webster, speaking at the International Air Transport Association annual conference in Singapore, said: 'We may have to do a frequent flier programme cheaply. It would be along the lines of a coffee shop stamp on a card.' He denied that such a programme would amount to easyJet adding frills. But in analysts' opinion, the move would inevitably further blur the distinction between low-cost and full-service airlines. In the end, easyJet didn't introduce the scheme, deciding that such frills didn't fit in with its low-cost plan, and perhaps also that it could fall victim to fraud.

Meanwhile, easyJet was experimenting with fully automated check-in kiosks at East Midlands Airport to replace check-in staff and counters. 'In due course, this could revolutionise the airport process in the way that the Internet revolutionised the booking process,' said Webster. The airline announced that if it was successful the system would be rolled out in other airports across its network, which would 'ultimately see kiosk-only check-in'.

EasyJet injected a degree of optimism into the sector when it announced that trading in its last quarter had been better than expected, with load factors remaining in the high 80s during the summer. The airline now expected pre-tax profits for the year to the end of September 2004 to top £60 million, up 16 per cent on 2003, improving on its previous predictions that profits would 'at least' exceed last year's £52 million. In the end, easyJet's full-year profits nudged higher than expectations. Profits rose to £62.2 million, up 21 per cent on a year earlier. The shares rose 2.86 per cent to 188½p on the news. The annual load factor, or how many seats were sold, improved to 84.5 from 84.1 per cent. With planes fuller, easyJet crossed the £1 billion turnover barrier for the first time, with sales up 17 per cent to £1.09 billion. But increased competition led to a fall in passenger yield to £42.28 in 2004 from £43.28 in 2003.

The airline warned the remaining winter months would be 'challenging'. Like other airlines, easyJet was facing pressure on overheads after its annual fuel bill increased by almost 22 per cent on a year earlier to £146.9 million, representing 14 per cent of spending, which had itself risen 20 per cent to £929.3 million.

High oil prices and stiff competition prompted a further drive to focus on costs. EasyJet said it planned to outsource some information-technology operations and achieve savings by using more fuel-efficient Airbus A319s. The airline also aimed to reduce spending by pulling out of poorly performing markets and over-priced airports. Airports and ground handling charges accounted for almost a third of easyJet's operational costs – a higher proportion than for most other airlines.

As part of its costs drive, on 31 October easyJet axed its Luton to Zurich service, which it claimed had become its most expensive route, and switched its Swiss services to Basel Mulhouse EuroAirport. The carrier accused Zurich Airport of ripping it off, describing a 132 per cent hike in landing charges over the previous two years as 'ludicrous', while castigating the airport's 'onerous operating restrictions'. Webster said Zurich 'now realised' that carriers would go to other destinations if airport operators thought they could raise prices as they wished. 'At any one time we are talking to a number of airports about future services – to date we have six new European cities for this winter,' he continued. 'Airports that "get it" and grasp the new reality will be rewarded with growth from Europe's leading low-cost airlines.'

Zurich wasn't the only airport to be shunned by easyJet. The airline reduced the number of flights it operated to Copenhagen Airport, scared away by its high airport tax of 75 kroner per passenger, and also decided to discontinue flights from Amsterdam to Barcelona and Nice as a result of rising landing fees, reducing the number of easyJet flights from Schiphol each day from twenty-seven to twenty-two. EasyJet was the second largest airline user of the airport after the national carrier, KLM. The total number of low-cost passengers at Schiphol in 2004 was around 4 million, almost 10 per cent of all passengers using the airport, and easyJet flew around half of those passengers. Leon Verhallen, manager of the passenger marketing business unit at Schiphol, said the airport was 'working hard to reduce its visit costs in general, but also to offer special facilities to reduce cost reductions'; the airport planned to open a new pier that it hoped would be attractive to low-cost carriers and free space in the central terminal area for airlines with a high level of connecting traffic.

Meanwhile, easyJet was still trying to establish a footing at French airports. The airline had boosted its number of flights out of Orly and Roissy from zero to thirty-five over the past two years. But as easyJet pointed out, it had taken only three months to build a comparable network in Germany. The airline asserted in a statement in *Les Echos* business newspaper that 'the French market is still closed to the development of airlines capable of competing with Air France . . . it is incomprehensible that a country such as France, which sees itself at the forefront of European legislation, does so little to permit the emergence of real competition to the national company'.

EasyJet's next area of conquest was Italy. Both easyJet and Ryanair, lured by Italy's position as the second largest low-cost airline market in Europe, announced plans to extend their reach in the country following the collapse of Italian no-frills airline Volare, which had declared insolvency. EasyJet planned daily services starting in April or May 2005 from Gatwick to Olbia, Luton to Cagliari and Berlin to Olbia and Pisa. The airline said it expected to see its passenger numbers on all Italian flights 'significantly increase' in 2005. Ryanair, meanwhile, said it would start a twice-daily service from Paris Beauvais to Venice Treviso and also announced that it wanted to hold talks with the Italian airports affected by the collapse of Volare about beginning low-fare domestic flights within Italy on routes previously served by the Italian carrier.

Then both airlines started to aim punches below the belt. In September Ryanair announced it would start flying from Britain to provincial Spain, previously seen as the preserve of easyJet. In a matter of days easyJet launched a surprise attack on Ryanair in the latter's home territory, announcing plans to introduce its first routes to the Republic of Ireland in January 2005. Weeks later, Ryanair said it would launch on the same Irish routes out of Gatwick as easyJet. The new easyJet services from Gatwick to Shannon, Knock and Cork were the only routes in Europe on which the two airlines competed directly.

In a side-sweep at its Irish rival, Webster declared: 'These are our first services to the Republic of Ireland, where air fares, in many cases, have remained stubbornly high and have generated consistently strong year-round returns for the incumbent airline.'

Ryanair co-deputy chief executive Howard Millar hit back: 'They are free to fly where they want to and if they want competition they can have competition. We will be happy to take the game to them.'

EasyJet's move into Ireland was ironic news for Ryanair. O'Leary had spent years calling for Irish airports authority, Aer Rianta, to be privatised. Eventually, in mid-2004, the Irish government proposed a bill which would break up the company that ran Ireland's three major airports by April 2005. Aer Rianta was to be split into three separate, competing state-run authorities operating the airports in Dublin, Cork and Shannon respectively. It must have come as a blow for the Irish CEO that the airports immediately chose to strike a deal with his competitor.

Meanwhile the two airlines battled to keep costs as low as possible. Whereas O'Leary famously banned highlighter pens from the office, Webster banned photocopiers, which he considered a more compelling example of cost-cutting. EasyJet employed more than 4,000 people but its headquarters remained in what Stelios had dubbed a 'giant Portakabin in Luton'. Not even the most senior managers had PAs; they all did their own administration.

EasyJet ran paperless offices, with documents scanned into the intranet where they could be picked up on a screen wherever employees might be in the world. An accountant complained in a flyer on the wall at easyJet's headquarters that she found 1,113 sheets of printer paper in the rubbish. 'If you rely on technology to run the business then you don't need pieces of paper,' said Webster. 'The problem with paper is that if you want lots of people to be involved you need lots of bits of paper. The great thing about technology is that 500 people can read the same piece of information simultaneously, three or four seconds after it was sent. It is not about the cost of paper. It is about unleashing the management potential by ensuring people have access to information as quickly as possible.'

The airline's only major administration expenses were IT costs, the lease on the head office and the salaries of management staff. EasyJet kept to its original formula of keeping costs low by selling directly to consumers, cutting out middlemen like travel agents, call operators and sales staff, with nearly all of its reservations made online; it sold a higher proportion of seats online than any other airline. Not paying commissions to travel agents added a healthy 6 per cent to the bottom line, and being a ticketless, web-based operation contributed another 3 per cent. Instead of a ticket, passengers received an email containing their travel details and confirmation number when they booked online. This avoided the cost of issuing, distributing and processing millions of tickets each year.

EasyJet reckoned they could get people on their planes quicker when people didn't have allocated seats. This was because people would be anxious to sit together and so would make sure they were at the gate, ready to board as soon as possible. Lone travellers, who didn't have anyone to sit next to, were a minority. Passengers were normally called to the gate by the number on their boarding pass number so the earlier they checked in the better the seat choice. EasyJet passengers also handed in their boarding card at the gate rather than the door of the plane where possible and used two sets of stairs, front and rear. Again, these were time-saving measures, necessary if easyJet were to achieve its tight turn-around times.

EasyJet worked hard to 'sweat the assets' by making sure that its planes were as full as possible and up in the air as many hours as possible. It wasn't unusual for an easyJet plane to make eight or nine hops around Europe in a day, beginning before dawn and ending around midnight. The planes had to be checked between each flight and the airline had to have a stock of spare engines and parts should any of the fleet need repairs. All planes had to undergo a yearly MOT, which required them to spend a day or more in a hangar being given the once-over.

Many fixed services, such as handling and maintenance, were outsourced to reduce costs. EasyJet held an outsourcing agreement with Danish-owned FLS Aerospace, under which base maintenance was carried out at a fixed price plus the cost of materials and time. Component maintenance was charged by the flight hour, while technical services, which included maintenance planning, was charged on a per aircraft basis. Ground handling covered the cost of check-in staff, baggage handlers and the workers who refuelled the planes. These employees were usually employed by an outside agency, such as Servis-Air or Aviance, who had a deal with the airline. At its large bases, such as Luton and Geneva, easyJet employed its own check-in staff.

In total, easyJet enjoyed a massive profit per employee. According to a study from the European Cockpit Association, easyJet's profit per employee was an impressive 350 per cent greater than that of the traditional airlines. Overall the cost per available seat kilometre, the industry yardstick, worked out at around half that of the full-service carriers and revenue per employee was almost double.

Flight crew working for the likes of easyJet weren't paid peanuts, as was often assumed, but pilot pay was still around 25 per cent lower than at traditional carriers. A captain with easyJet would earn around £80,000 a year, a first officer (the second in command) £50,000. And unlike large airlines, low-cost operators expected their staff to arrive fully qualified. Air France, British Airways and Lufthansa counted between twelve and fourteen pilots per aircraft in their short-haul fleets, while easyJet and Ryanair had between nine and ten, as its pilots and planes were more productive. Cabin crew earned significantly less than pilots, with salaries ranging from £14,000 to £17,000.

Of course, easyJet could employ fewer staff than full-service airlines as it eschewed free food service, which kept costs low. Plastic trays of reheated food were not the low-cost way and feedback indicated that most customers would prefer to pay less for a short-haul flight than be given a big meal, saving a surprisingly high 6 per cent from the bottom line. EasyJet had even managed to turn inflight catering into a money-earner. From the trolley on easyJet flights passengers paid £3 for a can of lager, £1 for a small tub of Pringles and £1.60 for a cup of tea or coffee. The decision to charge for coffee on easyJet flights generated two sources of additional revenue: one from the brew itself and the second from the fact that easyJet could eliminate one lavatory from its planes thanks to lower demand for them, making room for a few extra seats.

EasyJet managed to wring an average of £2.52 from each passenger for food, drinks and duty-free goods, on top of its average £38.06 fare. Perhaps unexpectedly, the airline gave away its in-flight magazine, *easy Come easy Go*. As it said on the cover, the magazine was 'easyJet's only freebie, get it while you can!' But in fact the publication provided another way for the airline to make money, thanks to advertising revenue brought by scores of adverts for second homes and ski resorts close to easyJet destinations.

Clearly the price paid for the aircraft, and each seat, was a key element in easyJet's low-fare business model. EasyJet had managed to secure lower aircraft prices via its mega aircraft order with Airbus. Getting more aircraft helped fleet economies. The newer the jets, the easier they were on fuel and thus the cheaper to run. Packing as many seats as possible into each aircraft played an important role in keeping costs low. The high-density seating configuration in low-cost carriers' aircraft provided an average 16 per cent cost advantage compared with the full-service airlines, which typically would offer business or first-class cabins in addition to 'cattle class'. With almost all of easyJet's costs incurred whether the aircraft was full or empty, it was desperately important to get as many bums on seats as possible. EasyJet managed to get 83 per cent of its seats filled on an average flight but worked as hard as it could to get more. An empty seat at take-off was money lost. Any price it could get for it was worth having, which was what drove it and other budget airlines to offer seats at lunatic prices. EasyJet made full use of its sophisticated yield management system, the brainchild of Webster, to work out the optimal fares. The software-driven pricing system could set an almost infinite number of fares for a given flight.

By using a number of secondary airports such as Stansted, Luton and East Midlands instead of Heathrow and Manchester, easyJet avoided congestion and paid lower airport charges per passenger. BAA Plc, which ran Stansted, charged £4.89 per person and TBI at Luton charged £5.50 per passenger. Heathrow, also a BAA airport, was more expensive, at £6.48 per person.

EasyJet's determination to hack away at costs and overheads wherever they occurred sometimes meant it took an unconventional approach, such as in its decision to supply dual-purpose sick bags on-board. The airline teamed up with

Scottish-based film laboratory Klick Photopoint to combine airsickness and photo development in one handy bag. Passengers who did not empty their stomach contents into the pre-labelled bag could leave their holiday films inside, to be sent off for processing by Klick, from whom easyJet received a commission. The Klick/sick bags were found in the seat backs of all of its aircraft marked with the catchy motto, 'Don't be sick, try out Klick – yes'.

'We thought this was an excellent value for money service,' said Alastair Gilchrist, head of commerce at easyJet, 'but I hope passengers don't post the wrong contents off to be developed.'

12. Go east

ON 1 MAY 2004 a swathe of former Communist countries, from Estonia in the north down to Slovenia on the shores of the Mediterranean, became proud members of the European Union. Budget airlines were swift to recognise the enormous business potential in Eastern Europe. On 24 April easyJet launched services from Gatwick to Prague, followed six days later by bmibaby on the same route. On 29 April, Jet2 began flying between Belfast and Prague, then on 1 May easyJet started services from Stansted to the Slovenian capital Ljubljana, and from Luton to Budapest, from £6.99 one-way.

Airlines wanting to fly into the new EU countries no longer had to wrestle with mountains of bureaucracy to obtain a licence. Out went complex bilateral agreements, which favoured a country's national carrier, kept competition to a minimum and ensured that fares cost hundreds of pounds. All of a sudden, it was a free market and airlines could fly anywhere they wanted. 'Within a couple of years, there will be a large number of airlines travelling to these new countries, within these countries and between them,' said Toby Nicol, the head of corporate affairs at easyJet.

The Iron Curtain was well and truly down, and easyJet and other budget operators benefited from the enormous increase in travellers flying in and out of Eastern Europe. For the first time citizens of the new EU countries could work legally in Britain without permits, and more than 175,000 Eastern Europeans arrived in Britain in the twelve months to 1 May 2005 – about twelve times the UK government's highest estimate.

Prohibitive prices had kept generations of Eastern Europeans on the trains and away from the airports. But the low-cost airlines changed all this. Many of the travellers from new European Union members such as Slovakia, Hungary and Poland were flying for the first time. Tens of thousands of immigrants flew into Britain using budget airlines to seek high wages in the service industries or professional jobs. The Lithuanian Association, for example, predicted that as many as 50,000 Lithuanians arrived in London – propelled from the Baltic State by mass unemployment. Migrant workers were needed to fill vacancies in the UK building industry, restaurants, hotels, food production and farming. They also found jobs as plumbers, labourers and lorry and coach drivers. Stagecoach Group, one of the UK's biggest bus operators, planned to recruit 100 Polish drivers, saying it had struggled to hire British staff.

Ryanair thanked the thousands of Eastern European migrants who flew with the airline for its 21 per cent increase in profits to £44.4 million in the three months to June 2005. Passenger numbers were up by almost a third on 2004 to 8.5 million – and a large proportion of these new passengers were people from former Communist countries. 'Back in the old days, we started off flying migrants from Ireland to England. Now we fly to Lithuania, Poland, Slovakia and the Czech Republic,' commented Howard Millar, Ryanair's deputy chief executive.

Moreover, the quick journeys and cheap tickets offered by easyJet and its competitors meant that the thousands of Eastern European immigrants who worked in cities such as London could now fly home cheaply to visit their relatives. Inevitably, the ease of travel brought problems with it too; according to an official police report quoted in the *Daily Mail*, organised crime bosses were also taking advantage of the cheap tickets, smuggling illegal immigrants from Africa or Asia into Eastern Europe and then using fake documents to board flights to the West. 'The widespread availability of low-cost flights provide a relatively cheap method of transporting illegal immigrants to the UK,' the report stated.

No-frills travel changed the lives of Eastern Europeans who ventured west to earn a living; it also changed the lives of their families back home, as Western tourists in their millions discovered the beautiful landscapes, eye-opening cultural heritage and astonishing low prices of the former Communist bloc. Budget airlines were expected to bring some 340,000 tourists to Hungary in 2004, raising direct revenues from tourism by some €90 million, according to regional development minister Istvan Kolber. At the beginning of 2004, one out of every eight tourists landing at Budapest's Ferihegy airport flew in on a budget airline. By October, that figure had risen to more than 22 per cent of all arrivals. Tourists arriving in Hungary on budget airlines stayed an average of 2.7 days in the country and spent around €100 per day, said Gabor Galla, managing director of the state tourism office.

In October 2004, easyJet increased its range of Eastern European services with new routes to Krakow and Warsaw in Poland and more services to Budapest. The airline now offered five flights to Prague a day, with services from Newcastle, Bristol and London. Meanwhile, Ryanair announced that it would operate flights to Riga from London starting at €50, while easyJet planned a Berlin–Riga route at €21. Other airlines operating in the region included

Wizzair, Germanwings, Snowflake, AirBerlin/Niki and Air Polonia.

At the end of October 2004, easyJet started flying from London Stansted to Tallinn, with one-way fares from as low as £26.99. Ryannis Capodistrias, easyJet's marketing manager for Greece, Italy, Hungary, Slovenia and Estonia, said that the company hoped to serve 185,000 passengers in twelve months on its Tallinn–Berlin and Tallinn–London daily flights. 'We plan to seize a 65 per cent share of the Tallinn–London route, and we predict that passenger traffic on this particular route will increase by 150 per cent after our arrival,' said Capodistrias.

The new easyJet route would raise the number of travellers to Russia as well as to Estonia, courtesy of the eight-hour bus journey linking Tallinn to St Petersburg, said Dimitry Paranyushkin, editor of waytorussia.net. 'About 47,000 British tourists visited Russia in 2003 according to Moscow's information office,' said Paranyushkin. 'At the same time, there are a few million independent travellers in the UK who would like to go to Russia but don't want to pay €400 for a ticket. Once the travellers learn about this offer, I reckon the number of travellers will double.'

Cities like Prague welcomed the huge increase in tourists shipped in by the budget airlines. 'It was all quite flat two years ago because of SARS, the Iraq war etc.,' said Iveta Schoppova, press officer with the Czech tourist board. 'EasyJet flying to Prague has meant that more young people now visit the city. The young generation now come here for a long weekend to profit from low-cost flights. Prague is not just for older people visiting museums and monuments. There has also been a boom in new hotels and lots of new and lively bars.'

Cheap flights had a cost too. By day, Prague's Old Town was a delightful area of cobbled streets and pavement cafés. Tourists of all nationalities mixed without trouble, taking in the culture and history of a city that since its Velvet Revolution had been happy to open its doors to the West. But come

nightfall, capitalism in its brashest form came to Wenceslas Square as the stag parties emerged, running from bar to bar and screaming in the streets. Thousands of Britons, dressed in wigs, tutus and rabbit costumes, descended on the Czech capital every weekend on budget flights that could cost just £18. The men were often already drunk when they arrived for their 'last night of freedom', which tended to involve copious quantities of alcohol and the services of local strippers.

Bored with glugging Guinness in Dublin and puffing pot in Amsterdam, the British hordes were seeking pastures new and heading east. The invasion began with Prague and Budapest, where they rapidly wrecked Britain's reputation with central Europeans, whose touching belief in the gentility of the British was replaced by a far darker image. Cheap flights and cheap alcohol then took thousands of holidaymakers and stag parties to Tallinn, a quaint city of cobbled streets, which soon filled up with young British men. Latvia's Riga developed into a hotbed of post-Communist carousing and Slovenia's Ljubljana became a magnet for British stag parties, drawn by the cheap beer and strip joints in a Disney setting.

It didn't take long for businesses in the UK to get in on the scene. Praguepissup was one of the companies which organised stag weekends to the Czech capital. The blurb on its website said it all: 'An all-nighter costs less than five quid . . . a night exercising the ferret costs 30 quid! Pub crawls, strippers and milkmaids – it's stag heaven.' The company boasted of its database of hundreds of girls, adding that they were the company that had exclusive rights to Andrea Miss Strip Czech Republic 2002. The weekend's cultural highlight was often a brewery tour.

Praguepissup was set up by thirty-five-year-old Tom Kenyon after he went to the city for his own stag weekend. The Mancunian moved to Prague in 1996, married a Czech girl and began his business with 'a mobile phone and a piece of paper'. By the end of 2004, he and his business partner had twenty staff and his clients could stay at more than 100 local hotels.

Kenyon soon added stag party tours to Budapest and Tallinn. Prague remained by far the most favoured destination, but Tallinn soon became popular too, though the Estonian city was so small that its founder said its capacity was limited to 500 to 600 groups a year.

'Low-cost flights and stag parties in Eastern Europe go hand in hand,' Kenyon explained. 'Low-cost flights are most definitely the number one driver in the whole business. We've been operating to Prague for more than five years now. During the first few years, business was okay but it was more of a hobby as it wasn't that easy to get cheap flights. Then it all really mushroomed when easyJet started adding flights to Prague and other low-cost airlines started operating here. Our business has taken off. It has more than quintupled, growing in direct relation to the number of flights on offer.

'The other direct effect of easyJet and the other low-cost airlines is that they've brought down the prices of the regular airlines too, such as British Airways. It used to cost me about £200 to fly from Prague back home to Manchester and now it is more like £100.'

Kenyon's customers were attracted by cheap flights, cheap accommodation and cheap beer. An average weekend booked through the agency, plus flights, cost around £200. 'Everything is so much cheaper when you get there that it almost pays for itself,' said Kenyon. 'You can pay £200 for a good weekend in Prague, which is the same price as a weekend in London as everything there is much more expensive. It's become such a good proposition because of the cheap flights. Without the likes of easyJet it would be just for the well-heeled stag parties.'

Praguepissup's typical client flew over from London Stansted, and was in his mid-thirties. Some 99 per cent of customers arrived on the Friday and stayed until the Sunday. After a spot of sightseeing on the Friday, the men started drinking beer before heading to a strip show. 'We don't employ prostitutes but only professional strippers and steer away from drugs,' Kenyon explained. 'After dinner, the men will head to a strip club or night club and stay out until 3 a.m. or 4 a.m., getting drunk.'

Additional entertainments of a boyish sort, such as machine-gun firing with live rounds, were a pull for macho refugees from safety-mad Britain. Some men, it was rumoured, had even paid locally for the privilege of firing rocket-propelled grenades at live cows. 'They'll get up at midday on Saturday and will then do some adrenalin sports such as shooting, go-karting or paint-balling,' Kenyon continued. 'Then Saturday night, it is the same again – beer and girls. Sunday they'll spend recovering and might do a bit of sight-seeing or something cultural like a museum, before flying home.'

Kenyon emphasised that he steered his parties towards hotels, bars and restaurants that liked his kind of business. 'I wouldn't send them to a small family-owned hotel,' he said firmly. 'We spread them around as much as possible in big hotels. We operate in a hundred hotels in Prague and thirty-five in Tallinn. Plus we have guides with all the groups, who tell the lads what they can or can't do. We take them to places where stag groups are welcome and which don't have any nastier connections.'

The delights on offer appealed to a certain type of customer. 'Couldn't have managed it without you, especially Ulla. We lost one lad who fell in love with a lap dancer and isn't coming home but everyone else got back okay, which is the best I hoped for,' posted one punter called Phil on the company's website, www.praguepissup.com.

It wasn't just the 'lads' who were succumbing to the temptation of a cheap flight away and a riotous weekend in Europe's eastern lands. Women were increasingly flying with the likes of easyJet to Prague for their hen weekends. 'I had a wicked time, all the activities were quality and have already recommended you to my mates for a great piss up weekend, as I want to join them!!!!' posted Tracy on the Praguepissup home page.

The revellers were big spenders. Research for Morgan Stanley Credit Card showed that friends of a bride or groom spent an average of £365 each celebrating a final fling, and that money went much further in Eastern Europe than it did back home. 'Beer 50p, hotel 13 quid, cocaine 10 quid – you wouldn't get more than a bread roll, a cardboard box and a packet of aspirin in London for that,' declared one happy reveller, twenty-three-year-old Gareth from Port Talbot.

Prices were just as low in Tallinn, which was becoming the second most popular stag destination after Prague. Prior to 2004, the relatively few Brits that had visited Estonia had for the most part charmed Tallinn's citizens: the British tourists were considered friendly, laid-back and polite and tipped well. About 2.7 million foreigners visited in 2003, attracted by the high-quality eating and drinking, high culture and fascinating history. Behind the fastidiously well-preserved façades of the medieval buildings were chic bars and expensive boutiques. You could have been in a fashionable part of Stockholm or Helsinki.

But things changed after easyJet and its rivals added Tallinn to its network. An increasing number of Internet-based tourism companies started to market the city as the new destination for binge-drinking Brits. Targeting stag parties in particular, they promised cheap deals, cheap beer and cheap women. It wasn't long before the locals started to notice that a new breed of Brit was coming to town.

EasyJet marketing manager Capodistrias dismissed the importance of stag parties to the airline. 'Stag parties happen at weekends,' he argued. 'We fly every day. You can never make money by flying a route on weekends. You cannot rely on seats you sell on a Friday heading out and a Sunday coming back.' And, as easyJet pointed out, the airline operated a policy of zero tolerance to alcohol on board its aircraft and could hardly be held responsible for the behaviour of their passengers once they had reached their destination.

But although stag parties were a minor part of the airline's business as a whole, they had a disproportionate effect on the cities that suffered invasion. Kenyon said that his company's annual bookings to Tallinn tripled between 2003 and 2004 to 1,500 following easyJet's flights into the cities. 'We chose to add Tallinn as a destination after we heard that easyJet would be offering flights there,' he explained. 'We're going to expand in the future wherever easyJet is going. We plan to set up a new place a year and are currently looking at Sofia, Bucharest and Warsaw. It depends though whether the cheap airlines will be flying there in the future.'

'Stare at the buffage with ample cha-chas,' read the company's website, www.Tallinnpissup.com, which, with a nod to the city's history as a Hanseatic trading city, offered a 'medieval lesbian stripper show and banquet'. Among the other 'bonking good' activities on offer in Tallinn were ten-beer pub crawls and 'tottie tours'. Britain's press was also getting in on the act. 'Tallinn-ho!' shouted the headline of one red-top newspaper. 'It's cheap, full of some of the world's most gorgeous babes and is fast becoming the destination for Brit stag parties.'

But the combination of cheap flights and Tallinn's growing reputation as a stag destination were making some locals worried about the future. The Estonians, a reserved people, were puzzled by British stag parties. 'The Finns have been coming here for year but they just fall asleep,' said one. 'The British are different – they get loud and then they want to take their trousers off. We can't understand it.'

Unsurprisingly, Tallinn's café and bar owners were starting to tire of stag party antics. Aimée, manager of Café Anglais on Tallinn's Town Hall Square, said: 'A lot more people have come to Tallinn since the introduction of easyJet flights. I've seen a lot of trouble caused by young and single English, Irish and Finnish men. They can be very drunk and do stupid things. The men dress up in women's dresses and skirts and scream and shout in the middle of the street. Sometimes there are nice, well behaved people but unfortunately the groups are mainly always drunk and noisy.'

Several hotels had 'taken measures' against stag parties who offended other guests with their drunken behaviour, and the Estonian embassy in London was growing critical of companies offering 'cheap, low entertainment'. Behind the scenes, the Tallinn city authorities had already asked the police to crack down on noisy Brits. Kalle Klandorf was one of Tallinn's most senior police officers and had years of experience dealing with foreign troublemakers. 'The city authorities have asked us to deal with Brits making noise on the streets. Until now we've taken a liberal standpoint.' Klandorf added, 'We'd like people to come here and behave well. British tourism companies might try to attract people here who are wealthier and interested in other things apart from drinking.'

Unsurprisingly, like the residents of Dublin and Amsterdam before them, the inhabitants of Prague, a conservative people with strict rules of behaviour, were also beginning to tire of the stag weekenders. Journalist Johana Grohova talked of her resentment of the drunken men who boarded the bus she took home: 'They bother the women on the bus. They come here thinking this is a poor place and they have money and can do whatever they want. They treat us like we are stupid.'

The tourists who sought out Prague for its culture were equally unimpressed. A columnist in the English-language *Prague Post* proclaimed: 'Those all-time record holders, the Americans, have been dethroned as the No.1 tourist plague of Prague . . . When instant gratification isn't provided, the English can be expected to put on a dazzling display of chair throwing and beer glass smashing.'

Martus Havira from Prague Holiday Company said, 'We welcome the increase in tourists from the flights. But when it is a stag party of twenty young men from England then sometimes it isn't very nice. I heard of one instance when six to seven men checked in to an apartment and totally wrecked it. There was blood in the elevator because of fighting. A neighbour asked them to be quiet and they sent over one of the escort girls as a present. The neighbour was so angry.'

The police on patrol in the city centre were equally unenthusiastic. The citizens of Prague boasted reputedly the world's best beer and the highest consumption rate – an estimated 330 litres, or 580 pints, per person per year – but they noticeably did not roam the streets in packs of twenty, wearing false breasts and singing loudly. 'We are the biggest beer-drinking people in the world, but there is a difference,' said one policeman. 'We can handle it.' The Prague city police increased their numbers and improved their language skills to deal with weekend rowdies. The British embassy conceded that budget flights had brought a new type of tourist to Prague, along with a sharp increase in the consular workload: lads visiting brothels often got their passports stolen. The Czech Ministry of Foreign Affairs also urged the British government to address the problem. 'We are discussing the problem with British authorities to try to find ways to stop British men behaving violently in Prague,' said a senior official.

Czech officials remained reluctant to criticise any visitors publicly because the city wanted the money and they did not wish to admit to a problem that might put off other tourists. This was understandable, for tourism was worth 4 per cent of Czech GDP. But a form of apartheid developed in response to the rising flood of revellers. Several bar and restaurant owners in the city centre rolled up their sleeves and took action. The sign taped to the window at Legends Bar in the city read: 'Please, no groups of drunken British men allowed.'

At Prague's Bombay cocktail bar, a 'no stag groups' sign was put up when the owner finally lost patience after a fight. 'We don't allow stag parties in anymore because they cause too much trouble,' said Deepak Sharma, the manager. 'We've had problems with them in the past and like every bar right now, we don't want them. They are English guys in big numbers of ten to fifteen and think that they own the place. The main problem is fighting. A couple of times they've been really violent, also to our staff, who have been badly injured, as well as to our customers. One Czech man broke his hand after they picked on him because he was out with his girlfriend. He didn't hit them back. They were just looking for some way to create a problem.'

Moskva, a famous café, bar and restaurant looking out over Tallinn's Vabaduse Square, was another establishment that chose to limit its entry. 'If a group of young English guys tries to get in then we reject them,' said manager Timo Tirs. 'We've had tourist groups before asking for catering but if we find out that it is a group of twenty young English guys then we say no.'

Some bars tried to keep a balance between the potential profits the stag parties brought and the possibility of loutish behaviour. 'We've tried to ban the stag parties and groups of English lads altogether but we did retreat from that as we were losing business,' explained Frank Haughton, manager of Caffrey's, who said that in his experience the troublemakers were invariably English; the Scots, Irish and Welsh were well behaved. 'So since then we've tried to be selective. We have a door policy and try to make a judgement on whom to let in. We observe the ones we let in and try to identify the leader so we can make him our ally and then try to calm things down if the situation gets out of hand. Basically, we want the business and are dealing with it.'

In the meantime, Estonia's top brewery, Saku, was opening a 'beer hotel' on Tallinn's waterfront to help large numbers of marauding Brits celebrate their 'last night of freedom'. The conflicting demands of profit and local culture showed no sign of going away, and as easyJet, Ryanair and their rivals opened up more routes to former Communist countries the lives of more Eastern Europeans and their cities would change irrevocably.

13. Home abroad

EASTERN EUROPE IS not the only region to have been changed for ever by the cheap flights phenomenon. At one time, Marbella was synonymous with Britain's movie stars and bank robbers. Recently it has seemed that the Spanish town is becoming more akin to Cheshire-on-Sea. According to Costa del Sol estate agents, some 12,000 properties were built in Marbella in 2002. A study of the real estate figures showed that 70 per cent of all new development purchases in the Spanish town were snapped up by the British and of these buyers around 60 per cent hailed from Cheshire.

Marbella-based Cheshire Estates opened its first UK branch – in Wilmslow – to meet growing demand. 'The demand for Spanish properties among people in Cheshire is phenomenal,' commented manager John Eason. 'Since we opened the UK branch, we have been inundated with enquiries. I think it is a lot to do with the broad wealth of people in Cheshire; anybody who knows the Costa del Sol realises it is not just millionaires and glitzy lifestyle.'

EasyJet and bmibaby flights from Liverpool and Manchester provide the explanation for the migration of the new Cheshire set. Many people are happier to jump on an easyJet flight than to head up the M6 motorway to traditional weekend getaway spots such as the Lake District. 'There are affordable properties and good investments to be made out there, coupled with the low-cost airlines, there has never been a better or easier time to buy,' Eason continued.

The thirty-seven-year-old manager, whose brother-in-law opened the Marbella branch ten years ago, lives most of the year near Macclesfield with his wife and two children. In 2004 they bought a £200,000 house on the fringes of Marbella. 'Our Spanish home is similar to the house over here,' Eason said. 'We also have lots of friends out there. It is like Cheshire in the sun.'

Many of the recent arrivals are men and women in their forties, lured by 360 days of sunshine each year, designer shops, good schools and private hospitals. 'It attracts young, good-looking people who drive around in Ferraris, looking glamorous,' the local Cheshire paper quoted a model called Miki as saying. 'The shops are fantastic too – all the designer names – and there's always a familiar face from Cheshire to chat to.'

Retired people are also attracted by the promise of a better lifestyle in the sun, with cheap links back to the homeland courtesy of the likes of easyJet. 'We don't have any regrets,' said Robert Wilson, who took early retirement and bought a £77,000 home in Spain. 'It is very relaxed and a world away from our old life. The only thing we miss are our children and grandchildren but we tend to see them quite often.' Others enjoyed a more relaxed lifestyle overseas and simply commuted back to the UK for work. John Williams describes himself as 'one of the easyJet generation'. He lives in Spain with his wife and two-year-old daughter, Chloe, and works as a website designer, taking cheap flights to the UK for business meetings every few weeks.

Owning a property abroad has suddenly become an achievable goal for many people. Low interest rates, a relatively weak euro and budget airlines like easyJet and Ryanair mean it has never been cheaper to get to mainland Europe. Before they knew it, would-be buyers could be rubbing shoulders with Claudia Schiffer in Malaga, Elton John in the south of France or Madonna and Cliff Richard in Portugal.

Cheap flights, the promise of sunshine and a slower pace of life prompted more than half a million people to buy a property abroad in 2003, according to a survey by market analysts Mintel. Aviation analysts believed that 15 per cent of all passengers on low-cost flights to southern Europe from the UK were on house-hunting missions. Mintel found that Spain was the most popular country for Britons seeking a holiday home, with 41 per cent of overseas properties bought on the mainland, in the Balearics and Canary Islands. Britons bought 84,000 second homes in Spain between 2001 and 2003, with most properties having a swimming pool and easy access to supermarkets and airports. France was second in popularity, with 32 per cent of overseas properties bought by Britons seeking 'la vie en rose', followed by other European countries, with 10 per cent.

'The time to buy in Europe has probably never been better, with estate agents reporting large numbers of Britons seeking to buy cut-price second homes,' commented the Council for Mortgage Lenders, the trade body representing banks and building societies. Mintel predicted that the value of UK Spanish property market, already worth £12 billion, would reach £21 billion within five years. By then, the company estimated that a further 99,000 new properties would have been sold to disillusioned Britons seeking a better quality of life abroad.

Of those with homes in Spain, 65 per cent said they were attracted by the climate, 45 per cent wanted to spend more time outdoors and 40 per cent were lured by the cheaper cost of living. Tony Holmes and his wife Elisabeth had just bought a villa near Malaga in Spain for £146,000 for themselves and their children, Shaun, eight, and Melissa, five. 'It has always been our dream to buy overseas and we'll eventually retire there – but for now it's a holiday home,' Tony explained. 'Friends recommended a Spanish lawyer who speaks perfect English, and all the documents were translated and verified before we signed. Elisabeth and the kids will spend the school holidays there and I'll join them as much as I can. The kids are even learning Spanish.'

Property-mad Brits were attracted by the fact that houses in Europe were on average cheaper than in Britain. The average price of second homes owned in Europe was £109,000 in 2003, and a run-down property in north-east France could go for as little as £25,000, according to the Council for Mortgage Lenders. On the Costa del Sol, apartments and small two-bedroom properties, usually with a communal garden and swimming pool, were readily available in seaside resorts from about £48,000, and larger, individual properties in the area started at about £100,000. Estate agents advertised bungalows in retirement villages in Malaga for £92,000. Two-thirds of buyers rented out their second home, while the rest used it as a holiday house or a long-term investment, according to the Council for Mortgage Lenders.

Many people remortgaged their own home to provide some or all of the finance for a second home abroad, and British buyers were contributing to a sharp increase in property prices. Data from the Royal Institution of Chartered Surveyors showed that house prices rose by about 15 per cent in 2003 in both France and Spain after similar double-digit rises in the previous year. Portugal and Italy saw a slower pace of price increases, closer to 6 or 7 per cent. Legal experts warned that while property abroad often seemed cheaper than the UK, it would probably take longer to complete the purchase, and that it would often be more expensive in terms of agent fees, local taxes and legal costs. One solicitor said: 'Study the domestic laws of the country you are moving to, you may find out you will be paying the legal costs of the seller as well as your own.'

Property dreams can quickly turn into nightmares. Some people signed the wrong contract and ended up with a different house from the one they thought they had bought, while others discovered that property developers didn't actually own the land in the first place. The dream certainly turned sour for Bob and Jane Alburg, who paid £120,000 for a substantial villa on the Costa Blanca that was supposed to be finished in 2003. A year later, it still wasn't complete and the Alburgs feared the unscrupulous developer who sold them the property would never build it. Their position was made worse because they did not have the completed deeds to the property, having merely signed the preliminary sales contract with the developer.

Still, the overseas property boom continued, and easyJet took plentiful advantage of it. The airline included adverts for estate agents, finance brokers and lawyers specialising in overseas purchases in its in-flight magazine, along with features explaining how best to buy a property in areas served by the airline. Homebuyers quickly learnt to buy close to low-cost airline destinations if they wanted to make money. 'The basic rules that property investors need to apply are how close is the property to an airport and how often there are flights,' said Mike Hayes, editor of *Home Overseas* magazine. 'If you are more than half an hour away from an international airport, then your rental potential drops by 20 per cent.'

'We've seen a steady increase in overseas property over the last couple of years and have seen a lot of more savvy investors,' Hayes continued. 'A third of the market is looking for retirement homes, a third is looking for holiday homes and a further third is looking at property as an investment. The latter third is keeping an eye in particular on low-cost airlines. The Central and Eastern European capitals are full of history and very cheap and are becoming massive weekend break markets. The property investors are certainly looking to follow the low-cost airlines to these destinations.'

A new low-cost flight on the map marked the spot of a future invasion by British homebuyers. Areas of Spain that were neglected before, such as the south-west Atlantic coast of Andalucia, were being opened up to homeowners thanks to the promise of low-cost flights to a new airport, said George Sell, editor of *Viva España* magazine. On the eastern coast in the Valencia area, a new airport was being constructed at Castellon, between Barcelona and Valencia.

'The property market and the tourism market are literally licking their lips and getting ready for a new influx of Brits,' said Sell. 'It is expected to be one of the next hot spots, directly as a result of the new airport and the entry of a low-cost carrier. Low-cost flights are a major, major factor in people buying property overseas and where they buy.'

The French department of Gers was also seeing growing numbers of Brits, thanks to the easyJet service to nearby Toulouse and Ryanair flights to other airports in the region. Jamie Crewe moved his young family from Sussex to Gers after tiring of life as an investment banker. He explained what prompted their life-changing decision: 'Rainy mornings, getting up at 5 a.m. and never seeing my children were enough to make me go – plus the fact that we're still young, so why not give it a blast?' In 2003, Crewe bought a 'great, big, old farmhouse, a ruin' and moved his children into the local school. At first they were the sole British pupils but in 2004 five other English pupils joined them, as purchases and enquiries from British buyers continued to rise following the introduction of easyJet flights.

'We've been getting so many recent requests for this region that we've decided to expand into the area,' said one local agent. But he sounded a note of caution to potential buyers over easyJet's new route: 'It's great when budget airlines expand their routes but this should not be the main factor that buyers base their decisions upon. After all, what if something happens and the airline pulls off the route?'

UK buyers were increasingly seeking second homes on the Costa Blanca, located in south-eastern Spain and including the resorts of Alicante and Benidorm. The Costa Blanca enjoyed 320 days of sunshine annually and an average temperature of 20 degrees Celsius. The World Health Organisation described the region as the healthiest place to live in Europe because of its temperate climate. It had also been changed forever by mass tourism.

The northern part of the region remained largely agricultural, with orange, lemon and olive groves in picturesque valleys, complemented by attractive and historic seaside towns. The southern part of the region, dubbed the Golf Coast, offered more than thirteen championship golf courses between Alicante and La Manga, with ten more planned or under construction. What was more, flying time with easyJet from the UK to Alicante took just two-and-a-half hours.

Ultra Villas Ltd of Cheltenham, an international estate agency offering UK buyers knowledge of the Costa Blanca property market, was currently expanding its operations north to the Costa del Azahar, an area relatively unknown to British property buyers. Huge investment was planned in the wake of the announcement that Valencia would host the Americas Cup in 2007. Low-cost flights with easyJet to Valencia, Alicante and Barcelona was making the area more accessible for Britons wanting to be among the first to invest in properties at prices around two-thirds of those for comparable homes on the Costa del Sol. 'Clients are aware of low-cost carriers and they look for ease of access, to and from the airport, when looking at property,' said Steven Grist, business development director of Ultra Villas Ltd. 'I'm a property owner myself in Alicante and know that I can get from door to door in six hours at less than the cost of a train to London.'

Ultra Villas was also expanding its operations west to the Costa del Almeria in the Andalucia region of southern Spain. The area, which offered spectacular scenery, beautiful beaches and the best weather in Spain, had seen little development so property prices were affordable. Typically a three-bedroom, two-bathroom villa with a private pool twenty minutes from the coast could be bought for as little as £120,000.

But the main reason the estate agency was attracted to the area was the introduction of easyJet's flights to Almeria airport, making it more accessible by air from the UK. The airport had just been opened up to international airlines and the former San Javea military airport was to be replaced by a large, new international airport in 2006. 'Nine out of ten of our clients are happy flying to their second home with low-cost airlines,' said Grist. 'After all it is only a short flight. We subsidise the flights for people who want to view a property and use low-cost airlines as it makes more commercial sense for our business.'

Investors could only hope that beautiful Almeria wouldn't be taken over by an orgy of building as mass tourism turned Andalucia into yet another Costa del Concrete. After forty years of breakneck development, vast stretches of the Spanish coast are built on, including three-fifths of the Andalucian seafront. The Spanish government is even considering buying seaside land itself to stop developers getting their hands on it. Some 70 per cent of the Costa del Sol is already choked in concrete and asphalt. Irish pubs offering Guinness, cafés selling English breakfasts and uninspiring, high-rise apartment blocks litter the view between Torremolinos and Marbella. Greenpeace believe that almost 45,000 houses have been constructed illegally and that 34 per cent of the first kilometre of Spain's Mediterranean coast is built up; around Malaga the figure rises to over 50 per cent. And yet more people keep on buying. In 2003, 1.7 million Spanish homes were owned by foreigners, mostly from the EU. Acute environmental problems have ensued. Development in the wrong locations has destroyed beaches; in Malaga's coastal area alone, 150,000 cubic metres of sand are being added artificially. And unplanned urban growth has caused pollution problems. In July 2004, the European Commission said that almost 200

Spanish municipalities did not respect guidelines on urban sewage for towns of more than 15,000 inhabitants.

Always on the look-out for attractive and unspoilt areas, the estate agency was considering Croatia and Cyprus for possible future properties, as it knew that easyJet was hoping to add the destinations to its network. 'Whether a low-cost airline flies to a destination has a major impact on our decision-making,' continued Grist. 'Low-cost airlines bring a new market to that region. We take stock every time we hear that there is a new route opened up by a low-cost carrier somewhere. There has been a tremendous upsurge in business to Alicante, for example, following the introduction of easyJet flights there. About 25 per cent of passengers on an easyJet flight to Alicante will be either looking at property there or going back to spend time at their property there.'

Meanwhile, the city of Barcelona was emerging as a desirable place for Britons to buy second homes in Spain. A new breed of 'Barça Brits' could be heard converting square metres into feet as they ogled the property brochures and nibbled tapas around the bars in Las Ramblas. The number of Britons buying and looking to buy holiday homes in the Catalan capital rose more than five-fold between the start of 2003 and mid-2004 according to Spanish Property Insight, a company that helped foreigners buy in Spain by introducing them to companies and professionals. Prices were rising by a London-like 20 per cent a year and by up to 50 per cent in the most fashionable districts of the city – to the delight of foreign investors, but less so of Barcelona's inhabitants, many of whom found themselves priced out by the British incomers.

EasyJet flew to the Spanish city from the UK airports of Newcastle, Liverpool, Bristol, Stansted, Luton and Gatwick. The budget airline also offered flights to Barcelona from Paris Orly, Basel-Mulhouse, Geneva, Dortmund and Berlin. Some 1.1 million easyJet passengers were expected to board the low-cost carrier bound for Barcelona by the end of summer 2005. Indeed, Barcelona was easyJet's second most popular summer city break, topped only by Amsterdam, with 2 million passengers due to fly there in summer 2005. 'Britons used to head straight for the Costa del Sol or the "pueblos blancos" of Andalucia without thinking, but they are realising that the real gem of Spain is Barcelona,' commented Mark Stucklin, who ran Spanish Property Insight. 'Barcelona is enjoying a cracking overseas property boom and Britons are big players.'

John Weller was one of the new UK investors in the city. He 'fell in love' with Barcelona and splashed out almost £200,000 on a one-bedroom flat in the newly hip Borne district. The Weller family visited their second home four or five times a year. Among the Wellers' neighbours were Graeme Jones, who had invested a similar sum in a three-bedroomed modern flat in a converted nineteenth-century tenement block, and Robert Collins, who had bought a £220,000 duplex flat. The Wellers, the Jones family and Collins all saw Barcelona as the perfect second-home city, largely because budget airlines made it cheap and easy to get to. 'My son studies, works and plays here, while my wife and I can enjoy terrific culture, good shopping and lazy days on the beach,' Weller explained.

Collins praised Barcelona as a 'proper international city, not a holiday resort'. The city beat the Costas any day, they all agreed. 'We've seen all the unspeakable, football-shirted trash that gathers in the concrete jungles of the Costa del Sol and we don't want any of that,' said Weller. Jones added: 'I'd never invest down south. We've had some great holidays in Marbella, but two weeks of sun, sand and sangria is quite enough.'

Stucklin chucked at the Barça Brits' criticism of the Costa del Sol, where holidaymakers had been flocking to enjoy kids' menus, shopping malls and Robin Hood pubs after Franco opened up Spain to the world in the 1960s. 'Ah, the penny has finally dropped,' he said. 'People may now realise that if you sit around all day in a manicured, culture-free golf resort, reading the *Daily Express* and drinking beer with a bunch of perma-tanned expats, you end up a miserable old alcoholic. Barcelona isn't for everybody but it is perfect for sophisticated people looking for a Mediterranean climate, beautiful architecture and a stimulating cultural environment close to great beaches and mountains.'

EasyJet may have pledged to bring flying to the masses but it wasn't only blue-collared workers boarding the airline. Some flights, such as those to the new stag destinations of Prague and Tallinn, may have attracted the shaven-headed type of punter whose main aim was getting drunk. Other flights, meanwhile, were full of more discerning passengers with fat wallets who were off to visit their overseas property. The rich people who set up home in sunnier climes provided a major boost to easyJet's passenger numbers. The advent of cheap flights might have meant that people could afford an annual trip to Malaga rather than to Blackpool but the real boom in air travel was caused largely by a rich minority taking several foreign holidays a year, according to figures released from the Civil Aviation Authority in November 2004.

Poorer people tended either not to fly at all or to make only one trip abroad a year, according to the CAA figures. Second homeowners took an average of six return flights a year. By contrast, half the population did not fly at all, and a further 25 per cent took only one trip abroad in a year. The CAA's figures, based on 180,000 interviews at airports, revealed that even at Stansted, where low-cost airlines such as easyJet accounted for nearly all the flights, the average income of British passengers was more than £50,000. Even low fares were failing to tempt the poorest section of society to fly; a smaller proportion of them took to the skies in 2003 than in 2002. Those in social groups D and E, which covered low-skilled workers and people on benefits, took only 6 per cent of the total flights in 2004, despite making up 27 per cent of the population. At the opposite end of the scale, the As and Bs, the professionals and senior managers who made up 24 per cent of the population, took 40 per cent of flights.

Of course, the richer passengers flew with the airline more often; and many of the lower-paid passengers who flew with easyJet wouldn't have contemplated travelling abroad before easyJet made flying affordable. And those passengers who previously flew with charter carriers were often choosing to fly with budget carriers instead. The proportion of passengers at UK airports flying on UK scheduled airlines reached 50.1 per cent in 2004, its highest level for the last twenty years, an increase of 8.9 million passengers on 2003, according to the CAA. This contrasted with the proportion of passengers at UK airports flying on UK charter carriers which, at 15.1 per cent in 2004, reached its lowest level in the last twenty years, a decrease of 1.3 million passengers on 2003. Still, the CAA figures undermined the government's argument that airports must be allowed to expand so that less affluent families could continue to enjoy the benefits of air travel. The UK government proposed constructing new runways at Stansted, Heathrow, Birmingham and Edinburgh to accommodate an expected surge in passenger numbers – the total number of flights was expected to grow from 200 million in 2003 to 500 million in 2030. Ministers claimed that the average return air fare would rise by more than £100 unless new runways were built.

John Stewart, chairman of ClearSkies, which campaigned against airport expansion, responded: 'The CAA's figures show that the massive expansion in air travel planned by the Government will almost entirely benefit the rich. The absence of any tax on aviation fuel or VAT on air tickets amounts to a £9 billion subsidy for the better off to enjoy their jet-setting lifestyle.' Stewart also argued that the CAA survey also challenged the Government's claim that expansion was necessary to help British companies to do business overseas; it showed that leisure air travel was growing three times faster than business air travel and in 2003 accounted for 77 per cent of all flights.

EasyJet said that the CAA survey confirmed its own

findings that the rapid growth in budget airlines was being fuelled by people with very high disposable incomes who booked dozens of trips a year. 'We have at least 1,000 people who fly every week from London to their second homes in Nice, Malaga, Palma and Barcelona,' said an easyJet spokesman. 'There is a misconception that budget airlines are used mainly by people on lower incomes. If you are in the airport car park at Luton, you will find it full of BMWs and Mercedes.'

14. Kicking up a fuss

IN MARCH 2004, a group of fifteen friends on their way to Portugal for a golf weekend were banned from easyJet for life for an unusual misdemeanour. 'When the plane landed at Faro we discovered some of them had urinated in their seats and seat back pockets,' said easyJet spokeswoman Samantha Day. 'We are absolutely disgusted and we won't welcome them on easyJet ever again.'

One golfer was told to leave the flight before take-off when his boisterous behaviour towards staff turned 'abusive', Day added. The rest of the group, from Cardiff and Abergavenny, South Wales, carried on with the trip and only became aware of the ban from the airline when they tried to check in for their return flight. They were forced to make their own way back from Faro, costing each of them an additional £170.

Outraged by their treatment, the golfers demanded that easyJet prove its claim that they had urinated on the seats. Bob Bennett, forty-eight, denied easyJet's accusation, saying:

'Nobody would do that on a plane. I got up ten minutes into the flight to tell the stewardess my seat was damp. She brought me a different seat cushion and that was it. I am absolutely appalled at easyJet's claim. Let's have the evidence.' Steve Pandeli, another member of the party, added: 'It is ludicrous what easyJet has been saying. If there had been other people in the crowd doing that we would have been the first to put a stop to it. The main issue isn't compensation; it is about our own reputations. I couldn't care less if I don't fly with easyJet again.'

Whether Bob and his friends relieved themselves in easyJet's seat pockets or made use of the aircraft's sole lavatory remained to be proved. Possibly the most amazing thing about the incident was that such behaviour was perceived as possible on-board an aircraft. Flying was no longer a case of hoping that the passenger next to you didn't snore or jostle for elbowroom on the arm-rest. In-flight entertainment was clearly changing for the worse. Unruly behaviour in the skies was increasing at an astonishing rate in terms of both numbers and severity of incidents.

Air rage wasn't purely a low-cost phenomenon. All airlines suffered from it. Air-rage incident after incident filled the newspaper headlines as abusive passengers turned their aggression against other travellers and often against flight crew. But two factors seemed particularly likely to provoke air rage among low-cost airline passengers. The first was delays. Passengers grew frustrated by the fact that budget carriers often not only failed to inform them why their plane was late but adopted a 'you get what you paid for' attitude towards them. The second factor was the tendency of 'the lads' to use low-fare carriers for their alcohol-fuelled jaunts abroad. In one incident, two men from Ireland allegedly pinned a female flight attendant against the wall of the plane and attempted to sexually assault her during an easyJet flight from Belfast to Liverpool's John Lennon Airport. Both men, in their early thirties, had been drinking.

EasyJet invested heavily in staff training to ensure all employees were able to deal with any situation – no matter how violent. A conflict management course taught staff to calm and even restrain passengers if necessary. 'Obviously restraint is a last resort, but if you are flying at thousands of feet you can't allow a violent passenger to run riot on an aircraft,' explained Samantha Day. 'The course deals primarily with how to calm people.'

Sometimes staff decided that the easiest way to deal with troublesome passengers was simply to stop them from boarding the aircraft, such as the case of one easyJet pilot, who refused to allow 127 drunken Rangers and Celtic fans on an easyJet flight from Glasgow to Belfast after a Scottish Premier League clash at Ibrox. However, angry passengers in Glasgow blamed the trouble on flight delays. 'We were kept waiting at the airport for ages,' complained Gavin Doyle of Dublin. 'There was nothing else for the fans to do but sit in the bars.' The bars were eventually closed in a bid to stop the fans drinking through the night. Airport officials then had to bring in police with dogs after fights broke out. By morning, the passengers were subdued and headed home to Belfast, after being asked to remove scarves and turn all football shirts inside out.

It wasn't just men who were guilty of behaving badly on-board aircraft. Estelle Willoughby was one of the female passengers who were guilty of air rage on an easyJet plane. Willoughby downed three bottles of red wine on the flight before she decided to get to know her fellow travellers by shoving cigarettes in their faces. The drunken woman then stunned easyJet air crew at 35,000 feet during a flight from Copenhagen to Bristol when she put on her rucksack and tried to leave the aircraft, announcing, 'I'm getting off.' She was arrested at Bristol but not before biting stewardess Kelly Brewer on the hand and kicking a police driver. She later told North Somerset magistrates that she had recently lost her job as a mobile phone worker and her relationship had broken up.

But it wasn't just easyJet passengers who were accused of air rage. In well-publicised incidents on other airlines, passengers beat up crew members and even sexually assaulted their own seats. Electrician Lee Thresher was imprisoned for fifteen years for attacking two passengers and punching out part of a window on a British Airways flight from London to Bangkok during which he had been drinking. The pilot had to divert to Delhi.

The question was what caused such atrocious behaviour. One likely trigger was the stress caused by cramming people in an enclosed, claustrophobic space and restricting their movement, industry experts concluded. 'Flying in a plane is a particular set of circumstances and produces a particular set of problems,' explained Dr Helen Muir, a professor of aerospace psychology at Cranfield University. 'That some people cannot cope with those circumstances is not so surprising. If you put mice into a small cage and heat it, they will end up eating one another.'

Leading health expert Professor John Ashton, the UK's North-West Director of Public Health, criticised the cramped conditions economy class travellers faced and called on the industry to plough profits into passenger improvements. 'Evidence is stacking up about the restrictive conditions causing deep vein thrombosis,' he warned. 'When you take that together with recycled air causing respiratory infections and people being cooped up in cramped conditions that can cause fear and panic, it is obvious that things must change. Poor conditions like these turn planes into slave ships without oars and are conducive to air rage, especially when alcohol is available on-board. It is time something was done to improve air travel, especially as the number of flights is expected to increase substantially in the next decade.'

Alcohol makes matters worse as it restricts the amount of oxygen that flows to the brain. A glass of alcohol in the air has the same effect as two on the ground, and the same applies to any recreational drugs. Smoking bans irritate already frayed nerves and have played a part in air-rage increases.

One thing guaranteed to enrage passengers is the chaotic stampede that often results from easyJet's policy of not allocating seats. Mark from Munich dubbed his last flight with easyJet 'a real farce' as he fought to find a place for himself, his wife and his eighteen-month-old daughter. 'We were pleased that we wouldn't have to struggle to get a seat as easyJet tried to board elderly passengers and families with small children first,' he recalled. 'How wrong we were. After our boarding pass was checked, we passed through a door and went down an escalator only to be confronted with a closed door and a bus waiting on the other side to take us to the plane. After a few minutes, all the other passengers were checked through and joined us at the closed doors. It wasn't long before my family and I were squashed against the still closed doors, waiting to get onto the bus. Eventually the doors opened and the free-for-all scramble began as passengers fought to claim a seat on the bus. But that was nothing compared with the fight on-board as we struggled to find seats next to one another. I just don't understand the point of boarding the elderly and young first!'

Laura Wood from London was also enraged by easyJet's policy of not allocating seats. 'I got to the airport four hours before my flight, sat down and watched how all the Germans had already started queuing to make sure they got seats at the front,' she remembered. 'It was ridiculous. Some of them sent their kids to the front of the queue and told them to sit down and make room for them. There was loads of pushing and shoving. When a gate change was announced, I couldn't believe how fast people ran and shoved others out of the way! I felt like I was being pushed along in a herd of cows.'

Sitting around in an airport terminal for hours on end doubtless doesn't calm passengers' nerves. The International Air Transport Association, which represents the industry, suggested that airlines could reduce the potential causes of disruption by trying harder to ensure that flights left on time and explaining why when they didn't. 'The best information should be relayed to people at all times to release tension,' said a spokesman.

Occasionally easyJet employees managed to assuage rising tempers with a sense of humour. One passenger who was waiting at Luton Airport for a delayed flight to Amsterdam was spotted berating an easyJet representative, who responded: 'I'm sorry, sir, but what else do you want me to do?'

'Sing me a carol,' shot back the angry customer. The hapless rep left his desk, rustled up a couple of colleagues, and broke into an apt rendition of *In the Bleak Midwinter*, which seemed to do the trick.

Other passengers, such as the group of easyJet passengers who were delayed twenty-one hours on their way to Belfast, needed more than a burst of song to cheer their spirits. The group's flight from Luton was turned back because of a technical problem. Some then took the option of travelling to Liverpool in the hope of catching an alternative flight but were left stranded because of severe fog and a power failure. One of the passengers, Simon Corless, described the delays they encountered. 'They drove us from Luton, through the night, to Liverpool. From there, we were stuck in a minibus. We never had overnight accommodation or anything. When we got here to get on the plane, to book in, the plane never came. It was delayed due to fog. The service has been terrible.'

EasyJet insisted that it had done 'everything in its power' to take care of them. Indeed, easyJet tended to be praised for its punctuality. The airline published weekly punctuality data on its website. For the week ending 7 August 2005, for example, 74 per cent of all easyJet flights were on time and 94 per cent arrived within an hour.

Simple mishaps caused other delays. Thousands of passengers were left stranded in May 2004 when easyJet cancelled eighteen flights and grounded forty planes after forgetting to put vital insurance documents on-board its fleet. The documents were legally required to be present on the plane for inspection, and more than ten airports in the UK and overseas were plunged into chaos as pilots refused to fly. The cock-up delayed 5,000 holidaymakers by up to eight hours.

Sometimes people resorted to a peaceful protest to express their discontent, such as the group of easyJet passengers who staged a sit-in protest. The problems started when a flight from Nice to Luton was grounded because of technical problems. EasyJet decided to move its passengers onto another aircraft, while a new aircraft was flown in from Britain. But the passengers refused to get off. One passenger told the BBC: 'All of the passengers on our flight protested. There were chants of "no, no, no" and "everyone stay on the plane" and "don't let them do this to us".' The protest resulted in delays of as long as five hours for two other easyJet flights. Their 280 passengers received full compensation but those who staged the sit-in weren't reimbursed.

Other passengers arrived on time at their destination but were then wound up by their experience in the airport terminal. Jesenka Veledar from Bosnia was pleased to see her suitcase appear on the luggage carousel after her flight with easyJet to London. But she wasn't so pleased to discover that her bag had been destroyed. 'It had a huge cut down the side and had clearly been mishandled,' she lamented. 'It was too badly damaged to use again so I bought a new one for the return journey.' She then couldn't believe her eyes when she landed after her return flight and found her new suitcase in tatters. 'The pockets on the outside were torn from top to bottom and one of the wheels was broken. It looked a right mess. So one short flight had cost me two suitcases!

'I would fly with easyJet again as it represents the cheapest deal,' Veledar admitted. 'This time, though, I've bought an indestructible-looking Samsonite suitcase that I've been assured can easily be replaced if need be. I don't want to risk losing another suitcase!'

Travellers also became irritated when they experienced

poor customer service or hostile staff attitudes. Often the problems started at the check-in desk. Norwegian Gunvor Ellingsen described how she was left nearly in tears after 'rude' check-in staff stopped her from boarding her flight with easyJet. Like many fellow passengers, Ellingsen was already stressed when she arrived at the airport after initially forgetting her passport and then battling through London traffic. On getting to the airport, she was relieved to find out that her flight had been delayed by forty-five minutes.

'I ran with my two suitcases to the check-in desk and waited there, only to be told by a sour-faced woman that I was at the wrong desk,' Ellingsen recalled. 'The check-in woman pointed instead to a long queue. Eventually I reached the front of the queue, and feeling very stressed and trying not to cry, I explained my situation to the easyJet employee behind the counter.

'He wasn't at all sympathetic. There was still forty minutes before the flight was due to take off but he insisted that I had to be there forty minutes before the original flight time to get on the flight. I was so upset by the way I was treated.'

EasyJet was particularly slated for its treatment of disabled passengers. In May 2004, easyJet gave compensation of £500 each and free flights to eleven people turfed off a flight minutes before it took off because they were deaf. The friends, from a centre for the deaf in Liverpool, were going to Amsterdam for the weekend in October 2003 when the pilot booted them off. 'EasyJet has apologised profusely for the humiliation and embarrassment they caused,' said the group's spokesman, Geoff Noon. 'But those involved still feel very bitter at their treatment.' Peter Edwards, the solicitor representing those involved, commented: 'One can't imagine the distress they suffered when they were told at the last minute that they would not be able to fly. The fact is that a group of people were denied the right to travel simply because they have a disability.'

EasyJet argued that the disabled people didn't have enough

carers and therefore threatened the safety of the flight, since rules stated that flight crew must be able to evacuate the plane within ninety seconds. The group were later allowed on a different flight after another easyJet pilot overturned the decision, but not before losing precious hours of their holiday. One passenger said: 'The pilot thought that because we were deaf we would not be able to follow emergency instructions. He made us feel like young children.'

EasyJet vowed to retrain its staff to handle disabled people better, but just five days after winning their apology from easyJet, one of the group members was again stopped because of his disability before boarding an easyJet flight. Sign language teacher Steve McKenna was told that he would not be able to understand emergency procedures as he tried to board his return Liverpool-bound plane at Belfast International Airport.

'I felt reassured flying with easyJet because I thought they had learned their lesson,' McKenna recalled wryly. 'The flight to Belfast was fine, and then it happened. A member of the flight crew approached me as I walked through the departure gate. She was trying to speak to me then got into a panic as she realised I am deaf. She was using huge mouth gestures, which made it even more difficult for me to understand. After speaking to the pilot she returned and we could not take off. It was only after they took advice that I was allowed onto the plane. The plane was late taking off and there was great hostility from other passengers. The trip to Belfast was for an international sign language conference – none of the other delegates were treated in this way.'

Just a couple of days later, easyJet caused further embarrassment when it tried to stop thirteen students with learning difficulties flying back from a football tournament, where they represented Wales. The eighteen- to twenty-two-year-olds and five staff had flown with the low-cost airline to Geneva but were initially told they could not board the return flight because they did not have a high enough ratio of carers to

students. Student Andy Brown said: 'It's disgusting the way they treated us just because we had a disability.'

The football players – none of whom had severe physical or behavioural problems – were eventually let on the plane after other passengers said they would act as carers. But they were made to wait until everyone else had boarded the jet to Liverpool. 'We have been treated like shit,' complained student David Byrne. Their college, Pengwern in Rhuddlan, North Wales, wrote to easyJet to complain, urging the airline to change its policy on disabled passengers. EasyJet defended its actions by arguing that there should be one carer for two disabled people to evacuate the cabin within ninety seconds in an emergency.

Barry Smith was another disabled passenger who suffered from easyJet's actions. Twenty-five-year-old Smith, who had cerebral palsy, flew from his home in Glasgow for a two-week holiday at a disabled centre in the Midlands. But when he tried to board the return flight, staff at East Midlands Airport told him he could not fly back to Glasgow alone. Instead he had to travel back by train.

Smith's distraught mother, Yvonne, accused easyJet of 'blatant discrimination'. 'They left him stranded,' she fumed. 'They did nothing to help him. He was beside himself with fear and is still very upset.' EasyJet employees admitted they had made a 'huge error' and offered Barry and his mother free return flights on any of their routes, once again promising to put together a new, improved policy for disabled travellers.

EasyJet wasn't the only budget airline to be criticised for its approach towards disabled customers. In January 2004 Ryanair lost a discrimination case brought by a man forced to pay £18 to use a wheelchair – nearly twice the cost of his £10 flight to the South of France. The Central London County Court ruled that Ryanair acted unlawfully by not providing Bob Ross, who had cerebral palsy and arthritis, with a wheelchair free of charge at Stansted Airport. Ross needed the wheelchair for the half-mile journey from check-in desk to departure gate and had to hire one instead. Ryanair immediately described the judgement as 'defective' and imposed a 50p levy on all of its flights to compensate, which it described as a 'wheelchair tax'.

Ryanair's move was condemned as 'obscene' by the Irish Wheelchair Association. 'The levy is low and grotesque, even by Ryanair standards,' said assocation spokesman Olan McGowan. 'Other airlines, including Aer Lingus, absorb the cost of wheelchairs. They hire them for their disabled passengers and pay for them.' Indeed, all other airlines, including budget and charter carriers, met the cost of the service. British Airways offered disability awareness training for all customer service staff and said it was 'delighted' to carry on-board wheelchairs or mobility aids for passengers with additional needs.

It was clear that easyJet and its fellow low-cost airlines still had some lessons to learn about service. Simon Evans, spokesman for the Air Transport Users' Council, the government-funded consumer watchdog, estimated that the council received proportionally more complaints about the main low-cost airlines than it did about other 'full-service' carriers. The council added that a rise in complaints about cancelled flights was probably due to the increased number of low-fare airlines. Figures released by the watchdog showed complaints by passengers about cancelled flights rose to 740 in the twelve months to March in 2004, compared to 558 in 2003 and 354 in 2002.

'The increase in complaints about cancellations is becoming a cause for concern,' commented the council's chairman. 'It appears likely that the rise in no-frills traffic is fuelling the surge. So while we commend the success of no-frills carriers in bringing down fares and hugely expanding the range of destinations on offer, we call on them to convince us that the inconvenience and financial costs suffered by passengers when flights are cancelled are not the flipside to the benefits these airlines bring air passengers.'

The problem for passengers was that they were used to being looked after by an airline when things went wrong. Because low-cost carriers worked to tight margins, they tended not to offer the sort of back-up that passengers had grown used to. Evans said that low-cost carriers as a group were far less generous with compensation and tended to fall back on the strict conditions of carriage, which left passengers with very few clear rights.

For example, if a flight was heavily delayed, or cancelled, passengers were not even entitled to a free cup of tea while they waited – let alone the proper refreshments and overnight accommodation that traditional airlines offered. Evans said he had come across many cases where customers had simply been offered refunds or told that they might have to wait days for the next available flight.

But it seemed that many easyJet passengers were prepared to put up with problems if they felt they were getting a good deal. A survey by the Consumers' Association magazine *Holiday Which?* provided an authoritative account of what passengers thought of low-cost airlines. The survey rated all the budget airlines poorly for their catering, legroom, seat comfort and the cleanliness of the toilets. Yet when rated overall, easyJet was in the top ten places in the survey, above major short-haul airlines such as KLM, Air France, British Airways and all the charter operators. Ryanair came halfway down the table. Passengers' perceptions that they were getting value for money often overrode their discontent.

Some disgruntled passengers preferred to put up a fight rather than accept any mishap. One such passenger was Brian Camp, a solicitor from Merseyside, who won undisclosed damages against easyJet after beginning legal action following a cancelled flight to Paris. He had planned to celebrate his wife Julie's fifty-third birthday, in the company of four friends, with a sumptuous meal in a private dining room aboard a bateau mouche on the River Seine. When the party arrived at Liverpool's John Lennon Airport they were pleased to see that their flight was on time. But, according to Camp, the smiling staff already knew the plane would be going nowhere because there was no flight crew available. He claimed he had learned that easyJet was aware the flight would not operate hours before it was due to take off, and alleged that staff went through a charade of checking in would-be passengers, knowing they would face a fruitless wait.

EasyJet said the problems were caused by delays earlier in the day which were out of their control. 'We did have some disruption during the day which was a combination of air traffic control delays and the effects of a new rostering system,' a spokesman explained. 'This flight was supposed to depart at 19.50 and was delayed to 21.00 but the crew was running out of hours. This meant they would not have been able to operate all the way to Paris. All the other crews were working because we had had delays. We did do everything we could to avoid cancelling this flight. Safety is paramount at easyJet and we accept that, last thing at night, a cancelled flight causes lots of problems. We offered transfers, hotels and refunds.'

The solicitor demanded £10,000 in compensation and encouraged all his fellow disappointed passengers to follow suit. Eventually Camp agreed to accept damages from the airline in a private settlement, with an undertaking that he would not disclose the amount entailed.

New European draft regulations in February 2005 awarded air passengers new rights for compensation for overbooked, delayed or cancelled flights, in cases such as Camp's. The legislation, hailed as a victory by consumer groups and MEPs, meant compensation of as much as £420 for travellers who were bumped off flights due to overbooking. Serious delays also meant compensation for passengers on any EU airline flying to or from Europe, including charter flights and low-cost airlines.

Under the Brussels proposals airlines would be banned from charging elderly or disabled passengers for any special help they needed. They would also be unable to refuse such passengers permission to board their planes. About 7 million European airline passengers need special help each year. Under the new rules, European airports would be responsible for providing free assistance for these passengers, while the airlines would contribute to paying for the expenses. However, according to the Commission the costs should not amount to more than €5.9 million per year.

Jacques Barrot, the European commissioner for transport, argued that the boom in air travel needed to be backed by new consumer rights, and officials in Brussels rejected airline claims that costs would inevitably rise, dragging up ticket prices. According to the European Commission, around 250,000 air passengers were denied boarding at EU airports each year because the flights were overbooked by the airlines. Under the new laws, compensation for passengers not allowed on flights because of overbooking would be £175 for flights of 1,500km or less, with £275 in compensation for those between 1,500 and 3,500km and £420 for longer flights to destinations outside the EU.

Compensation would be the same for cancelled flights unless the carrier could prove they were not responsible or had given passengers at least two weeks' notice. Delays of at least two hours would trigger a range of benefits, from free drinks, meals and phone calls to a free hotel room when the next flight was a day away. Financial compensation was also available after five hours. Previously the maximum compensation offered by airlines had been £205 and budget carriers often offered none. Airlines failing to comply with the new rules could face substantial fines, with the Civil Aviation Authority responsible for complaints affecting UK carriers.

The measures angered the industry, which argued that it would be subject to harsher rules than competitors in other parts of the world. EasyJet said the compensation package for passengers bumped off flights was 'probably the most flawed piece of European legislation in recent years', arguing that it would damage the industry. 'We will look after our passengers and will implement the legislation,' chief executive Ray Webster promised. 'But what started as a good piece of legislation to prevent traditional airlines bumping off passengers through overbooking has become a bad piece of legislation and will cause unnecessary confusion and conflict.'

Still, at least the new rules might calm down the next passenger who was threatening to explode in a fit of air rage.

15. Viking invasion

THE VIKING DESCENDANTS landed in Luton in October 2005. EasyJet became the focus of frenzied takeover speculation after Icelandair snapped up an 8.4 per cent stake in the carrier, splashing out £50 million following a day of hectic trading.

In a statement to the stock exchange, Hannes Smárason, Icelandair's chairman, announced that the deal fitted in with the Icelandic national carrier's strategy of investing in rival companies where it had specialist knowledge. 'The Icelandic Group is financially strong and the company is seeking ways to improve the return on its cash,' Smárason explained. 'We have kept our eyes open for opportunities in airline-related securities.' Icelandair added that it would not be averse to buying more shares in easyJet in the future, since it viewed its easyJet stake as a long-term investment.

Analysts praised Icelandair's investment choice. 'I consider Icelandair to be a sensible investor as it is clearly taking the long-term view about easyJet,' commented Andrew Lobbenberg, airlines analyst at ABN Amro. 'It was a very good deal for Icelandair.'

More than 40 million shares in easyJet changed hands that day and the airline's value rose to £620 million. Shares were driven 16 per cent higher on the news, closing up 21 pence at 152p, as rumours spread through the market about Icelandair's purchase.

Icelandic investors had been among the busiest players in the UK stockmarket in recent months – led by the acquisitive group Baugur, which owned the Goldsmiths, Karen Millen, Oasis, Whistles and Coast chains in the UK and was in talks over a possible offer for Iceland-to-Booker group Big Food. Local analysts had been anticipating investment action from Smárason. The Reykjavik-based airline made little secret of its enthusiasm for overseas expansion. 'We are looking for opportunities to grow in neighbouring countries by mergers and acquisitions,' declared Smárason in an interview with Reuters news agency the week before the investment. 'Our intention is to become very aggressive.'

Educated at America's MIT university, Smárason was a former finance director of DeCode, a controversial biotechnology company that had built a database of the genetic make-up of Iceland's entire 300,000-strong population. One of Iceland's wealthiest entrepreneurs, Smárason was appointed chairman of Icelandair in March 2004 and owned 32 per cent of the airline's shares.

Established in 1937, Icelandair flew to five destinations in America and sixteen in Europe, carrying 1.1 million passengers annually on its twelve Boeing 757 aircraft. Icelandair's Reykjavik hub was popular among travellers seeking a cheap route from Europe to the US. The airline employed 1,000 staff with annual profits of £11 million and a market capitalisation of £174 million. Its biggest investor, with 33 per cent of the holding company, was the Straumur Investment bank.

But the airline was only a fraction of the size of easyJet. After all, Iceland only had a population of 290,000 – fewer than easyJet carried in a week. In contrast, easyJet, at the end of 2005, operated seventy Boeing 737s and twenty-four Airbus A319s to fifty-six destinations in Europe, carrying 20.3 million passengers annually. Its employee count was 3,450 and profits had reached £96 million with a market capitalisation of £608 million.

Despite its small size, Icelandair's management had succeeded in turning the minnow perched on the edge of Europe into a canny investment fund. Icelandair was so confident the market was wrong about easyJet that it went out and sold 420 million new shares to institutional investors at 9.10 ISK per share, raising a total of 3.8 billion ISK (approximately £33.1 million). The airline combined the funds from the share sale with the £60 million in cash it had on its balance sheet to finance its investment in easyJet.

Through buying the shares, Icelandair alerted the market to the possibility that things might not be as bad in the budget airline sector as had been suggested and injected some long-term confidence back into the industry. 'I talk to Icelandair regularly,' commented JP Morgan's airline analyst Chris Avery. 'They are a very well-run small airline. They've got cash to invest and they are airline people. They know about leasing plans and average revenues and all those types of things. They've made the judgement that easyJet is the best investment of all the budget airlines – as I have.'

Another analyst also thought Icelandair had made a wise long-term investment: 'The market at the moment is garbage but in three years' time easyJet will still be here and the world will look different.'

Icelandair increased its stake in easyJet to 10.1 per cent later in October, with the purchase of an extra 6.73 million shares. 'If we want to find ways to grow, we have to look beyond Iceland,' Smárason said. 'There will be consolidation in the low-cost sector and easyJet's fundamentals are strong.' On 1 July 2005, the Icelandic airline purchased a further 2.12 million shares in easyJet, amounting to around 0.5 per cent of the company and thus increasing its stake to 11.5 per cent. Speculation mounted that a takeover bid was in the pipeline.

In common with other low-cost airlines, easyJet had been battered by high oil prices and fierce price competition, making it vulnerable to a bid. Fares had fallen to record lows and, despite the launch of dozens of new routes, the airline had warned that in 2005 it would only marginally beat the previous year's profits of £52 million. But Webster dismissed bid speculation. 'I have no idea,' he replied to questions. 'But we're delighted that at least someone recognises the underlying value of the airline.'

Morgan Stanley analyst Penny Butcher pointed out that an outright takeover bid by Icelandair would be difficult because the Icelandic company was valued only at £180 million. '[A bid] would deviate significantly from [Icelandair's] stated business strategy which is focused almost entirely on north Atlantic routes,' she said. In addition, Icelandair would also have to get round foreign ownership laws, which put a cap of 40 per cent on overseas holdings in airlines. And any takeover of easyJet would require the consent of Stelios, whose family still owned 41 per cent of the shares.

Stelios informed easyJet that he didn't have any plans to take the airline private or sell out. He vowed always to keep a stake in easyJet, although he would not specify how big, adding that he would not support a takeover of easyJet unless he was assured that the buyer would not do anything that would tarnish the brand. 'I am not about to sell out to any Tom, Dick or Harry,' he declared. Meanwhile, easyJet could continue to act as a source of income for Stelios's burgeoning easy empire. 'I don't think that Stelios wants to sell out,' said ABN Amro's Lobbenberg. 'Stelios likes to use his stake to sell it down to provide cash for his other easyGroup companies.'

Stelios was still busy adding more creations to the easy

empire. *EasyCruiseOne*, easyCruise's first ship, embarked on its maiden voyage in May 2005. The 'floating hotel' with orange ceilings, orange walls, orange bathrooms and orange beds regularly set sail up and down the French and Italian Rivieras between St Tropez and Portofino. Holidaymakers paid as little as £20 a night on the world's first no-frills cruise liner to share a four-berth, fluorescent orange cabin. The cabins were described as 'unique' and 'minimalist' – they didn't even include windows or portholes to escape from the sheer orangeness of it all.

EasyCruise was aimed firmly at the young. Facilities on board the 88-metre, 4,077-ton ship were minimal: there was a sports bar, a coffee shop and a cocktail bar – with a hot tub. Gone were lavish gourmet dinners at the captain's table. People had to pay extra for food and drinks: a burger and chips for £3.90, or a pint of lager for £2.30. Passengers could hop on and off when they fancied but had to stay a minimum of two nights. The venture has met with initial success; more than 83 per cent of its cabins were booked in August 2005.

Meanwhile, easyJet was preparing itself for a winter of discontent as the fare wars intensified. Webster warned that the refocusing of charter carriers such as First Choice and Airtours away from the Caribbean and on to European holiday routes the previous summer was likely to continue: 'These carriers are still desperate and we are assuming that will continue again as early as January on popular ski routes.'

Package tour operators and charter airlines were reeling from the impact of easyJet, Ryanair and other low-cost carriers, which had taken away business by introducing travellers to the concept of booking cheap getaways independently. To meet the challenge, Thomson, a subsidiary of Frankfurt-based TUI, had chosen to restructure itself completely. The company launched a new carrier in December 2003 called Thomsonfly, which began scheduled service in March from

Coventry to cities on the continent for less than £20 each way. Thomas Cook's charter affiliate, Condor, was also trying to compete head-on with low-cost carriers by increasingly focusing on selling just flights rather than traditional holiday packages.

EasyJet's annual sales rose 17 per cent as passenger numbers increased 20 per cent to 24.3 million. But Webster was disappointed that softer yields, the average amount paid per customer, pushed underlying profit before tax down 11 per cent to £85.4 million. The average fare fell by £1 to £42.28, largely due to increased competition from charter airlines and budget challengers such as Ryanair and flybe.

EasyJet's next piece of news stunned the industry. In May 2005, after nearly ten years manning the airline's flight deck, Webster announced his retirement, saying that he intended to resign from the board as soon as a successor was found, although he agreed to continue in a consultancy role until 30 November 2006 before severing his ties entirely.

Webster told investors that he was leaving the airline for personal reasons. The fifty-eight-year-old New Zealander said that his time at easyJet had been the highlight of his career, but that it had come at a heavy personal cost. He continued: 'For the company, it is the right time to step down. For me, it is two years too late. I have lost my mother and father this year and that really accelerated my decision. I had hoped to spend a couple of years with them. I have a nine-year-old grandson and since he was born, I have spent three days with him, which is appalling. I love the outdoors and would love to take him and my two other grandchildren camping while I am still able to. Over the next decade, it is important to protect myself and my family.'

While Webster wasn't pushed, analysts suspected that he was probably encouraged to think about his future at the airline. 'Webster did wonderfully well at building up the airline but then he allowed the company to deteriorate quite sharply in financial terms, while Ryanair was driven far harder under rapid expansion,' said one analyst, who didn't want to be named. 'He didn't always serve as an appropriate figurehead: he wasn't a very high-profile figure internally and didn't have a great profile with investors or the public. I suspect that one of his weaknesses was building a team.'

One employee certainly didn't seem that upset by Webster's departure; a pilot who went by the nickname of 'A Tree' on PPRuNe, the pilot web message board, posted: 'Good old Ray, how we shall miss him. The man who thinks that staff travel is a waste of money and has done as little as possible to allow it to happen at easyJet.'

Webster said that he and his Parisian wife would continue to be based in London, where he hoped to build up a portfolio of non-executive and consultancy jobs. But easyJet would be his last full-time executive role, allowing him to spend more time in his native New Zealand and Australia. He said it was unlikely that he would work for another airline in any capacity.

His successor would be chosen from outside easyJet and would not necessarily be expected to have a background in aviation. 'We are a fast-moving consumer business, which carries 29 million passengers a year,' the company said. 'We will be looking for consumer-driven experience.' Webster said that headhunters had already been appointed and that he hoped a replacement would be in place by the end of 2005. Possible external candidates included American Airlines' chief financial officer James Beer and Gulf Air chief James Hogan. Former Go boss Barbara Cassani might also be interested, although after their history of spats she might find a working relationship with Stelios far from easy.

In some respects, easyJet was as much the creation of Ray Webster, its chief executive, as Stelios, the man with whom it was still identified. Stelios had the original idea, the money and the charisma but it was Webster who had designed the software behind the airline's yield management system that lay at the heart of its low-cost model, and who had steered easyJet to become the first airline to harness properly the selling power of the Internet.

It was therefore with some regret that the airline industry, investors and fans of easyJet alike received the news of Webster's impending departure. Almost as shocking was news that Stelios would be rejoining the board as a non-executive director with immediate effect. The City was in two minds as to whether this amounted to a reasonable trade-off. In his last year at easyJet, Stelios had annoyed investors by trying to change the articles of association to give himself the power to appoint the chairman and two non-executive directors, and he had also sold down his shareholding, which helped finance his other business ventures but didn't do a lot for the easyJet share price.

On the other hand, Stelios knew the business better than anyone, and as a major shareholder he had every incentive to make the company work. 'I hope to make a contribution based on my close understanding of the easyJet business model, and appreciation of its markets and its unique culture,' the Greek entrepreneur announced.

Stelios's return to the board certainly represented something of a U-turn. It was only two years previously that he had quit the board, declaring he had 'taken note of the concerns of institutional investors' about his role at easyJet when he was spending more time building other companies in his easyGroup empire. Now, all of a sudden, Stelios was returning as a non-executive to replace Amir Eilon, his representative on the board and his long-standing corporate finance advisor. Eilon, a former investment banker, joined the board in 1999 before easyJet's flotation and was due to resign at the annual general meeting in February 2006.

Analysts speculated whether Stelios's decision was influenced by the declining fortunes of his other easyGroup companies. 'Not many of his catalogue of easy-branded investments have been successful to date but easyJet was,' one commented. 'Also Stelios had a lot of capital tied up in the

airline. No doubt he wanted to take a close look at what was going on given its recent performance.'

EasyGroup's bright orange hadn't always translated into business success. EasyCinema had failed to expand beyond its flagship, a weathered building in Milton Keynes, and continued to face resistance from distributors. EasyCar still hadn't broken even. It had grown to fifty sites since its launch in 2000 but now mainly acted as an online brokerage for 1,100 car-hire firms across the world and was criticised for the large number of disclaimers in its rental contracts. On the introduction of the central London congestion charge, easyCar plastered pictures of London mayor Ken Livingstone on its UK fleet, announcing its customers would not have to pay the £5 charge, but this pledge was quietly dropped by managers.

EasyInternetcafé was suffering from the growing popularity of home Internet access and continued to lose money. EasyBuses were still chugging around but few passengers were keen on journeying between north-west London and Milton Keynes. As for easyPizza, many doubted whether the appeal of ordering a pizza a week in advance would really work.

It was early days for easyMobile, launched in March 2005. While the company carried the easyGroup logo, Stelios had no ownership stake and was being paid only for use of his brand. EasyMobile was 80 per cent owned by Danish phone company TDC, with 20 per cent held by a consortium including Frank Rasmussen, the founder of Telmore, a Danish virtual operator.

Calls to any British network were 7.7p a minute, versus rates often three times higher for full-service operators like Vodafone and Orange. Prices were low because easyMobile was as bare bones as possible. It neither owned nor operated a network, instead leasing spare capacity from Deutsche Telekom's T-Mobile unit, which was happy to get the extra revenue. It also had no retail stores, no marketing, and a tiny customer-support centre. EasyMobile didn't even sell phones.

Instead, customers signed up over the Internet and receive a SIM card in the mail that they slipped into just about any handset, then topped up their accounts online.

Analysts' reactions to Stelios's return were mixed. Morgan Stanley's Penelope Butcher said that the easyJet board changes could lead to a strategic switch, with Merrill Lynch's Anthony Bor saying that Stelios had always been a 'talismanic' focal point for the airline. Ian Jones of the CIS, meanwhile, was quite happy to see Stelios back as a non-executive, adding that easyJet should take the opportunity to increase the number of independent directors on the board.

Stelios said he foresaw no major change to his relationship with the airline he launched. 'By becoming a non-executive director myself, rather than operating through a representative on the board, I expect it to continue to be business as usual,' he said. 'I would like to stress that my role will be in a purely non-executive capacity, given my business commitments with the fourteen other easy-branded businesses.' He told the *Daily Mail* newspaper that he didn't want to be chairman, even though he retained the right to unseat easyJet chairman Sir Colin Chandler as long as he owned 10 per cent of easyJet's shares.

Stelios wasn't returning at a prosperous time for the airline. EasyJet was suffering from rising fuel costs, as oil reached $60 a barrel, as well as increased competition. Losses for the six months to 31 March deepened to £31 million from £27 million in the previous year after fuel costs leapt by 51 per cent. EasyJet said that the high cost of oil would continue to push pre-tax profits below the level of 2004. 'Fuel now represents 18 per cent of our cost base,' Chandler explained, 'and the high prices experienced over the winter months show little sign of abating.' EasyJet shares fell nearly 6 per cent.

In summer 2005 British Airways decided to address its annual fuel bill of some £1.2 billion by introducing a surcharge on ticket prices – £2.50 on all flights, with an additional £12 on long-haul return flights, with the aim of raising £70 million. Virgin Atlantic followed suit, increasing its fuel surcharge from £8 per flight to £24.

EasyJet didn't follow their example. The budget carrier maintained that its financial performance was in line with expectations and the pressure of high fuel prices had masked successes elsewhere, including a 25 per cent increase in the number of passengers on its flights and a 26 per cent hike in group revenues to £553 million. Travellers were spending more money on services such as in-flight food, with ancillary revenues per passenger up by 16 per cent, helping group turnover to continue to grow.

EasyJet had launched forty routes over the previous six months and started flights to fourteen new airports, passing milestones such as the delivery of its hundredth aircraft. The increase in routes meant that a total of 13.5 million passengers travelled on an easyJet flight during the six-month period.

Meanwhile, the airline experienced a further sting in the tail as it discovered that construction of a second runway at Stansted, one of its key bases, might be postponed. The second runway was due to open in 2011–12, but airport operator BAA claimed it would not be ready until 2013 at the earliest due to the UK government's slowness in planning new road and rail links. Moreover, under the existing regulatory regime, enforced by the Civil Aviation Authority, any expansion at Heathrow, Gatwick or Stansted had to be financed by the passengers who used that airport. But funding the £4 billion project entirely from those flying from Stansted would require an increase in charges from £3 to up to £11 per passenger, and would delay completion of the runway 'for several years'.

BAA said, however, that there was an argument for reverting to a 'system' approach to financing the runway on the ground of the wider economic benefits that it would generate in the south-east. If Heathrow and Gatwick passengers paid an extra 50 pence to £1 and Stansted passengers paid airport fees of between £7 and £8, the runway would be able to open in 2013. If the runway were to be self-financing, Stansted charges would have to rise to up to £11.

Ryanair and easyJet, the two biggest operators at Stansted, accused BAA of dropping a 'bombshell' on them by proposing to raise airport charges by almost 300 per cent 'just to finance another BAA Taj Mahal'. Indeed, the two low-cost carriers demanded that BAA return to the drawing board and produce a scheme for Stansted for which its customers were prepared to pay.

Mike Clasper, BAA's chief executive, said that the earlier that an additional runway was built at Stansted, the greater the capacity and the more the competition between airlines, driving down fares and benefiting the economy generally. He rejected claims that BAA was proposing to 'gold-plate' the new runway or build another 'Taj Mahal' at Stansted, and also denied that by airing the possibility of cross-subsidisation BAA was effectively starting the campaign to change the regulator's mind.

Any additional expense was a heavy burden for easyJet, which was battling hard to lower costs and to win customers' affections amid the competitive environment. Webster said the company was basing its longer-term yield forecasts – the amount of money it made per customer – on an outlook of 'continued intense competition'. There were now forty-seven low-cost airlines operating in Europe and all were finding conditions hard. Ryanair reported a 16 per cent drop in third-quarter net profit, blaming high oil prices and intense competition, and British Airways reported a 41 per cent drop in third-quarter earnings.

The low-cost airlines gained some ground by refusing to impose fuel surcharges on customers, thus increasing the price differential with the full-service airlines. EasyJet also saved money by adding more fuel-efficient Airbus A319s to its fleet and withdrawing from poorly performing markets or airports that charged high fees. More full-service carriers were being forced to copy the no-frills carriers' spartan service tactics in a bid to lower their costs and fares in response to their budget rivals. Heathrow-based bmi announced it was to scrap its business-class cabins and make all passengers pay for food and drink in a desperate bid to lift the airline into the black after four consecutive years of losses. New bmi chief executive Nigel Turner launched the shake-up, admitting the former British Midland had lost touch with its customers.

EasyJet, meanwhile, was busily thinking up ways to differentiate its product and raise extra revenue in the cut-throat European market. One innovation was easyJetLounges, which it introduced in June 2005. The lounges offered free drinks, snacks and magazines, as well as the standard flight information and access to phone, Internet and email. Offering a lounge, normally the domain of business-class passengers, seemed a move away from easyJet's no-frills approach, but it was intended to attract the many passengers who flew with the airline on business. And true to easyJet form, passengers had to pay for the privilege of using the lounge. Prices started from £12 per person including VAT.

In a further move, easyJet announced that in the future it would quote fares online that included taxes and charges. From early summer 2005, when the carrier had completed an upgrade of its software systems, easyJet's web bookings would show the complete fare payable, including government tax, airport tax, insurance, security and other charges. Previously, the complete fare was only shown in the last stages of making a booking.

From summer 2005 all-inclusive fares had to be quoted in newspaper, television and outdoor advertising. EasyJet had previously had its knuckles rapped by advertising watchdogs over its fare promotions, including one incident in 2004 when the Advertising Standards Authority upheld a complaint about its cheap flight offers from Newcastle to Barcelona. The ad was headlined 'lots more low fares!' and stated 'Newcastle ultimate irony being, of course, that easyJet eventually bought Go.

The world of travel has been reinvented during the past ten years. In 1980, the cheapest return fare on what was then the world's busiest international air route – London to Paris – was around £70, which then represented a week's wages for the average British employee. Nowadays, if you book in advance on easyJet, the fare has fallen to as low as £50, while wages have risen to the point where Mr or Ms Average need work for barely half a day to earn enough for a trip to the French capital.

Today, few people laugh at the idea of easyJet. They are more likely to thank the airline for allowing them to explore Europe on the cheap, visit Auntie Mavis in Edinburgh, and meet regularly with that important new business client in Paris.

Stelios Haji-Ioannou and Michael O'Leary have transformed Europe's airline industry. 'What easyJet and Ryanair did was identify a niche,' said David Bryon, managing director of bmibaby. 'They took out ticket restrictions, kept their cost bases low and reduced their fares, undercutting the prices offered by the major airlines. The pair of them went out there with the message of price, price and price. They stimulated the marketplace and created incremental growth.'

Low costs were essential to their business model. 'The root to being a low-cost airline is to start with a new or renewed focus on operating costs,' said Tim Jeans, managing director of Monarch Scheduled. 'You need to look from the top to bottom at an airline's costs. You need to cut out anything that you don't need that costs you money. Basically you need to be as close to a train as possible.'

The budget airlines' route structures marked a further change in the short-haul market. Most major airlines like British Airways operated a hub-and-spoke system with a major centre like London Heathrow acting as its principal hub from which all flights radiated. The problem was that this could

to . . . Barcelona from £22.49 single'. But an investigation by the ASA revealed that less than 10 per cent of all tickets sold were at that price; by regulation, at least 10 per cent of all tickets sold had to be at the advertised price.

Meanwhile, easyJet was working on another scheme to combat another leading passenger complaint, namely its 'sit anywhere' policy on its flights. The airline had been allowing up to ten passengers on each of its flights from Luton to jump the queue for £10. EasyJet claimed the scheme would benefit passengers wanting more legroom or the choice of a seat in a particular part of the aircraft, but admitted there had been a 'mixed response'.

Slightly more popular was the airline's policy of slowly introducing self-service, automated kiosks for passengers to collect their tickets and boarding cards at its sixty European airports, after successfully testing the scheme at Nottingham East Midlands Airport. The trademark orange kiosks, shaped like slot machines at an amusement arcade, enabled easyJet to handle more passengers for a larger number of flights at the same time.

Ultimately, easyJet and other airlines claimed, the whole airport process would become even easier. One plan was to introduce a system where air tickets were replaced by individual barcodes for each passenger. Baggage tags, meanwhile, could be replaced by new 'smart tags'. The tags each had tiny chips in them that could be tracked by radio, to speed up baggage handling and put an end to the problem of lost and mislaid luggage. Only security checks and passport control would still involve the human touch.

Airline industry executives admitted that the new techniques would slash their costs. By 2007, every ticket was expected to be an 'e-ticket' issued either by computer or through self-service kiosks – a measure that would cut checking-in costs by 90 per cent. Worldwide, that alone would cut airline costs by £1.5 billion a year. But there were risks with the self-service airport. The International Air Transport

Association, the largest of the industry bodies, admitted that airlines would have to prepare for a computer collapse or massive technical failure that could leave thousands of passengers stranded. Some things never changed.

16. Past, present – and future

WHAT A DIFFERENCE a decade makes. It was in 1995 that Stelios hatched the idea of easyJet, shocking the world with his concept of selling flights for the same price as a pair of jeans. At the time, most people stared, laughed or dismissed the fledgling carrier as ridiculous. Weren't those prices too good to be true? EasyJet surely couldn't survive more than a few months, they told each other, joking that the airline catapulted its aircraft and passengers into the skies using a giant elasti band. And the whole idea of a flight without free food or drin was outrageous, never mind the notion of booking your ow flight using the Internet, which in 1995 most people had n even heard of.

Even as easyJet's approach became more familiar, travelle speculated that the low-cost carrier didn't have enough pla and assumed that it wouldn't last long. They assumed t British Airways would soon quash the upstart; until, that BA copied easyJet's no-frills idea by setting up Go.

lead to multiple changes and longer journeys for passengers. EasyJet, by contrast, described its route map as looking more like a spider's web, operating routes from a network of central airports in cities including Luton, Liverpool, Amsterdam and Geneva. This enabled passengers to make more direct journeys.

Of course, easyJet did not only have to compete against the traditional airlines.'One of easyJet's strategic challenges is how to deal with Ryanair,' said Andrew Lobbenberg, airlines analyst at ABN Amro. 'The Dublin-based carrier is more aggressive in its business approach and how it deals with consumers and it delivers better on business reliability and punctuality. Basically easyJet doesn't know how to react to Ryanair. First of all it took the high moral ground, claiming that it offered better service. EasyJet then launched routes into Ireland and Ryanair came back with extra capacity, which brought down easyJet's stock price. EasyJet says it doesn't compete with Ryanair but everyone does compete with everyone else in the airline industry.'

EasyJet differs from Ryanair by competing head-on with the legacy carriers such as British Airways, and often operating to larger established airports such as Nice and Athens – then trying to capture a third or more of that market, said industry expert Professor Rigas Doganis. Ryanair's approach, meanwhile, is modelled on Southwest Airlines, which flies to secondary airports in major cities to take advantage of lower landing charges. It also flies on routes that would not interest a larger carrier, such as Trieste in Italy and Esbjerg in Denmark, and blurs the borders of Europe by describing the Swedish city of Malmo as Copenhagen, and Perpignan in France as Barcelona. 'Ryanair generally tends to fly on thinner, underserved routes and aims to become the dominant carrier on those routes and develop new markets,' explained Doganis. 'Where it competes head-on with the legacy airlines it is normally by serving secondary airports, such as Hahn (Frankfurt) or Torp (Oslo), very distant from the major centres Ryanair claims to be serving.'

Like Ryanair, easyJet has excelled in getting its brand well established, assisted by its in-your-face marketing campaigns and spectacular publicity stunts, such as Stelios and his easyJet crew turning up at Go's launch dressed in orange boiler suits. Nowadays, consumers immediately associate the neon orange shade with easyJet or the other easyGroup companies. 'EasyJet has two real strengths that its peers admire it for,' Tim Jeans admitted. 'The first is its brand, its styling, culture and tone of voice and that's been self-sustaining. The yield management system, thanks to Webster, is its other strength. EasyJet manages to extract the maximum revenue per flight by being very aggressive on pricing, meaning that it has very strong revenues per flight. EasyJet was set up to win, as was Ryanair.'

The carrier is often praised for looking after its customers better than Ryanair and other no-frills airlines. 'I would rather fly with easyJet than Ryanair any day and I'm an Irishman!' said regular easyJet user Ray Hanley. 'EasyJet employees are not as abrupt as those at Ryanair and have always been helpful if I asked about something such as extra luggage. Ryanair staff are always on the offensive – they always expect you to make a complaint, I guess.'

On the other hand, easyJet's costs aren't as low as Ryanair's. There is a 15 to 20 per cent cost differential between the two carriers, according to Doganis. 'Ryanair is much more disciplined about costs than easyJet,' said Jeans. 'If you cut a Ryanair person down the middle, like a stick of rock, you would see cost control written all the way through.'

EasyJet had other failings. Industry experts criticised the company for spending too much time and effort trying to sort out DBA, the BA subsidiary it tried to buy in 2003, instead of backing out at an earlier stage when it was clear that the proposed takeover wasn't going to work.

Furthermore, easyJet's record of communicating with the financial markets has not been always perfect. The City was outraged after easyJet gave two profit warnings within four weeks in May and June 2004, and did not forgive the company lightly. But the company learned its lesson and resolved to communicate more openly in future. Added to that, the airline has had a tendency to be too inward-looking. 'It took easyJet a long time to realise that it doesn't totally control its own destiny,' Lobbenberg commented, 'and that its revenues can be badly affected by what happens to other low-cost airlines and the market.'

One thing easyJet did recognise from the start was the importance of an impeccable safety record. The airline sought to impress on people's minds that low cost didn't equal low safety. EasyJet wasn't the only no-frills carrier to come to the same conclusion. Low-cost airlines agreed on hardly anything but the one topic on which they were unanimous was safety. Southwest, which had flown over 10 million flights without losing an aircraft in a fatal accident, saw 'safety as its most important priority every day', said the American airline's head of PR, Linda Rutherford. 'You can't be successful if you're not safe. Southwest has a better safety record than Qantas.'

EasyJet's emphasis on cost control was legendary but there could be no compromises on safety. As it strove to point out, easyJet invested in an even younger fleet than those flown by its full-service rivals. The airline was aware that less than perfect maintenance would be its most costly mistake. To quote one of Stelios's maxims: 'If you think safety is expensive, try an accident.' Avoiding crashes was even more crucial for no-frills operators than for traditional airlines. An accident could obliterate a carrier's reputation in an instant. Low-cost airlines only had to look at the example of ValuJet, which destroyed the lives of all passengers on-board, as well as its reputation, when one of its planes crashed in May 1996.

Fatal accident rates among airlines in Europe and North America ran at one in every million or two departures. Most accidents occurred during the take-off, climb, descent and landing phases of flight. Most other forms of transport are more dangerous per mile and even per trip than flying.

Engineers and safety inspectors scrupulously monitored the construction of an aircraft, checking every nut and bolt.

EasyJet is meticulous about what can or cannot be allowed safely on-board an aircraft, sometimes to passengers' annoyance. Donna Marie Parks was due to travel with her two young sons on an easyJet flight from Glasgow to London in June 2005. Desk staff and the cabin crew told her the baby seat was fine to carry her four-month-old son Daniel. But the captain disagreed and ordered the family off the plane. Her husband Gordon turned up two hours later with an alternative car seat, but she was again refused permission to fly. The family was only permitted to travel more than five hours later after an easyJet desk worker loaned a different car seat for Daniel.

'Although the car seat appeared to have the standard requirements, there was no way that this particular seat could be attached to an aircraft seat in a safe and secure manner,' an easyJet spokeswoman explained. 'Therefore, it was deemed inappropriate for travel. Once she had obtained a seat that was appropriate for travel, easyJet transferred them free of charge on to the next available flight.'

EasyJet's safety regulations caused Parks inconvenience. But before the advent of easyJet, she would no doubt have been making the journey by train or car, or not at all. No one could deny that easyJet had changed the world of travel and made flying easy. 'Stelios and Michael O'Leary are responsible for changing the whole travel culture in this country,' said Ian Briggs, press secretary at Luton Airport. 'You would never have thought of flying from London to Edinburgh before the days of easyJet. You would have taken the train or the car instead. Flying was just for wealthier people. Nowadays flying is the first thing people think of. They feel hard done by if they have to take the car or the train and that's purely because of the nuisance value and regardless of the costs involved.'

Before easyJet, who would have dreamed that you could jet out to the South of France for less than £37 return? Cheap fares changed every aspect of people's lives. 'My love life was hanging by a thread until you started flying from Liverpool to the South of France,' said one happy easyJet passenger whose fiancé lived in Nice. She could barely afford to see him before easyJet's arrival.

Flavia Collins, mother of a toddler and pregnant with her second child, was another who appreciated easyJet for allowing her to spend time with a loved one. Collins used easyJet to commute regularly between London and Amsterdam to visit her husband, Shaun, who was working in the Netherlands capital to set up an Internet business for an Anglo-Dutch company. Collins even found commuting with a toddler easy. 'The air stewardesses were very helpful with my son, Toby. Also, refreshments are more hassle than it's worth on a forty-five-minute flight with a toddler. They just get in the way, so I much prefer it when you don't get them automatically included.'

EasyJet changed working as well as flying habits. Cheap and easy flights meant that employees could work overseas and travel home for the weekend. Ray Hanley, an engineer for BMW, was one customer who used easyJet to travel to work. 'I was based in the UK for three years and worked over in Germany so I used to commute back and forth every couple of weeks,' he explained. 'Since then I've moved to Munich to work for BMW full-time, so in a way, easyJet has helped me get the job!'

The advent of easyJet flights encouraged executives to strengthen their links overseas and set up offices abroad. Clive France, business director of Internetics, a London-based Internet and new media design agency, often flew with easyJet between London and Barcelona after setting up an office in the Spanish city. 'When easyJet opened its route from Gatwick to Barcelona, we didn't think twice about making Barcelona our choice of city to expand our design team abroad,' he said. 'Barcelona is a creative city and the cost of living is relatively low, compared with London. I probably wouldn't have considered setting up an office in Barcelona otherwise but the reasonably priced flights out there have made it all possible. We've now set up a second office in Barcelona and taken on employees there. I fly out there regularly with easyJet. Low-cost travel combined with video conferencing and remote working tools have meant that we have been able to expand confidently and cheaply and the operation has been a huge success.'

France didn't just use easyJet for work. The airline and its low fares also encouraged him to fly around Europe for pleasure. 'EasyJet changed the life of my generation,' he declared. 'For a while there, I was jetting off every weekend to cities such as Venice, Barcelona, Nice and Athens. I was the boy about Europe.'

It was clear that the 'easyJet generation' was turning their backs on the traditional Mediterranean package holiday in favour of independent travel. The sun was setting on the package holiday, which traditionally comprised a charter airline's flight and a fortnight's pre-paid accommodation. Holidaymakers increasingly opted for DIY holidays, booking their own flights over the Internet and sorting out their own accommodation. The giant tour operator First Choice abandoned seat-only sales amid rising competition from the likes of easyJet while other operators tried to copy no-frills airlines by offering low-fare scheduled flights in a bid to survive.

'I guess I'm the typical easyJet customer,' France continued. 'I barely travelled apart from on package holidays before budget airlines came along. I used to work as a tour rep for Thomson Holidays and it was always easier and more convenient to take a package tour. Nowadays I wouldn't even consider going on a package holiday. EasyJet and budget travel has given me the confidence to take a flight and wing it when I get there. People like me can do their own thing and take off at any moment. The price is so low for flights that it almost forces people into taking a gamble, even if they would never have flown before.'

EasyJet attracts impulse flyers. People might see that the airline flew to Bratislava, decide that sounded interesting and fly to the city for the weekend. Europe was suddenly an exciting place to explore, full of intriguing cities just one or two hours' flight away. The British jetted off to Nice and Toulouse and the French landed in Liverpool. EasyJet helped join the dots between the various European cities and open up countries to their neighbours. Indeed, *The Economist* went so far as to suggest that easyJet and Ryanair had 'done more to integrate Europe than any numbers of diplomats or ministers'.

In addition, easyJet's cheap and easy flights encouraged the concept of the weekend break at a time when getting away from the office had never been harder. A survey by the Chartered Management Institute found that of more than 3,000 managers surveyed, only 53 per cent found time to use their holiday entitlement. As work pressures made it hard for many to get away for a full two weeks, more people took shorter breaks to Europe on a frequent basis.

Some people even decided to escape abroad just for the day. Before easyJet moved into Britain's airports, a day trip used to mean a quick jaunt to the seaside, equipped with bucket, spade and a picnic. An exotic day trip, meanwhile, usually meant catching a ferry to the Isle of Man. But thanks to the extraordinary expansion of our travel horizons courtesy of easyJet and its pals, sun worshippers could get a blast of sunshine with a day on the beach. Keen skiers were sloping off to the ski slopes for the day for a quick fix of the white stuff. The DIY sector of the ski market grew by some 50 per cent in 2002 as some snow fanatics took advantage of easyJet's early ski flights. These included the 6.30 a.m. flight from Luton which landed at 9.10 a.m. at Geneva, close to several excellent ski areas including Chamonix.

'The effect of the no-frills airlines? Huge – it has transformed this town,' said Simon Norris of the Hotel Eden in Chamonix. 'At least 50 per cent of our British clientele comes through easyJet.' Other popular day trips included the Venice

Carnival and playing roulette at the casino tables in Monte Carlo.

The popularity of low-fare flights helped the airline industry recover after a dramatic dip in sales following the terrorist attacks in the US in 2001. After two turbulent years in 2002 and 2003, the world's airlines clawed their way back to pre-11 September levels in 2004, with China and the low-cost carriers leading the overall recovery. EasyJet's Toby Nicol described 11 September as a 'watershed' in the global aviation world. 'Since then, the traditional airlines have been smaller, and low-cost airlines have mushroomed. After the terrorist attacks, we ran very major seat promotions and cut prices while traditional carriers put prices up due to extra security costs.' He added that until the attacks, the 'low-cost phenomenon' had not been truly accepted in Europe.

Now that they were established in Europe, how long would low-cost carriers survive? From high fuel costs and over-capacity to the threat of development aid taxes and likely eventual inclusion in climate-change emission controls, the challenges for the airline industry kept on mounting. In May 2005, European Union finance ministers agreed to impose a tax on plane tickets to fund development aid programmes in Africa. According to a document drawn up for the ministers' meeting, a tax of €10 on airline tickets for flights within the EU and €30 on flights outside the EU would generate about €6 billion for development spending. The tax would be compulsory in some countries, such as Belgium, France and Germany, while other countries would make it optional.

The move was seen as a major blow by airlines, particularly cut-price carriers such as easyJet. A spokesman for easyJet said the proposal was 'confused'. 'Why only target airline passengers, why not bus passengers?' he asked, arguing that there would be no side-benefit for the environment as the tax would not give any incentive to people to alter their behaviour. 'Aviation could put hundreds of millions of pounds into the Treasury and it would have no impact on the environment.'

But environmental groups were delighted by the news, seeing it as the first step towards making people pay the true cost of plane travel. Environmentalists pointed out that politicians such as Tony Blair denounced global warming as the greatest threat to the mankind while encouraging the development of a fifth terminal at London Heathrow, and as more passengers take to the skies green issues can only become more important. Environmentalists were cheered when a coalition of airlines formed a 'sustainable aviation group' in June 2005, claiming to take green issues seriously. EasyJet was one of the airlines who joined the green fold. One airline was notable by its absence: Ryanair. O'Leary announced cheerfully that Ryanair intended to increase its emissions of carbon dioxide, adding that if his customers were worried about the environment they should sell their car and walk.

The first wave of consolidation had already tightened up the market and many low-cost ventures had fallen by the wayside. EasyJet had taken over Go and Ryanair had bought Buzz. Another low-cost casualty, euJet, was laid to rest in July 2005. EuJet owner Planestation also went into administration, as did Kent International Airport, home for the airline, which flew from Kent and Shannon to more than twenty locations, including Ibiza, Malaga and Nice. EasyJet offered passengers stranded at their European destinations a rescue fee of £25 to return home to the UK. And it was certain that consolidation in the sector would continue at the expense of many more no-frills carriers. 'I see a lot of low-cost airlines in Europe disappearing,' Lobbenberg warned. 'The market simply won't support them all.'

But easyJet and Ryanair were clearly slated to survive. 'EasyJet and Ryanair have first mover advantages,' added Lobbenberg. 'They became established in and outside the UK as pan-European brands, unlike say the German low-cost carrier Air Berlin. Indeed, the majority of low-cost airlines have unknown brands outside the UK. Air Polonia even launched flights to the UK without initially having a website in

English. By being based in the UK and Ireland, easyJet and Ryanair also benefit from the country's low labour costs and flexibility.'

Most industry experts expected only one or two low-cost airlines, apart from easyJet and Ryanair, to stay alive. 'It is certain that many new entrants are not going to survive beyond two to three years,' said Doganis. 'SAS's no-frills subsidiary, Snowflake, is already being phased down. Duo, Volare and Air Polonia all collapsed during 2004. The market simply can't absorb so many low-cost carriers. There will be consolidation around two to three carriers, namely easyJet, Ryanair and possibly one further carrier based in mainland Europe.'

Other industry members, such as bmibaby's David Bryon, were more optimistic. 'I think it will be more like ten no-frills airlines that are doing okay, with a core of five to six major low-cost players in Europe and three to four just starting up,' the airline CEO said.

Monarch Scheduled's Tim Jeans insisted that there was room for some new entrants to squeeze into the market. 'While Ryanair competes on secondary or tertiary routes, it always leaves room for people to compete against flag carriers on primary routes. The French, Spanish and Italian markets have hardly been touched compared with Germany and the UK. I'm more bullish than most. Monarch is taking on three new aircraft this year. The people most at threat here are the legacy flag carriers, who are still in denial and wishing that the whole low-cost thing will go away,' Jeans continued. 'These include carriers such as Iberia and Alitalia who are seeing their yields in freefall.'

Alitalia was still being bailed out. In early June 2005 the European Commission gave its conditional approval to the debt-ridden Italian carrier's restructuring plan, which included a €1.2 billion recapitalisation of its new subsidiary AZ Fly. Despite three government bail-outs since 1997, Alitalia was still losing money; it lost €620 million in the first half of 2004 and cut-throat competition was forcing its market share downwards.

Meanwhile, consolidation was continuing among national carriers. In 2003, Air France, Europe's second largest carrier, bought KLM, Europe's fourth largest, in a deal that created the biggest European carrier and the number one worldwide in terms of sales. Air France held 81 per cent of the group, led by Air France chairman Jean-Cyril Spinetta, with KLM owning the remainder. EasyJet, by now the second biggest operator in the French market after Air France in terms of traffic, opposed the takeover on the grounds that it damaged competition.

But the no-frills market share in Europe had yet to reach anything close to US levels. The US low-fares market is 'probably in its adolescence or maturity whereas the European market is still in its childhood', said Southwest's Linda Rutherford. 'There is a tremendous amount of growth in Europe in the cities that can be served and the number of passengers that can be carried.' Nevertheless, low-cost carriers' rate of growth would inevitably slow down; otherwise, they were in danger of overheating by expanding too rapidly, concluded Doganis. 'Low-cost carriers will grow faster than scheduled airlines but their growth rates will settle down to a rate of 15 per cent to 20 per cent per year, not the 40 to 60 per cent of recent years.'

There was no doubt that the key driver of growth in the budget airline market was the airlines' rock-bottom prices, as they slashed fares to win passengers. The battle for European skies was in full swing, and the big winner was the consumer. Ryanair, for example, continuously grabbed the headlines with its offer of 99 pence one-way flights and offered some routes for free, claiming to undercut traditional carriers by an average 70 to 80 per cent. At easyJet, the model was 'the earlier you book the lower the price': a one-way trip to Palma from London might start at £30 several months in advance, but could rise to £200 the day before travel. This compared with British Airways' efforts to compete with a limited number of seats at £80 to £160 return on routes such as London to Paris.

The good news for the consumer and the bad news for the airlines is that low fares at their current levels seem here to stay. Gone were the days when airlines set the fares. Nowadays, Ryanair even pays people to fly on its aircraft, offering total fares for less than the combined taxes and charges. 'The market is setting the fares for us and we have to manage our costs to tie in with the available revenues per flight,' said Jeans.

Future fares will, of course, be influenced by external factors, such as fuel prices, taxes, US dollar exchange rates and government regulations. Airlines such as easyJet will also be forced to maintain their low fares by cutting out any remaining excess costs in their operations. And they will endeavour to make money by additional revenues such as the food, drink and goods sold on-board and by re-introducing traditional 'frills' such as in-flight entertainment and business lounges, which passengers will have to pay for. 'Airlines will almost become retailers, with the flight viewed as a classic loss leader and the value of the customer becoming highest,' Bryon prophesied.

EasyJet maintained that in the next ten to fifteen years the vast majority of short-haul traffic in Europe would be on low-cost airlines, though if you flew long-haul you would still travel with a traditional airline. But many passengers, pleased with their cheap flights to Malaga, were beginning to ask when they would be able to buy a no-frills flight to Florida or another long-haul destination. If low fares worked so well within Europe, why couldn't the formula be transferred on to long-haul routes? The hypothesis seems simple enough but aviation history is littered with airlines that went bust applying no-frills principles to long-haul: PeopleXpress of the US, Wardair of Canada, Civair, whose secondhand Boeing 747 never got off the ground from South Africa to Stansted, and of course, Laker's Skytrain. Like many others in the industry, Stelios believed that his short-haul model did not adapt to longer flights. 'The controllable costs where you can make a difference are swamped by uncontrollable costs like fuel and air-traffic control charges,' he argued.

In any case, it seemed that Stelios had enough to keep him busy within Europe. According to a publication of the European Commission, air transport was the fastest growing transport mode and was expected to account for 10.8 per cent of passenger transport activity by 2030, compared with 5.4 per cent in 2000. According to the same study, the volume of passenger traffic using air transport should be twice that of the railways by 2030, reaching the level of 923 billion passenger kilometres.

And whether as a result of the bad weather or because the UK had given birth to a nation of would-be explorers, Great Britain remains at the epicentre of the budget airline explosion. The UK might be only the world's twentieth-biggest nation in terms of population but it accounts for 14 per cent of all international air travel – more than any other country in the world. The number of Britons who fly has increased more than six-fold over the last thirty-five years, from 32 million journeys a year in 1970 to 217 million in 2004, and is expected to increase to about 400 million by 2020. Half the population now fly at least once a year and a substantial percentage five times or more. And mostly for pure pleasure. Only one-sixth of the trips made by UK residents are for business purposes. Thanks to easyJet, the British have become a plane-crazy nation of holidaymakers. We fly because we can afford to and because it is as 'easy as travelling on a bus', once you remembered that buses didn't offer you anything to eat, simply got you from A to B and were subject to delays.

In 2005, the British public, as well as many Europeans, can fly cheaply to most corners of Europe – a prospect that would have seemed like pie in the sky just a decade ago when easyJet was born. 'By 2008, no one will be flying on traditional airlines in Europe,' promised Stelios. It certainly looks as if planeloads of passengers will continue to head cheaply into the sun with easyJet. No doubt, you, I and other members of the easyJet generation will all be cursing our neon-orange friend under our breath the next time we get caught in a stampede for a window seat or traipse home in dejection after being refused on a flight for not checking in early enough or forgetting our passport.

But meanwhile, property owners will visit their holiday homes in Spain and France. Stag weekenders will stagger drunkenly around the medieval cobbled streets of Eastern Europe. Businessmen will continue to commute between cities and jet back home for the weekend from their overseas offices. And lovers, friends and families will continue to be reunited courtesy of the bright orange British airline that no one took seriously ten years ago.

Index

to . . . Barcelona from £22.49 single'. But an investigation by the ASA revealed that less than 10 per cent of all tickets sold were at that price; by regulation, at least 10 per cent of all tickets sold had to be at the advertised price.

Meanwhile, easyJet was working on another scheme to combat another leading passenger complaint, namely its 'sit anywhere' policy on its flights. The airline had been allowing up to ten passengers on each of its flights from Luton to jump the queue for £10. EasyJet claimed the scheme would benefit passengers wanting more legroom or the choice of a seat in a particular part of the aircraft, but admitted there had been a 'mixed response'.

Slightly more popular was the airline's policy of slowly introducing self-service, automated kiosks for passengers to collect their tickets and boarding cards at its sixty European airports, after successfully testing the scheme at Nottingham East Midlands Airport. The trademark orange kiosks, shaped like slot machines at an amusement arcade, enabled easyJet to handle more passengers for a larger number of flights at the same time.

Ultimately, easyJet and other airlines claimed, the whole airport process would become even easier. One plan was to introduce a system where air tickets were replaced by individual barcodes for each passenger. Baggage tags, meanwhile, could be replaced by new 'smart tags'. The tags each had tiny chips in them that could be tracked by radio, to speed up baggage handling and put an end to the problem of lost and mislaid luggage. Only security checks and passport control would still involve the human touch.

Airline industry executives admitted that the new techniques would slash their costs. By 2007, every ticket was expected to be an 'e-ticket' issued either by computer or through self-service kiosks – a measure that would cut checking-in costs by 90 per cent. Worldwide, that alone would cut airline costs by £1.5 billion a year. But there were risks with the self-service airport. The International Air Transport

Association, the largest of the industry bodies, admitted that airlines would have to prepare for a computer collapse or massive technical failure that could leave thousands of passengers stranded. Some things never changed.

16. Past, present – and future

WHAT A DIFFERENCE a decade makes. It was in 1995 that Stelios hatched the idea of easyJet, shocking the world with his concept of selling flights for the same price as a pair of jeans. At the time, most people stared, laughed or dismissed the fledgling carrier as ridiculous. Weren't those prices too good to be true? EasyJet surely couldn't survive more than a few months, they told each other, joking that the airline catapulted its aircraft and passengers into the skies using a giant elastic band. And the whole idea of a flight without free food or drink was outrageous, never mind the notion of booking your own flight using the Internet, which in 1995 most people had not even heard of.

Even as easyJet's approach became more familiar, travellers speculated that the low-cost carrier didn't have enough planes and assumed that it wouldn't last long. They assumed that British Airways would soon quash the upstart; until, that is, BA copied easyJet's no-frills idea by setting up Go. The ultimate irony being, of course, that easyJet eventually bought Go.

The world of travel has been reinvented during the past ten years. In 1980, the cheapest return fare on what was then the world's busiest international air route – London to Paris – was around £70, which then represented a week's wages for the average British employee. Nowadays, if you book in advance on easyJet, the fare has fallen to as low as £50, while wages have risen to the point where Mr or Ms Average need work for barely half a day to earn enough for a trip to the French capital.

Today, few people laugh at the idea of easyJet. They are more likely to thank the airline for allowing them to explore Europe on the cheap, visit Auntie Mavis in Edinburgh, and meet regularly with that important new business client in Paris.

Stelios Haji-Ioannou and Michael O'Leary have transformed Europe's airline industry. 'What easyJet and Ryanair did was identify a niche,' said David Bryon, managing director of bmibaby. 'They took out ticket restrictions, kept their cost bases low and reduced their fares, undercutting the prices offered by the major airlines. The pair of them went out there with the message of price, price and price. They stimulated the marketplace and created incremental growth.'

Low costs were essential to their business model. 'The root to being a low-cost airline is to start with a new or renewed focus on operating costs,' said Tim Jeans, managing director of Monarch Scheduled. 'You need to look from the top to bottom at an airline's costs. You need to cut out anything that you don't need that costs you money. Basically you need to be as close to a train as possible.'

The budget airlines' route structures marked a further change in the short-haul market. Most major airlines like British Airways operated a hub-and-spoke system with a major centre like London Heathrow acting as its principal hub from which all flights radiated. The problem was that this could

Chapter Fifty-Seven

This is proving to be a very long night. I gulp down my wine. It's as good an anaesthetic as any. The weird thing is that I've wanted to come to this restaurant for ages – it's the current 'in' place to go in London. Of course, that means it's packed and over-priced and the service is terrible. Their stick-thin surly waiters are as legendary as their small portions.

I pick my way through my *poussins*. Little chickens. Nothing more grand than that, despite the posh name. I look up at Alec. He has been talking for a very long time about investments. I try, and fail, to stifle a yawn.

'I find unit trusts so fascinating,' Alec says. 'Do you?'

'Fascinating,' I echo vaguely. For a man with great looks and a trendy name, Alec is proving to be a crashing bore. The only positive thing I can say about him is that he would fit in perfectly well at family parties that involve my sisters' tiresome husbands, Dreadful Dickie and Awful Austin. He could become Atrocious Alec. Does he have to sit so absolutely upright? Perhaps he isn't suave and sophisticated after all. Perhaps he's just starchy.

We exhaust his knowledge of art in about ten minutes. He looks as if he knows what he's talking about, but he's a bullshitter. And he's the worst type of bullshitter, because he doesn't think he is one; he actually thinks he knows what he's talking about. He didn't buy anything from the gallery either, which automatically puts a black mark against him.

Alec works in the City in one of the huge financial institutions, like Leo. But unlike Leo, he's enthralled by his work. And thinks everyone else should be. Whereas, the only head for figures that Leo has is for female ones.

I had a late and sleepless night last night, plus an early start at my shrink's. It's no wonder I'm exhausted. It isn't yet nine o'clock and already I can feel myself sliding down my chair with fatigue. I'm still trying to fight sleep, when the waiter comes to top up our glasses. Alec puts his hand over his wine glass. 'No. Goodness. Not for me thanks,' he says with a disapproving look. 'One glass is more than enough.'

'Slug it in,' I instruct the waiter. 'One glass isn't nearly enough.' Through a rapidly developing drunken haze, I grin cheesily at Alec.

My date looks faintly alarmed. 'I have an early start in the morning.'

I think Alec looks like the type who jogs. At six o'clock in the morning. He is a high maintenance boyfriend. The sort who wouldn't appreciate waking up next to ancient sheep-patterned pyjamas. He'd want something filmy from Agent Provocateur on his woman.

I stare at him through bleary eyes.

'I think I'll get the bill,' he says crisply, as if reading my thoughts. 'Shall we split it?'

Uptight and cheap, I think bitterly. No dessert, no coffee. And, after my measly main course, I'm still starving. Yet, I know in my heart of hearts that it is definitely time to go.

Outside, on the street, the fresh air hits me. Suddenly, I feel very tired and very alone. My limbs are heavy and aching.

Alec is shrugging on his coat. It isn't cold enough for a coat. My father will be the only other person in London who'll be wearing a coat tonight.

I put two fingers in my mouth and whistle for a cab that's passing – a very useful trick that Leo taught me. Alec doesn't look impressed by my skill. Obligingly, the driver pulls up in front of me. The end of this interminable evening is in sight.

'Well,' Alec says tightly. 'Thank you for a pleasant evening.'

'Yes,' I say politely. 'It's been very . . . very . . . Well. Thanks.' We both know that it has been perfectly awful. 'Come into the gallery some time.'

'I will,' he says. And we both know that he will never darken its door again.

He waves briskly and then marches off down the street – into the balmy summer night in his coat. If I'd turned round and looked again just a moment later, I would have seen that damn woman – that *Isobel* – in exactly the place where Alec had been, wearing a very oversized coat and a satisfied smile on her face. Then I would have realised that there is something very strange going on in my life. But I don't. I'm so grateful to have hailed a cab, I climb into it without a backward glance and collapse back in the seat.

'Where to, love?' the driver wants to know.

Before I know what I'm doing, I rattle off Leo's address – I blame the drink myself.

The cab swings out into the evening traffic.

'Oh Leo,' I wail loudly. 'Why do I still love you?'

The cab driver, I note, closes his dividing window.

In the end, I had the taxi driver drop me at the bottom of Leo's road when I see that the Doner Kebab takeaway is still open. I buy myself the biggest, greasiest kebab on the menu and it tastes a lot better than the scraggy *poussins* that I paid ten times the price for in the trendy, rip-off eaterie.

Now I'm sitting on the bonnet of Leo's manky old car, Ethel, opposite his flat. And really I have no idea why – except that I know it's another hundred and fifty quid of psychiatrist's fees up in smoke. I also need to feel close to Leo – in distance if nothing else. It's still relatively early and yet Leo's bedroom light is on and the curtains are closed. They're probably curled up in bed together having just made mad, passionate love, I think, and the chilli sauce from my kebab burns an acidic hole in my stomach. Thank goodness there aren't any shadows moving against the curtains. That would have been too hard to bear. I might have been tempted to brick in Leo's windows.

I seethe as I sit here. I want my boyfriend back and, make no mistake, I'm going to get him. By hook or by crook. All I have to do is come up with a foolproof strategy. How hard can that be? I'm an intelligent and resourceful woman. Intelligent and resourceful enough to know that it's time I was going home. The walk back to my own flat isn't too far even though it will be filled with only my lonely footsteps.

Jumping down from the bonnet, I brush the dirt from my

skirt. It's a shame that Leo never washes his car, but then the grime is probably the only thing holding Ethel together. Leo, with his usual scant appreciation of security, has left his car window open. Screwing up the paper that my doner kebab has been wrapped in, I push it in through the window. Punishment for Leo making me sit outside his flat without him. The car will stink in the morning. No doubt Leo won't even notice.

Chapter Fifty-Eight

'How did you get on with Emma last night?' Lard asked.

'I didn't "get on" with Emma,' Grant admitted. 'I "got on" with her best friend, Caron.' He gave Lard a sheepish grin.

'What? Are you turning into Leo?' Lard wanted to know as he crammed another chocolate croissant into his mouth. All this emotional turmoil was doing his diet no good at all.

'I hope not,' Grant said. 'I just realised that it was a very bad idea to pursue his ex.' The fact that Caron had been great company had certainly helped to persuade him of the fact. But it was more than that. He didn't want anything to spoil his friendship with Leo. 'I want to be his mate again, not his enemy.'

Grant looked at the clock. 'Speaking of which,' he said, 'where is the Boy Wonder? This is very late, even for Leo.'

It was nearly lunchtime and they'd still heard nothing from him.

'Perhaps he's going for a personal best?'

Grant craned his neck and checked in Old Baldy's office. A frown creased his forehead. 'Isobel isn't here either.' He suddenly felt a frisson of worry. 'Isn't that odd?'

'Seeing them fly across the sky on balloons is what I call odd,' Lard said flatly. 'This doesn't even register as a blip.'

Grant scratched at his ear. 'Something's not right.'

'He's probably still in bed,' Lard said. 'Ring him.'

'I can't ring him,' Grant puffed. 'He's still not talking to me. We need a bit of time to make our peace. You do it.'

Lard tutted. 'I hope you realise that all this falling out is giving me dyspepsia,' he complained as he reached for the phone with one hand and another croissant with the other.

Leo could hear the phone ringing in the hall and realised that he must, after all, have dropped off in the wee small hours. Glancing over at Isobel, he was relieved to see that she was still here at least. But she didn't look good. She was fast asleep, but her breathing was troubled and her face was contorted with pain.

Leo's legs were numb where he'd been sleeping in the chair. Tiptoeing out to the hall, he closed the bedroom door so that he didn't disturb Isobel and picked up the phone. When Leo heard Lard's cheery, comforting voice he nearly passed out with relief.

'Mate,' Lard said. 'Where are you? There are cakes here for the eating.'

'Isobel's sick,' Leo replied. Even he could hear the panic and strain in his voice. 'She's very sick. I think she has to go back.' His throat was so clogged with emotion that he could hardly speak. This was the first time he'd voiced his fears. 'I don't know what to do.'

'Leave it to Uncle Lard,' his friend said and hung up.

As Lard hung up the phone he turned to Grant with a worried look. 'Isobel's sick,' he said. 'She has to go back.'

'Go back where?'

'I don't know,' Lard admitted with a grimace. 'To where she comes from, I presume.' He shrugged. 'Leo sounded really screwed up. I think he might need our help. He doesn't know what to do.'

'Do we?'

Grant and Lard both turned and looked at the computer together.

'Not yet,' Lard said, flexing his fingers and cracking them in a decisive manner.

'Thank goodness for the internet,' Grant said. 'Useful not only for nailing down the cheapest prices for Viagra and Russian brides, but also for finding out all you need to know about fairies.'

Grant pushed Lard out of the way and started tapping away at his computer. Feeling beads of sweat gathering on his forehead, he could only hope that he was right.

Lard sat down next to him. 'I feel an excess of calories coming on.'

Chapter Fifty-Nine

I decide to do something mad. Really mad. Leo-type mad. I want my man back and I'm going to shock him into noticing me again. He'll soon tire of that fluffy, fragile little woman he's with – she isn't robust enough to stand the rigours of Leo – but I'm not sure I can wait long enough for nature to take its course. I have to do something desperate.

I look at the huge cardboard box in my lounge. This certainly could be classed as desperate. One of the life-size wire-mesh figures was delivered in it to the gallery, so there's no doubt that it's fit for my purpose. As soon as my master-plan popped into my mind, I'd jumped out of bed, sprinted down to the gallery and struggled back with the box through the narrow cobbled streets of Shad Thames, just as the rest of London was emerging from sleep. I also left a note for Caron saying that I'd be late for work – although, with a bit of luck, I won't be turning up at all today. Explanations can come later.

Now to put phase two into action. Picking up the phone, I make a provisional booking with the specialist delivery company we regularly use at the gallery. They aren't too shocked by my request – perhaps they've seen it all before in the art world – and give me a price that won't break the bank. And they're used to handling fragile packages, which is a bonus. When that's done, I punch in Leo's work number. 'Can I speak to Grant Fielding, please?'

After a moment Grant comes on the line.

'It's Emma,' I say.

'Oh.' There's a slight pause. 'How are you?'

'Terrible,' I tell him. 'And you?'

'Fine. Fine.' His voice sounds strained.

'Look, Grant,' I say, 'can you do me a favour?'

'Anything.'

'Can you tell me if Leo is in work today?'

Another pause. 'Not yet.'

'Is he sick?'

'I don't think so.'

'Is he at home?'

'Er . . . yes.'

I sigh. 'This is like pulling teeth, Grant. I need to know if he's likely to be alone.' I can't imagine that he would have let that woman move in with him. Whatever else Leo is, he's resolutely a bachelor. We've been together for five years and yet he's managed to avoid any kind of formal commitment at all costs. His new woman is, hopefully, at work – whatever that might entail. 'Is he alone?'

'Er . . . yes,' Grant says.

I sag with relief. That will make life so much easier.

'Thanks, Grant. I owe you one,' I say, realising that I probably owe him several.

Hanging up, I eye my cardboard box again, taking a deep breath. This is a bold scheme. I'm going to get myself delivered to Leo. My plan is to spring out of the cardboard box and give him the surprise of his life. I smile at my own ingenuity. I'll make him realise what he's been missing! If I was going to be delivered to his office, I would have needed to remain suitably attired. As I'm going directly to his home I can opt for something considerably more risqué.

I pad through to my bedroom. More risqué involves the red silky thong that Leo bought me as a joke last Valentine's Day. It's emblazoned with the legend MISS FUNNY FANNY in white embroidery and giggles when you pressed a padded button in a strategic place. Perhaps Leo is right, I have lost my sense of fun. For some reason I didn't find it remotely amusing when he presented it to me. Perhaps it was because Jo had received a gold bracelet from her current squeeze and Caron had been bombarded with bouquets of red roses from several unidentified admirers.

Now I can see that it has its uses. Slipping off my clothes, I step into the red thong. It certainly isn't in keeping with my usual underwear style. You can tell the length of a relationship by the lingerie choices, I think. Comfy pants have generally replaced anything sexy or lacy – except on high days and holidays and birthdays, of course. Delving into the drawer once more, I find a big red ribbon that had been round the Easter egg that Leo bought me and I know now that I've been wise to save it for a special occasion. It's just long enough to wind round my ample breasts and tie in a bow at the front.

Risking a glance in the mirror, I gasp out loud. 'Oh my word.' I close my eyes in shock. I look like something that's wandered out of a Spearmint Rhino establishment. Leo will love it. And although it seems a very good theory, in practice I'm not quite sure that I'm up to this at all. I don't think

I'm a natural temptress. Hasn't one of the main reasons for loving Leo been that he hasn't expected very much from me in that department? Well, that's about to change. I'm going to show him that I can be fun. FUN. FUN. FUN.

Back in the lounge, I call the delivery company to confirm my booking. They agree to pick me up in twenty minutes. Literally.

I try out the cardboard box for size. Perfect fit. Even though I have to curl up in a ball at the bottom to squeeze in. It does, however, feel a bit flimsy. Wire-mesh sculptures, it seems, weigh considerably less than a thirty-year-old flesh and blood woman. What to do? There's no way I want the humiliation of falling out of the bottom of the box when they pick it up. I ease myself out of the box and go into the kitchen. The seams clearly needed reinforcement and I might have some parcel tape lurking in one of the kitchen drawers.

I pull the blind in case any of my neighbours are at home during the day and wonder what I'm doing in nothing more than sleazy underwear and a gift bow at my kitchen sink. Rummaging through the drawers, I fail in my quest to find parcel tape. I do, however, find a brand new tube of Superglue. That will do the job just as well. Doesn't it stick anything to anything?

I scuttle back to the lounge, superglue in hand. Time is running out – the delivery company will be here at any moment. One of the reasons why we keep using them is that they're ultra-punctual – something very rarely found these days, in humans or delivery companies. Snapping the top from the glue as instructed, I smear it along the bottom seam of the box, then along all the side seams, pressing the cardboard together. It oozes out of the seams, but I know better than to try to wipe it off. This stuff is lethal. Standing back, I admire my handiwork. That surely will hold my weight a bit better.

Quickly, I scribble on the top of my box: '*To Leo, with love*.' And, just as I've finished, my doorbell rings. The delivery company has arrived.

This is going to be the embarrassing bit. There's no way that I can avoid the delivery men seeing me like this. The box is too small for me to be able to put on some other clothes and then shrug out of them before I reveal myself – in more ways than one. I just hope it isn't Tom and Eric, the usual guys who collect items from the gallery – the young, fit ones – otherwise I'll never be able to face them again.

The doorbell rings again and I sidle towards it, covering as much of myself as possible with my arms. I hide behind the door as I open it. 'Hi.' A gulp travels down my throat. 'Tom. Eric.'

Their eyes are out on stalks.

'I need you both to close your eyes while I go and get in the box.'

They both nod, amazement having robbed them of speech.

I run to the cardboard box, not daring to look back to see if Tom and Eric have kept their side of the bargain, and jumping in, I settle myself down in the bottom, curled up in a neat ball. 'Okay,' I shout at the delivery guys.

A moment later, Tom and Eric peer over the top of the box. Their eyes shoot out further and I hear Tom clear his throat. 'Are you sure this is what you want?'

'Yes,' I insist. There'll be no bottling out now. 'It's a surprise for my boyfriend.'

'Well, I hope he's worth it,' Eric comments.

'I think so,' I say.

'Shall we carry you downstairs like this?' Tom asks. 'Then tape the top shut when we arrive at our destination?'

'No,' I say. 'It's not far. Ten minutes max, if the traffic behaves. Better to tape the lid up now. If Leo's looking out of the window, he might see you and wonder what's going on. I want you to drop me off, ring the bell and then zoom off quickly. I must be on his doorstep in my box before he knows what's happened. Surprise is the important element.'

Tom and Eric both look unconvinced. Eric sounds nervous. 'You won't sue us for this?'

'Of course not,' I snap. 'What could possibly go wrong?'

Another look passes between the guys. 'Can't say we've ever done this before.'

'It will be a breeze,' I reassure them.

Hesitantly, Tom pulls a roll of parcel tape from his back pocket. They both wave at me and I'm sure I can see a tear in Eric's eye. 'Bye,' they both say. 'Good luck.'

Tom closes the lid and suddenly everything goes very black. I've never experienced claustrophobia and it's something I'm now rather glad of. I hear the rasping noise as Tom tapes the top shut. Then it all goes quiet.

I can hear my own heart beat. Thank goodness I won't be in here for very long. Already I'm struggling to move. My knees are wedged under my chin and my feet are braced against the side of the box. The top presses down on my head.

Then there's a violent jolt as I feel Tom and Eric hoist me up.

'Careful,' Eric says, puffing heavily.

They stagger towards the door with me. This is a good idea, I tell myself. Really it is.

'Do you think we should have cut some air-holes in it?' I hear Tom lower his voice to a whisper. 'How long do you think she's got before she runs out of oxygen?'

It's only then that I start to worry.

Chapter Sixty

Leo was cradling Isobel and mopping her brow with a cold flannel. He didn't know whether she was too hot or too cold – it seemed to change by the minute. But he did know that, whatever was wrong with her, it was much more serious than a touch of the company hangover. What was that old wives' tale? Feed a cold and starve a fever? Where could you find an old wife when you needed one? Perhaps he should be making Isobel something to eat, even though she didn't look strong enough. Chicken soup – wasn't that what was called for?

Bits of Isobel were almost transparent and Leo didn't think that was a good thing. She looked so weak he could weep. Then the doorbell rang, which made him jump out of his skin, and he wondered who the hell it was.

As Leo kissed Isobel, promising her that he'd be back in

a minute, it rang again – someone out there was rather impatient – and so he plodded out of the bedroom to see what all the fuss was about.

When he opened the door, Grant and Lard were standing there. Lard was carrying a large holdall. Leo hoped he wasn't planning to move in with him. Grant and Leo eyed each other sheepishly.

'Stonehenge,' Grant said crisply.

'The same to you,' he replied.

'We've got to get there,' he told Leo. 'Fast.'

'And how exactly have you arrived at this conclusion?'

Grant held up a sheaf of papers. 'Internet. We Googled fairy legends.'

'Stonehenge is the gateway to the fairy underworld,' Lard explained as if it was an everyday thing; as if he was telling Leo which bus to catch to Marble Arch. 'The Land of Light.'

'And that's where Isobel is from?'

'It looks like it,' Grant confirmed.

Leo shrugged because he didn't know what else to do. 'Stonehenge it is.'

They shuffled into the flat and Leo caught Grant's eye. 'You're a mate,' he said. Relief flooded Grant's features and Leo clasped his friend to him. 'You're a real mate.'

Grant nodded his acknowledgement. 'We'd better get moving.'

'I'll go and get Isobel.' Leo's eyes filled with unshed tears. 'I'll tell her that the cavalry is here.'

'I hope we're right about this,' Lard leaned in towards Grant and whispered confidentially. He chewed his lip anxiously.

'So do I,' Grant admitted, with a tense exhalation of breath.

'We're doing our best for Leo. We can't do any more than that. I just hope it's enough.'

'If Isobel has to go back to her home, does that mean that Emma will get back with Leo?'

'I haven't a clue,' Grant said. 'And I don't even want to think about that now. Or any other implications of the stuff we're planning to do.'

Lard flashed a commiserating look at him.

'This is all getting far too complicated for me. We used to have such a quiet life. You, me, Leo, lots of chocolate, some curry, the odd beer. When did it all start to go pear-shaped?'

'Why did you tell Emma that Leo was going to be here alone?'

'I don't know.' Grant rubbed his hand over his face. He felt like he'd been up all night. Which partly he had – chatting, very amiably, with Emma's friend Caron. She was a lovely girl and he hoped that he'd see her again. Very soon. He did, however, wish that all of his cylinders were firing. It wasn't a good day to be feeling below par. 'I wasn't really thinking straight. I just didn't want to give too much away about Leo's circumstances. How could I tell her that Isobel was ill? I don't know what she might have done. As it was, I had a horrible feeling that she might be here when we arrived. It looks as if I was stressing unnecessarily.' Which seemed to be happening a lot at the moment.

Leo appeared carrying Isobel in his arms. She was wrapped in a blanket and looked pale and clammy and, frankly, not long for this world. 'We're ready,' he said.

'So are we,' Grant and Lard confirmed.

* * *

Leo carried Isobel out of the flat and down to his car, Ethel. Grant and Lard jumped in the back and he laid Isobel down on the front seat. Then he sprinted round to the driver's seat and slid in.

'Jeepers, Leo.' Grant held his nose. 'What the hell have you been eating in here? It smells like a Greek brothel.'

There was the vague odour of stale lamb. 'Kebab,' Leo said, rescuing the crumpled package from underneath his bottom. Though he had no idea when. He couldn't remember leaving it in there, but he was sure that he must have.

'You are such a waste of space,' Grant tutted. And Leo knew that they were back to normal. They were brothers once more.

He wasn't usually a litter lout, but needs must – and he tossed the greasy paper out on to the street, promising to clear it up later if it was still languishing on the pavement when he returned. Leo suddenly gave an involuntary shudder as he wondered when that might be.

'Ready?' he asked everyone. The boys, squashed together in the back, nodded their assent. Lard was chain-eating chocolate already. Isobel moaned softly. Leo squeezed her hand. 'Not long, darling. Hang on.'

Buckling up, he started the car and, with an anxious glance at Isobel, he set off down the street. Leo attempted the style of top racing driver, Ralf Schumacher and instead got demented kangaroo. 'Come on, Ethel,' he urged, patting the steering wheel. 'Do your worst!'

Chapter Sixty-One

Cobblestones feel very bumpy when you're banged up in a cardboard box. My bottom is numb already and I've lost all feeling from my legs before we've hit the end of my street. I'm beginning to regret my rashness.

Tom and Eric career round a corner and my cardboard box slithers to one end of the van. It's like being on the worst possible theme-park ride that you can imagine.

Then suddenly the van comes to an abrupt halt. It's either yet another set of traffic lights or we've arrived at Leo's flat. I sincerely hope that it's the latter. It couldn't come a moment too soon. My courage is leaving me with the speed of rats diving off a sinking ship. I hear Tom and Eric fling open the van doors and my sigh of relief is rapidly replaced by a surge of panic. Leo will find this funny – surely he will. This is the sort of thing he does all the time. It isn't, however, the sort of thing *I* do. Ever.

'You all right in there?' Tom's voice whispers close to my ear, slightly muffled by the cardboard.

'I'm fine,' I mumble back. Which is just as well, because no sooner do I speak than I'm hoisted into the air again. I can feel Tom and Eric struggling up the half a dozen steps to the main door of Leo's flat.

'This will do,' Tom pants. And I'm unceremoniously dumped on the ground.

'Oouff,' I say, and then am gripped by a fit of the giggles as I wonder what it must sound like from outside my box.

'We'll be going now,' Tom says, down by my ear.

'Right.' I hear the doorbell ring, much scuttling of feet, the slam of a Transit van door and then the screech of wheels as it roars away.

Then there's a silence, the like of which I never thought possible to encounter in London. I sit there waiting – excitement and terror mounting in equal measures. What if Leo takes this the wrong way? Then again, how many ways are there to take a woman – an ex-girlfriend – jumping out of a cardboard box on your doorstep dressed only in her underwear and a gift bow?

He should be coming down the stairs by now. I count the steps. Then count them again. Perhaps I've caught him while he's in the loo. I allow for a little time lapse – flush toilet, wash hands, dry hands. Then I count the steps again. Still no Leo. I check my watch, which thankfully, I thought to keep on. Five minutes have passed already. Perhaps he's nipped out to the newsagents at the end of the street to buy a newspaper or some chocolate or something. Or there's probably a beer shortage – that's the usual thing that lures Leo into the great outdoors. Whatever it is, I just wish he'd hurry up. Thankfully the weather is reasonably warm so I'm not likely to freeze to death, sitting here in my skimpies – cardboard is surprisingly cosy – but I'm getting mightily uncomfortable.

After twenty minutes the first shadow of doubt crosses my mind. Clearly Leo has gone out and, quite possibly, he's staying out. Leo doesn't indulge in any unnecessary movement, so he won't have gone jogging and he doesn't have a dog, so a brisk walk is pretty much out of the question. If he'd simply gone to the local shop, then he would have hurried back as quickly as possible to make acquaintance with his sofa once more. Perhaps Grant was wrong. What if Leo isn't at home at all?

I wish that I'd thought to put my mobile phone in the box with me. What was I thinking of? No self-respecting contemporary woman can operate without her phone. I could have at least called Grant again or Lard, or tried to track down Leo – although that was a mission impossible even Tom Cruise might shrink away from. Leo never usually manages to hold onto a phone for more than a few days at a time and, on the rare occasion that he does, he invariably forgets to turn it on. There's nothing else for me to do other than sit it out.

After an hour and still no sign of Leo – or anyone else for that matter – I'm now starting to panic. It's Tom's anxious words about oxygen consumption that have started to play on my mind. And, to be honest, there's nothing else to do whilst passing time in a cardboard box, other than to panic. And worry. And chew your own fingernails down to the quick. I can barely move now and I wonder if my muscles have started to waste away already. No wonder Hollywood features it so often in films – put people in a sweatbox for any length of time and they come out like gibbering idiots, too helpless to walk and weak with hunger. My stomach rumbles. It's been a long time since lunch. Is it just my imagination that I'm starting to feel faint? Perhaps my oxygen really is starting to run out. I wish that I hadn't sealed the seams with Superglue quite so lavishly now. If I hadn't, there might be more air gaps. Anxiety is prickling over my skin. This is ridiculous. I can't sit here all night on Leo's doorstep. Wherever Grant had got his information from, it was wrong and I'll have words with him at some future juncture. Assuming that I live to tell the tale.

That's it. I can't contain my fear any longer. I have to get out of here. I don't want to die in a box on Leo's doorstep in my undies – I still have so much living to do!

Outside the box there's the sound of a cat meowing at the front door. Surely someone will come down and let it in. The nice couple in the flat next to Leo have a cat – a white fluffy thing with a bad attitude – I hope it's theirs. I can hear it rubbing against the side of the box. 'Here, kitty, kitty,' I murmur sweetly. I've never been a cat-lover, but talking to anything is preferable to letting my mind race wildly over my predicament.

Dutifully, the cat meows back.

'Here, kitty, kitty.'

I can hear the cat scratching at my box now. Where's the wretched owner? Don't they know that their cat is out here begging to be let in? I should report them to the RSPCA. The cat meows again, rather pitifully. It's a very endearing sound. But the next sound isn't. It's the sound of the cat weeing on my box. The acrid stench of cat urine fills my airspace. 'Bloody hell!' I shout at it. 'Clear off, you mangy animal!'

The cat meows again. That's it. Now I'm being used as a toilet for the wildlife of the area. I've had enough. Scratching frantically at my box, I bang on the lid. There's no way I can even get a fingernail under a corner to lift it, let alone rip my way out. I'm so squashed in that there's no room to try to kick my way out. This cardboard is tougher than it looks. I should have thought to bring a knife or some scissors or some way of getting out of here. In fact, I should have thought the whole mad idea through a lot more carefully. There's only one thing for it.

'Help!' I shout feebly. 'Somebody help me!'

Chapter Sixty-Two

'I can't believe you drive like this even when you're not drunk,' Grant complained loudly from the back seat.

'Sorry,' Leo offered.

'There are creatures in the Australian outback that kangaroo less than this.'

Leo had his own particular lurching style of motoring. He blamed it on the fact that it was a very long time ago since he'd learned to drive and he didn't do it very often and he wasn't very good at it when he did. However, this was an emergency.

Leo hated driving in London and the route had, so far, been torturous – out towards the motorway and their ultimate destination. They were heading away from the smoke of the city to the gateway to the Land of Light which, according to the internet, was slap-bang in the middle of the ancient circle of stones that formed Stonehenge. Leo hoped that their source was reliable. Quite frankly, he didn't trust the internet at all. He'd bought three CDs on eBay once; two of them never appeared even though his credit card was debited and the final one, which did turn up, was supposed to be *The Best of Motörhead* but instead he received a copy of *The Nolan Sisters' Greatest Hits*. To be fair, it was in very good condition. Hardly played. It was slightly unsettling though, that they were relying on this rather erratic tool to help repatriate Isobel to her own home, time, land, whatever.

'Jeez, Leo,' Grant moaned again. 'I can't sit here while you take for ever to jump us all the way there. Pull over. Go on.'

Leo pulled Ethel into the nearest lay-by. Well, hopped, skipped and jumped into it really.

'Get out and let me drive,' Grant snapped.

'You're not insured to drive my car,' Leo objected.

'Does it matter at this point?' his friend wanted to know.

'No,' Leo said, too tired and anxious to argue.

'Not unless we're stopped by the police,' Lard pointed out from the back seat.

They both glared at him. Cars whizzed by.

'When was the last time you saw a policeman?' Grant asked.

Lard quietly conceded that police patrols were somewhat scarce on the ground in this, the age of the speed camera.

'Leo, you can get in the back with Isobel,' Grant said. 'Lard, come in the front and navigate.'

Leo bounded out of the car and went round to the passenger side, lifting the listless frame of Isobel into his arms. Grant squeezed out of the back and slipped into the driver's seat. Lard also climbed out, relinquishing the back seat. He helped Leo to settle Isobel across his lap, so that he could cradle her. If Grant employed his usual driving style they'd be going at warp speed to Stonehenge.

'Quick, Lard,' Grant said impatiently. 'Don't dolly about. Get in.'

Lard made the most sprightly move Leo had ever seen and positively sprang into the passenger seat.

'Are we quite ready?' the driver asked.

'Yes,' Leo said.

Isobel stirred. 'We're running out of time,' she whispered.

Leo stroked her face. 'Not long now,' he murmured. 'Not long now.'

Grant swung out into the traffic once more. Leo was happier now that he'd relinquished control to someone that he trusted with his life – with Isobel's life. He sagged back into the seat. 'Step on it, Grant,' he instructed. 'And don't spare the horses.'

Grant was driving as if he had a starring role in *The Italian Job*. He was hunched over the steering wheel, concentration etched between his eyebrows. The party had inched their way through the rush hour, but now the flow of traffic had picked up again and they were making good progress. Leo was sure that if Isobel had been stronger she could have magicked them all to Stonehenge in a trice – but then if she'd been stronger, they wouldn't have been going there at all.

Leo's heart was heavy and his head ached from his fitful night. Conversation in the car had died and they all sat in an uncomfortable silence. How different from their usual boys' road-trips, where the banter flowed as easily as the beer. They were weaving in and out of the traffic on the motorway, eating up the miles as they headed nearer towards Stonehenge. Grant normally drove a TVR Tuscan and Leo thought that he'd probably forgotten that most people had cars that don't go that fast. He hadn't thought that Ethel was capable of going over forty, but now under Grant's tutelage she was doing a ton and smoking. And Leo didn't mean 'smoking' in a trendy, street way – he meant that there was smoke coming out from under her engine and it was pouring out of the exhaust pipe in a great black plume. He now wished that he'd had her serviced more often – or at all.

Isobel was asleep in his arms. Sleep had slackened the lines of pain on her face and she seemed comfortable at least. Dusk was gathering, the cobwebs of clouds thickening in the sky. The sun was falling out of view and Leo hoped that there wasn't some sort of unseen, unknown deadline on this escapade and that their best really would be good enough.

Then, in the rear window, he caught a glimpse of a flashing blue light at the same time as the siren on the police car started.

'Oh bugger,' Grant, Lard and Leo said together.

The police car came alongside of them, so that they were in no doubt that they'd been clocked. Leo thought that 'it's a fair cop' would be an appropriate phrase at the moment.

Without further ado, Grant pulled over onto the hard shoulder. It would be futile trying to outrun a souped-up police Volvo in a decrepit Beetle, but it crossed Leo's mind to urge Grant to do so.

They sat anxiously awaiting their fate. Grant rubbed at his eyes, which must have been tired. The policemen got out of their patrol car, put on their peaked caps and ambled up to the side of Ethel – who they viewed with more disdain than was necessary in Leo's opinion.

Grant wound down the window. One policeman leaned on the roof. He was considerably younger than Leo. He gave them all a supercilious smile. 'In a rush, sir?'

'Yes,' Grant said, and took a deep breath. 'We have a sick fairy in the back of the car and we're trying to get her to Stonehenge.'

'A sick fairy?'

'Yes,' Grant confirmed. 'I believe in this situation that honesty might be the best policy.'

The policeman didn't look as if he agreed. He peered into the car and ran his frosty gaze over Leo and Isobel.

'Isobel,' Leo urged her. 'Get your wand out. Zap him. Zap him now.'

She managed to rouse herself, but said weakly, 'I can't, Leo.' She shook her head sadly. 'I can't.'

Then, he felt, they were doomed.

The policeman sighed. The word 'clowns' was written all over his face. He turned to Grant. 'Would you mind stepping out of the car, sir?'

Chapter Sixty-Three

'Hello?' the man says. 'Hello? Is there anybody in there?'

I sag with relief at the sound of a human voice outside my box.

'Yes there is. Help,' I say urgently. 'Help me. Please.'

'Are you okay?'

'I'm fine,' I say. Panic-stricken, stiff, hungry and getting cold, but other than that, fine. 'Can you just get me out, please?'

There's some tugging and pulling at my box and I brace myself against the sides. Then all goes still again.

'I need to go back up to the flat and get some scissors,' the man tells me with a disgruntled puff. 'I'll be back in a minute. I'm Dominic, by the way.'

'Hi, Dominic,' I say. 'I'm Emma. We've met on the stairs a couple of times before. I'm Leo's girlfriend. I *was* Leo's girlfriend.'

'Oh,' Dominic responds as if that explains everything. 'Won't be long.'

I know exactly who Dominic is. He's the dreamboat who lives next door to Leo with his equally gorgeous girlfriend, Lydia. Leo and I always used to row about Dominic and Lydia. Dominic cuddles his other half to death even when they're just going down the stairs. Leo isn't even that keen on holding hands in public. Dominic and Lydia were always very friendly when they passed in the hallway and, as couples, we always said that we'd get together and have a drink or dinner some time, but never did. Now I wish we had. It isn't a good idea to be formally introduced in this way. Maybe if we'd made time to have a quick pizza with Dominic and his girlfriend, I wouldn't be so mortified now. Why can't the person who witnesses my shame be one of the other folks from the apartments – the forty-two-year-old divorcée or one of the gay blokes or, preferably, a visiting relative who is less attractive than Dominic and also blind. I sigh and try to cheer myself up. Not long now and it will all be over.

I hear Dominic go back up the steps to the flats. 'Come on, Chloe,' he says pleasantly to the cat. 'Get down from the top of the box. There's a good girl.'

Wait till I get my hands on bloody Chloe – although to be fair the cat did come to my rescue in a roundabout way. I lean back in my box, looking forward to escaping my self-inflicted prison, but not relishing the next part. Exposing my folly to the world. That will teach me to try to be spontaneous and fun.

'I'm back,' Dominic says a few minutes later. 'Had to search for the scissors. Hold still. Have you out in a jiffy.'

Leo's neighbour gets to work with the scissors. I duck out of the way as the sharp points slice through the box. 'I knocked at Leo's door to let him know that you were here,' Dominic says. 'But he's out.'

I'd managed to work out that much.

'Good job that I came home early from the office,' he says cheerfully as he works away.

He's nearly got the lid off. I cover myself as best I can. This is going to take some explaining away. After a few more snips, Dominic flips open the top.

'Aargh!' I shout.

Oh no. My hair is stuck to the Superglue on the lid. 'My hair. My hair.'

Dominic quickly lowers the lid again and peers under it, before recoiling. 'Oh!'

So he's noticed the underwear then.

'I'm sorry about my appearance,' I say quickly. 'This is a prank that's gone very wrong.'

'I think you're right there,' he agrees and then peers in again.

I shrink away from him. This is supposed to be for Leo's eyes only. Perhaps Dominic will lend me some clothes to go home in. All I want to do is get away from here with some shred of dignity intact, climb into a steaming hot bath and consume some very strong drink.

'You've stuck your hair to the lid,' he says, tsking loudly. 'I think I'm going to have to snip some off.'

'Cut my hair?'

'There's quite a lot of it plastered to the box.'

I want to cry. This has been a hare-brained scheme from start to finish. Exactly the sort of thing that Leo would do. And I'm beginning to have some empathy with his more idiotic pranks. I was so well-intentioned and this has gone so horribly wrong. There's no way though, that I deserve this humiliation. 'Cut it,' I instruct. 'Just be careful.'

Dominic gingerly slips his scissors inside and slices at great hunks of my hair. It feels like a re-run of *Edward Scissorhands*.

Erratic snip, snip, snipping echoes in my ears. I just hope that Leo doesn't turn up now in the middle of all this. The only thing I want to do now is hide myself and run for the hills.

My rescuer flips the lid again and I gulp in the fresh air, glad that the overpowering smell of cat wee is out of my nostrils.

'There you are.' Dominic smiles at his handiwork.

'Thank you,' I say gratefully. 'Thank you.' I go to stand up but can't move.

'Easy there,' Dominic advises. 'I expect you're a bit numb. Been here long?'

'Yes,' I admit. 'Hours.' Hours and hours and hours and hours. For most of my adult life. At least, it feels like that.

'Do you mind me asking,' he says. I know the question before he asks it. 'Why exactly are you in a box on our doorstep?'

'It was a prank,' I explain. 'A silly joke. Leo and I have split up. I thought this would be a fun way to get his attention again.'

Dominic looks as if he doubts my sanity.

'I realise now,' I say, before he decides I'm a complete headcase, 'that I have made a terrible mistake.'

'Here.' Dominic offers me his hand. 'Let me help you out. I'll avert my eyes,' he continues, doing anything but. He has a good ogle at my MISS FUNNY FANNY thong.

Reluctantly, I let go of the gift bow covering my breasts and reach out my hand. The skin on the back of my arm rips painfully. 'Arghh!' I cry out and withdraw my hand. What the hell is that?

I try to move it again. But it's stuck fast. 'Oh no,' I say, panic returning. 'Please no.'

I try to move my legs, but the bottom of my feet are firmly attached to the seam of the box where I so fervently applied a liberal coating of Superglue. I try moving my bottom, but I can't budge an inch. I thought it was merely the confines of my cardboard box that were restricting my movements. Once again, I'm wrong. The glue must still have been wet when I settled myself in. How could I be so stupid? 'I can't move,' I say tearfully. 'I can't move at all.'

'Oh dear,' Dominic comments, frowning worriedly.

'I Superglued the seams of the box before I got in it,' I admit. 'I think it was a bad idea.' One in a long line of bad ideas.

'It does look like you're rather stuck.'

I feel that's something of an understatement. 'What am I going to do? How am I going to get out, Dominic?' I turn my eyes to plead with him.

'Er . . .' He nibbles his lip. 'It's dastardly stuff, this Superglue,' he informs me.

'I know. I know.'

'This isn't going to come off with a bit of Fairy Liquid and a nailbrush. If I try to prise this off, it could seriously damage your skin.'

'*Seriously* damage?'

'I reckon it needs specialist treatment.'

A cold shiver runs over me. 'What sort of specialist treatment?'

'I think there's only one thing for it,' he says, shaking his head. 'I need to call the Fire Brigade.'

Chapter Sixty-Four

Ten minutes later, two bright red fire engines arrive, sirens blaring, and block Leo's street. As no cars are able to pass, the drivers waiting in the resulting traffic jam simply get an eyeful. To add even more discomfort to my predicament, a small and very curious crowd of neighbours start to gather. Even the guys from the greasy kebab takeaway wander up the road to take a peek.

By this time too, Dominic has managed to cut away some of the box. It means that I'm not feeling quite so encased or claustrophobic, but it also means that the entire street has a great view of my underwear. So I'm now sitting on Leo's doorstep, in gift wrapping and my smalls, framed by a cardboard cut-out sculpture. The rubber-neckers all crane to get a better view. The only person who isn't anywhere in sight is, of course, Leo.

Half a dozen fire-fighters – all male, all built like brick outhouses and all smirking – make their way up the steps to the flat. They come armed with a selection of axes and cutting tools and other things that look like instruments of torture which I really hope they won't need. I wonder if any of them are friends of Caron's brother. I sincerely hope not. All those hunky men to hand and look at the state of me. Why can't I have something dignified wrong with me that needs a sensible, life-threatening rescue, instead of having

Superglued myself into a box? I huddle into myself and pretend that I'm somewhere else, while Dominic kindly explains what has happened.

A couple of the burliest fire-fighters grab hold of the box and start trying to prise me from it.

'Aargh!' I cry out again. I shrink away from them and somehow the button on my MISS FUNNY FANNY thong gets pressed and my underwear starts to giggle maniacally.

The fire-fighters join in. So does Dominic. I want to die. I wish I'd just given up and suffocated in my box.

When the thong has ceased giggling, the laughter finally dies down and the fire-fighters stop rolling about on the ground. The men try to compose their faces into suitably serious expressions and turn their attention back to me.

'I think we need to call for an ambulance, miss,' one of the fire-fighters informs me.

'I don't think that will be necessary,' I say.

'That Superglue is terrible stuff.' He rubs his chin in a considered fashion. I think he might be trying to wipe the smile off his face. 'They'll be able to get it off in Accident and Emergency without you having to part with your skin.'

'Please, please,' I beg. 'Don't take me to hospital. Just get one of your axes and cut my arms and legs off instead. I'll be fine.'

'What you need is a little bit of solvent and it will be all over.'

'I don't . . .' I start to protest. My eyes fill with tears. 'I don't think I could bear it.'

'Trust me,' the fire-fighter says, holding up a hand to quiet me. 'It'll be for the best. A lot less painful. Your boyfriend can ride in the ambulance with you,' he goes on, nodding towards Dominic.

'That's not my boyfriend,' I say, and then give up. They're much more interested in my taste in underwear to bother themselves with my taste in men.

The fire-fighter wanders off, presumably to call for an ambulance – which is a shame because a ride in a fire engine might have offered some sort of compensation for my suffering.

'Do you want me to go and make you a cup of tea?' Dominic asks.

'I'm fine, thanks.' I'm desperate for a cup of tea, but I'm even more desperate to go to the loo and I'm not sure how I'm going to manage that with my knickers glued to my backside.

My rescuer sits down on the step next to me and I notice that he angles himself between me and the crowd, so that not all of the neighbours can get an eyeful of my lingerie. Which is very thoughtful. He's been really nice to me even though he hasn't been able to fully liberate me. 'I'm quite happy to come with you in the ambulance,' Dominic says.

'Won't Lydia be worried about where you are?'

Dominic shakes his head. 'She left me,' he explains with a shrug. 'A few weeks ago. Went off with someone from work.'

Suddenly, I notice that he looks tired and pale. 'I'm sorry to hear that,' I say. 'It happens.'

'I didn't think of posting myself to her in a box,' Dominic confesses. 'I've just been at home trying to drown my sorrows with passable red wine. This shows great ingenuity.'

'It shows great stupidity.'

Dominic laughs. 'This is more the sort of thing that I can imagine Leo doing,' he says. 'You always seemed more – well . . . reserved.'

'I wanted to break out of my box.' We both smile ruefully at my choice of metaphor. 'I thought Leo would like this. Instead, I'm sitting here covered in Superglue while he is off somewhere – who knows where – probably having a great time.'

'Leo's a lot of fun,' Dominic says. 'I wish I could be more like him. While the rest of us are burdened by responsibility, Leo has always managed to remain childlike.'

'Childish,' I correct.

At that moment, the crowd parts and the ambulance arrives. I let out a weary exhalation. 'Let the next part of the fun commence,' I state.

'I will come with you. If you want me to.'

'I'd like that,' I say. 'You're very kind.'

'I was going to watch the football this evening,' Dominic admits. 'This is much more interesting.'

Oh, I'm so happy that I've been able to provide him with an entertaining distraction.

Two paramedics get out of the ambulance and go over to talk to the fire-fighters who, with a cheery wave to me, then jump back into their fire engines and drive away. I can imagine that I'll be the talk of the station room for some time to come

'I'll go and get you some clothes for later,' Dominic says. He nips up the stairs and disappears into the flats.

The paramedics come over to me and, after taking in my underwear, also fall about in a fit of giggles. Just wait until they move me and set off my chuckling knickers again, I think miserably.

Dominic returns with a small holdall.

'We'll lift you and what remains of the box into the ambulance,' one of the paramedics says.

Dominic smiles at me and, putting his hand on my shoulder, says, 'Nearly over.'

He really is very sweet. I let my head fall back against the remains of the box. Just then, a truck with *LONDON LIVE* emblazoned on the side pulls up and a television crew leap out. Nearly over, it seems, but not quite. It looks as if I'm going to be on the evening news in my underwear. Oh good.

The reporter sprints over to me. Hot on her heels is a burly cameraman and a sound engineer with one of those big, furry boom things. 'How are you feeling?' She pushes her microphone into my face. 'Why are you doing this? Is it a protest against something? Who glued you into the box?'

'No comment,' I say. If I could get one of my arms free, I might punch her.

Dominic does his best to shield me from their attention.

'Just relax,' one of the paramedics advises me. And then they both hoist me into the air with a chorus of inelegant grunts and edge their way through the crowd, with the reporter in tow. Whereupon my underwear sees fit to burst into life once more and giggles hysterically all the way to the ambulance.

Chapter Sixty-Five

Grant was standing on the hard shoulder. The youngest and stroppiest policeman was making him blow into a breathalyser bag. Thankfully, Grant hadn't touched a drop of booze today – yet. But no doubt they would make up for that omission later on tonight.

Lard and Leo were looking sheepish in the car. They had no idea what to do and time was marching on. Isobel's eyes flickered open.

'We are in big trouble,' Leo told her, whispering urgently. 'The police have stopped us. Isn't there anything you can do?'

Her eyes were dilated black circles. She looked as if she'd been doing some heavy drugs.

'Where's your wand?' he asked. 'What about if I wave and you tell me what to say?'

She opened her mouth, but she hadn't the energy to speak. This was not a good place to be.

'Isobel, please try,' Leo urged. 'Please try. Otherwise we're stuffed.'

The policeman came back towards Ethel, and Grant followed him. The young man leaned into the car and took in the sight of Isobel draped across Leo's lap. 'Is she all right?' he asked.

'No,' Leo said. 'She's very ill. We're trying to save her.'

'Miss?' the policeman said. 'Miss?'

Isobel's eyes struggled open once more. 'Help me,' she mouthed and as she did, she opened her hand – a tiny unfurling of her fingers – and a silver butterfly fluttered out towards the policeman. It landed on his hand and stayed there opening and closing its wings. 'Help me,' she whispered again.

Leo looked over to Lard and saw that he had tears in his eyes too.

The policeman gazed in awe at the butterfly which fluttered slowly away, disappearing into thin air within an arm's length. Then the officer stood up and adjusted his hat. 'Right,' he said, twitching his neck. 'We'll give you a high-speed escort.'

'Thank you,' Leo breathed, hardly daring to speak in case he did something to break the spell. With Isobel so weak, he didn't know how tenuous this might be.

'Where did you say you were going?'

'Stonehenge,' Grant answered.

'Then you'd better get a move on, sir,' the policeman said. 'We'll take you as far as we can. That'll speed things up a bit.'

Lard and Leo nearly passed out with shock. Grant looked as if he couldn't believe his ears, but jumped back into the car and gunned it into life once more. The policeman returned to his car and, with lights flashing and sirens wailing, pulled back into the stream of traffic.

'You did it, Isobel.' Leo hugged her to him. But she had slipped away from them again.

'What happened there?' Grant said as he tried to keep up with the racing police car.

'I don't know,' Leo admitted.

'I had to say this heap was mine, Leo.' His friend was clearly affronted that he had to pretend to have such bad taste. 'And I still got a tug for speeding.'

'I'll pay the fine,' Leo said.

Grant shook his head. 'That doesn't matter,' he said. 'All that matters is that we get Isobel there in time.'

They were all quiet in the car as they continued their journey, zooming along the motorway after the police car. Ethel ate up the miles, complaining little at the breakneck speed. As they came off the motorway the police officers waved them a cheery goodbye and peeled away. They continued their journey alone, following the signs for Stonehenge. Leo was holding his breath as they rushed past fields, fields and more fields, endless swathes of golden hay gleaming in the last vestiges of late-evening sun. Grant sped along the narrow, unlit dual carriageway lined with mile after mile of dark, claustrophobic trees until, eventually, they burst out onto a stark, open plain. Ahead of them, standing proud on the horizon, were the towering black silhouettes of the monoliths of Stonehenge.

Relief flooded through Leo. He leaned over and kissed Isobel. 'We're nearly there, baby. Hang on.'

The night was now drawing in, darkening slowly, and the clouds had huddled together. The sun was on its downward path towards the horizon and the space between the earth and sky was spattered with splotches of pink and apricot and fire red. Leo hoped this was a good omen. Coming closer into view was the huge circle of stones – great monoliths outlined against the vastness of the sky.

Leo wasn't a man prone to this sort of thing, but he could feel the strong pull of ancient powers. Isobel shifted in his arms and he clung to her. Inside, Leo had a horrible empty sensation and he wondered how much longer their time together would last.

Even though they'd made it this far, Grant and Lard were looking decidedly worried. And Leo got the feeling that as one part of the journey was ending, another more terrifying part was about to begin.

Chapter Sixty-Six

It took two very patient nurses, two very long hours to peel away all the Superglue from my tender skin with some sort of foul-smelling solvent. My skin feels bruised and raw, but there'll be no permanent scarring – just a painful memory that I'd really rather forget.

Prior to this, there'd been another two-hour wait in a cubicle in the Accident and Emergency department – where they'd left me, still in the remains of my cardboard box, perched on top of a trolley, screened from too many prying eyes by nothing more than a pair of flimsy, ragged curtains.

Dominic has been fantastic. The nurses gave him some scissors while we waited and he quietly and methodically cut away at some more of my firmly adhered box, until I could actually straighten my legs. He endured, stoically – as I did – the parade of junior doctors who had clearly felt moved to come along to offer their vital medical opinion and not simply to have a gawp at me in my sleazy underwear. Eventually, one of the nurses brought me a surgical gown which Dominic tied round me to cover as much as he could. While we waited for the de-gluing to commence, we'd talked about Leo and Lydia and agreed what idiots they both were. It helped me to avoid thinking about what an idiot I am.

This is not how I envisaged the day would end. By now I should have been in Leo's arms, quite possibly in Leo's bed – he would have found it hard to resist me, I'm sure, in red giggling knickers. Instead, Leo's poor neighbour has been roped in to perform the role of knight in shining armour. I look over at Dominic, and my new friend smiles crookedly at me. I have to admit that he's done a very good job.

Now we're in a cab on the way back to my flat. Dominic had brought me some clothes in his holdall – clearly ones that the recently departed Lydia had left behind. They're a bit tight – maybe Lydia doesn't have my attachment to all things calorific – but they're certainly a lot more suitable than my previous ensemble.

I lean back on the seat of the taxi. I'm absolutely knackered. Being stuck in a cardboard box for the best part of the day has been an emotionally draining experience. Particularly when I've got nothing but a collection of red and very sore patches of skin to show for it. I glance over at my companion. Dominic looks completely done in too. For once it's quite nice to be the stupid one, while someone else takes control. I can now appreciate Leo's addiction to it. What on earth is making me act like this? What on earth is making me act exactly like Leo? My mind drifts to my ex-boyfriend and I wonder where he is now. Has he returned home to his flat completely oblivious to the fuss that has been created outside it all afternoon?

The cab pulls up outside my place. Dominic pays the driver and we get out.

The bars and restaurants on Shad Thames are still bustling. I want to crawl into my bed and sleep for ever. I limp towards the flat, all of my bones aching. It would have served me right if I'd never walked again or had spent the rest of my life in that hideous red thong. My bottom will bear the marks of it for weeks.

'I want to make sure that you're okay,' Dominic says into my moping. 'I hope you don't mind.'

'I'm fine now, really,' I insist stoically, when inside I don't feel fine at all. 'But I should give you Lydia's clothes back. Just in case she turns up for them.'

'I think that's unlikely,' Dominic admits.

'It might be better if I give you them back straight away. It would be easier than trying to explain to her why I borrowed them.'

Dominic laughs. He's a great-looking guy. Relaxed, tousled. Laid back, but with a good deal more commonsense than some I could mention. Someone like Dominic might well be able to turn my head. A lightness comes over my spirit – something that I haven't experienced in weeks. Perhaps my 'in-the-box' experience might have a worthwhile outcome after all. The thought makes me smile, even though my jaw aches with tension.

I open the door to my flat and let us both in. The red light on my answerphone is blinking away at me. Hopefully, it will be Leo having found out that I've suffered a cruel indignity on his doorstep and begging my forgiveness. If it is, I don't want to listen to the message while Dominic is here.

'Shall I put some coffee on while I go and get changed?' I ask. He must be starving too, as neither of us has eaten during our ordeal.

'I should be going,' Dominic says with a shrug. 'I've got work to do before tomorrow.'

I realise that I don't even know what work Dominic does and that, apart from a brief session of slagging off Lydia, I don't know much about his personal life either. 'Maybe I could take you out to dinner one evening soon,' I offer. 'As my way of saying thanks.'

'You don't have to do that.'

'But I'd like to.' And I realise that it's true.

'Then I'd like that too,' Dominic replies shyly.

'Scribble down your number while I change.' I indicate a pad by the phone.

'You've got a message.'

'Yes.' I feel myself flushing scarlet for the seventeen-hundredth time today. 'I'll listen to it later.'

Dominic doesn't question my motives.

'Make yourself comfy,' I tell him. 'I won't be a minute.'

My friend turns to write down his number and I slip into the bedroom. Pulling off Lydia's clothes, glad to be free of yet another constriction, I then yank on my comfiest tracksuit bottoms. All I want to do is sink onto my bed and never get up again. Instead, I root in my wardrobe, find a carrier bag for Lydia's loaned clothes and pop them inside.

Dominic still waits patiently as I emerge from the bedroom. He hasn't made himself comfortable, he's sort of hovering about the flat, and when I go towards him, I can see that he's looking at a picture of me and Leo together. I could kick myself that they're still displayed all over the place – masses of photos of me and Leo in giggling, romantic poses. We did have our moments. Rather a lot of them, actually.

'Here are Lydia's clothes.' I hand the bag over and he stuffs it into his holdall. 'Thanks again. That was very thoughtful of you.'

'You're welcome,' Dominic says. 'I'd better be off now.'

'Shall I call you a cab?'

'I'll walk,' he shrugs. 'It's a nice night. It might help me sleep.' My heart goes out to him. I know all about sleepless nights.

'I'll give you a call,' I say. 'Soon. And thanks again for everything. I don't know what I'd have done without you.'

'It was certainly an interesting experience,' Dominic agrees. 'Even from my point of view.'

'I promise to wear more clothes when we go out for dinner.'

'No need to on my behalf,' Dominic replies with a smile.

I kiss him on the cheek. Oh, it would be so easy to turn my head and kiss his lips. Quickly, I pull away. Perhaps I've got some Superglue on the brain.

'I'll speak to you soon.' And with that, Dominic leaves. I

think about watching him walk down the street from my balcony, but wonder if he'd misconstrue it. I wonder if he *should* misconstrue it!

I pick up Leo's photograph. Will it be possible to replace Leo in my affections? Who knows. It's too late and I'm too tired to think about it. Still, I'd better listen to his message – see what he's got to say for himself.

Flicking on the answerphone, I listen in. But it isn't Leo. My father's wavering voice rings out into the flat.

My father never rings me. Ever. That's my mother's job.

'Darling,' he says shakily. 'It's Daddy. And I've got some terrible news.'

Chapter Sixty-Seven

The towering circle of stones were so distinct on the horizon. An unmistakable monument to long-departed ancestors. Though to this day, no one really has any idea what Stonehenge is all about or how the gigantic slabs of blue Welsh stone came to be here. It looked like a great place for sacrifice and rituals and pagan worship and magic. Those Druids – or whoever built it – certainly knew how to pick their spot.

Leo and his friends turned down a small, dark country lane and bumped along towards the monument. As Grant pulled into the gravel car park at the Visitor Centre, Ethel's wheels made an intrusive crunch in the overwhelming silence.

Leaning down, Leo whispered to Isobel, 'We're here.' She managed a weak smile. And not a moment too soon, Leo could have added.

The area was absolutely deserted – theirs was the only car around. The snack bars were all closed up, the ice-cream vans and the tourists' coaches long gone. In the distance, Leo could see that the stones were surrounded by a high wire fence; he was sure that when he last came here as a boy, he'd walked right up to them.

Without talking, they all climbed out of the car. Lard helped Leo to lift Isobel into his arms. An officious sign announced that the Visitor Centre closed at 7.00 p.m. and went on to give a long list of rules for 'enjoying' the stones. The row of turnstiles were locked, clamped with padlocks, for the night. The pay booths were shuttered against them. Racks of audio commentaries stood idle. Even if they'd wanted to, the tiny group couldn't have parted with the extortionate entrance fee.

'Oh flip,' Leo said with a heartfelt sigh. 'It's shut.' In his haste to get there, he hadn't even considered that they might not be able to get access to the stones. He hoped that Isobel had one last wave left in her wand as they might well need it. 'What now?'

Lard picked up his holdall. With a flourish like a sword, their dark little friend produced a crowbar from inside. 'We go and find fairies,' he said.

Grant and Leo looked on in amazement as Lard marched up to the turnstiles and jumped over with a surprising degree of athleticism. They followed him, speechless, and Grant jumped over too and then took Isobel from Leo's arms while he did the same.

By the time they'd sorted themselves out, Lard was already at the door of the Visitor Centre. In fact, they were so surprised that they followed him, unspeaking, until they were all huddled round the door – Lard with his crowbar in hand.

'We have to go through here to get to the stones,' he told them.

'Isn't there another way?'

'No.' Lard shook his head firmly.

'We can't break in,' Leo said.

'We can,' Lard insisted, exhibiting an assertiveness previously unseen in his character and outside of *Terminator* films.

Leo looked to Grant as the voice of reason. 'Let's do it,' his friend said.

And, with a minimal amount of effort, Lard leaned on his crowbar and eased his way in. The front door gave amazingly quickly – they really needed to look at their security arrangements here. Grant and Leo exchanged a stunned look. They never knew that Lard had this in him.

'Have you ever done this professionally?' Leo asked.

'Leo,' he answered, 'if we get caught, I might not have any choice.'

Leo could see how having form for breaking and entering might not sit well with an accelerated career path in the City. But that was the least of their worries tonight.

They eased their way in and tiptoed past the waiting rack of books, DVDs and videos selling the story of Stonehenge from every possible angle. Leo would have thought that there might have been a burglar alarm in the shop, but then again, who on earth would hear it ringing out here in the middle of nowhere? The nearest police station must be miles away.

'Do we need anything from in here to help us in our quest?' he asked.

'What good is a Stonehenge thimble to us?' Grant said. 'Or Stonehenge playing cards?'

'I don't know,' Leo admitted. 'But I thought I'd check.'

They jemmied the door at the other end of the gift shop and slipped out into the tunnel which went under the road and linked them to the site of the stones.

The tunnel was lit with psychedelic spotlights in pink and green, picking out naive paintings of bare-chested Anglo-Saxons heaving stones on wooden rollers. They hurried along it – Leo panting with the weight of Isobel in his arms – until they came out onto the vast open plain. Leo's shirt was sticking to his back with sweat.

Despite the night being hot and clammy, there was a cool, steady breeze blowing. Leo turned his face to it, thankful for a moment's respite. Just ahead, there was a sentry box, but thankfully there was no security guard on duty. Instead, a huge metal gate barred the way.

'It's terrible that they have to go to so much trouble to protect the stones from vandalism,' Leo said with a sigh.

Grant and Lard turned to look at him.

'What?'

Lard opened his holdall once more and pulled out some bolt cutters.

'Why have you got all these things?' Leo wanted to know. All he owned was a Black & Decker drill – unused. And . . .

no, that was it. Just the drill. And Emma probably bought him that one Christmas in an attempt to domesticate him. What previous use had Lard had for a range of tools like this? Obviously, there was much that they didn't know about their little chocolate-eating friend.

Lard cut through the gate with his bolt cutters like a warm knife slicing through butter. They all slipped inside.

Once in the middle of the hallowed circle, they gazed in awe at the massive stones, humbled by the sheer audacity of their size. Leo felt as if they'd been standing waiting for them all this time.

'Wow!' Lard intoned breathlessly. Leo thought that his friend was quite taken aback by his own skill at skulduggery.

'Isobel's fading fast,' Leo told them. 'What do we have to do?'

'Lay her on the ground in the centre of the stones,' Grant instructed.

Leo kissed Isobel and held her to him tenderly, before gently laying her on the lush grass, thick with springy clumps of clover and a sprinkling of buttercups and daisies. The circle was no longer complete and some of the great slabs of stone lay higgledy-piggledy on the ground. Leo wondered what this place might have been – a temple to a Sun God, a prehistoric observatory or some sort of calculator for celestial activity? All of these things had been mooted by experts in the past. He'd never heard anyone say that it was a kind of underground station for fairies who needed to get home. Which worried him.

Grant and Lard exchanged a glance. 'Is this a bad time to mention that we're all supposed to be virgins?' Grant said sheepishly.

'Oh great!' Leo paced the ground. 'You've been shagging everything that moves for years.'

'Thanks.'

'None of us are exactly,' Lard interjected, 'well, pure. What's the opposite of virgins?'

'Slappers,' Leo said. 'We're all slappers.'

'Apart from Isobel,' Lard noted respectfully.

Leo gazed down at her on the grass and wondered how it could have come to this – that she'd had to put her trust in three City slappers and Google. He covered his eyes with his hands. 'What are we going to do?'

'I don't know,' Grant admitted. 'Perhaps we should all think clean thoughts while we do the rest of it.'

'What "rest of it"?'

His friends exchanged another dodgy look. They really were getting more and more like an old married couple every day, Leo thought.

Lard delved into his holdall once more and pulled out a ghetto-blaster which he placed, with some reverence, on the ground between them.

'I put new batteries in it,' he said proudly.

'Good.' Leo stood open-mouthed still awaiting some explanation. There was very little light left now and they were peering at each other in the dark.

Grant cleared his throat. 'We do a fairy dance.'

'What the hell's a fairy dance?'

'How should I know,' Grant snapped. 'That's all it said on the internet. It didn't give me the steps.'

'Marvellous.'

'Try to enter into the spirit of this, Leo,' he shouted. 'We are doing it for you, after all.'

'We're doing it for Isobel,' Leo said quietly. 'Come on. Let's get on with it instead of doing our Marx Brothers routine.'

Lard produced another packet from his seemingly bottomless holdall and with great solemnity handed out sparklers.

'Sparklers?' Leo asked, trying not to sound cynical.

'Sparklers,' Lard shrugged in response.

'Look, Leo,' Grant snapped again. 'Just accept that we do not understand the great unfathomable mysteries of the universe and go with the flow.'

Leo examined his sparkler. He hadn't had one of these for a long time – Bonfire Night circa 1980 would be his guess. It was rogue one and had burned a hole in his glove. He turned his attention to the ghetto-blaster. Leo hardly dared ask this question. 'What's that for?'

'Fairy music,' Grant said.

'Of course.'

Lard flicked the switch and a blast of tinkly piano music filled the air. Leo could feel a frown coming on.

'What on earth's that?' Grant demanded.

Lard looked offended. 'Liberace.'

Grant and Leo in unison. 'Liberace?'

'Fairy music,' Lard explained. 'I didn't have any Elton John so I borrowed this from my mum. It's just the job.'

Grant huffed with exasperation. 'It said to play some music *for* a fairy, you clot – not *by* a fairy!'

Liberace's latest fan shrugged. 'What's the difference?'

'Turn it off! Turn it off!' Grant shouted.

Lard clicked off the ghetto-blaster and the eerie sound of silence returned once more to the vast landscape. 'What else have you got?'

Rooting around in the bottom of his holdall, Lard muttered mutinously under his breath.

Leo could have wept. He could have wept for his beautiful girl, who was having to suffer this indignity.

Chapter Sixty-Eight

My father seems to have shrunk. The proud, bad-tempered curmudgeon has disappeared to be replaced by a small, frightened man who looks older than his years.

The man who is so meticulous about his appearance has dishevelled hair and a mismatched jacket over his trousers. I fly straight to him and hug him.

'Where is she?'

'Through there,' he says, indicating double swing doors. 'I just came out for some air.'

The reception of the private clinic my mother has been taken to is a far cry from the tatty Accident and Emergency department I've just left. It's decorated in soothing blues and is filled with sumptuous sofas and vases of delicate flowers. Tasteful modern artworks hang on the walls. Catherine would hate them.

'How is she?'

'Asleep,' my father tells me. 'She's comfortable.'

'Is she going to be all right?'

He shakes his head. 'It's hard to tell at this stage,' he says, his voice hoarse with tiredness. 'It seems to be a minor stroke, thank goodness, but she's lost her speech and the movement down one side. That might take some time to come back.'

'But it *will* come back?'

Daddy puts his arm around me. 'We don't know, darling. We simply don't know.'

I burst into tears and cling to my father. 'Mummy can't be ill,' I say. 'She's never ill.' It's my father who's been swallowing pills for his angina the best part of ten years, not my mother. She never takes so much as a headache tablet. She never even has a common cold. Catherine Chambers is the picture of health.

'We're going to have to do things differently from now on,' my father says. 'Your mother has always run the family. She's the powerhouse. We're going to have to take the pressure off her. We need to look after her now.'

'I don't want to see her like this,' I say.

'Come on, now.' My father rubs his thumb over my face, smudging my tears, and I think that it's probably the first time he has touched me like that in years. 'My big strong girl. You can cope. You always do. Catherine doesn't look any different. Just more vulnerable.'

And that's exactly how I feel. More vulnerable than I've ever felt in my life.

* * *

My mother lies on the hospital bed attached to an array of machines and drips. Something beeps methodically. She looks pale against the starched white sheets. I go over to her and kiss her on the forehead, which feels too cold and dry, but my mother doesn't stir.

My father pulls up two armchairs and we both sit down. He holds my hand, too tightly. I rest my head back. I'm so unbelievably tired.

'How did it happen?'

'Catherine was out shopping with Henrietta Gooding,' my father explains. 'She collapsed in Harrods. They were marvellous. Thank goodness she didn't keel over in a lower-class establishment,' he says with a shake of his head. 'She might not be here to tell the tale.'

I hide a smile. Even in this state, my father still manages to be a pompous snob.

'Henrietta is normally so feeble-brained,' he continues, 'but the woman came good this time, phoned me immediately. I pulled a few strings and we brought your mother straight here.' He pats his wife's hand and fusses with her bedclothes. 'Much better than that terrible general hospital. I called you as soon as I could, but they said you hadn't been into work today.'

I sigh. 'I had a small emergency of my own.'

My father raises an eyebrow in question. Thankfully, he hasn't been watching the television news.

'All sorted now,' I say quickly. 'I'm sorry it took me so long. Do Clara and Arabelle know?'

My father nods. 'They'll be here tomorrow. They both needed to make arrangements for the children to be cared for.'

'Will Mummy be in here for long?'

'We don't know yet, sweetheart,' my father admits. 'We'll have to see what the doctor says.'

We both settle back into our armchairs. I feel so helpless just sitting here, watching my mother; there's nothing I can do for her, except wait and be here. I close my eyes. It would be unbearable if anything happens to her. It seems as if my entire support network is being kicked away from me at the moment: first Leo, now my mother. Both people I've taken hideously for granted. Maybe it's God's perverse way of making me realise that I should have appreciated them both more.

'I do love your mother,' my father says into my thoughts. 'I don't think I ever showed it enough.'

'Of course you did, Daddy,' I insist.

'I should have told her more often. I should have taken her out more. She's a very beautiful woman.' His voice is laden with tears. 'I should have said so every day.'

'She knows you love her,' I tell him. She knows, but I realise that I've never heard my father say it to his wife. That suddenly seems too sad.

'You plan for the future,' my father continues heavily, 'but none of us knows how long we've got. We never understand the frailty of human life until it hits us in the face. We really are a very arrogant race. We always think we've got for ever.' My father fiddles with his watch. 'I'm going to take her on a cruise. She'll like that. A long one. Round the Caribbean. As soon as she's well. We must do the things we've always said that we'd do.'

He doesn't say 'before it's too late' but I know that's exactly what's on his mind.

'I'll work shorter hours,' he goes on. 'Maybe take early retirement.'

'But your work is your life, Daddy.'

'Your mother must be my life from now on. She's always been there for me – for all of us. Now I must do the same.' He turns bleak eyes to me. 'I don't want her to leave me. I don't know what I'd do.'

I hold my father to me. It surprises me to realise that this is the longest conversation I've had with him in many years. Normally, it's a few brisk exchanged words, before each of us rush off to do something more important. Why is it that sometimes the people you love the most, you know the least? Why do we build barriers around our feelings for our closest relations? Maybe I have some thinking to do too.

'She won't leave us,' I say determinedly. 'Mummy won't give up without a fight. She's an old battleaxe. That's why you love her.'

'I do love her,' my father says. 'I do.'

Suddenly I need Leo. I need to talk to him. Just to hear his voice. 'I'll be back in a minute, Daddy,' I say and slip out of the hospital room.

Outside the front door there's a tranquil Japanese garden. Rich burgundy acers flutter in the breeze. A fountain splashes lazily over a beach of smooth, grey cobbles. I find a small bench and sit on it, flipping out my mobile phone now that I'm out of the confines of the clinic. Slowly, I push the digits of Leo's number. I feel so alone without him. Like my father, I think I should have told Leo more often that I love him. I should have shown him more. It's only now that I've become aware that all the stupid, insane, irritating things he did filled the space that's inside me. Leo is the sun in my sky, the rain in my desert and, sometimes, the fly in my ointment too. But I should have loved him for it. All of him. Leo sees the magic in the world – in the small things – whereas I'm far too uptight to even imagine it. I love looking at Leo when he doesn't know I'm watching him. When he's relaxing, he has the face of a child – without guile and accepting. I'd lost my appreciation of his qualities and had become so concerned with what other people thought of my relationship with him that I'd forgotten what it meant to me.

His mobile phone rings and rings. Then there's a strange humming noise on the line and I can't tell whether Leo has picked up or not. 'Leo,' I say, choking back the emotion in my voice. 'Is that you? Where are you? I need to talk to you.' I speak quietly. No jumping out of a box in my underwear, no gimmicks, no coercion, no shouting, no emotional blackmail. 'Please call me. I need you, Leo. I really need you.'

There's no reply. So I hang up. All I can do now is wait.

Chapter Sixty-Nine

Lard lit their sparklers which burst into life, showering silver sparks into the sky and illuminating their pale, tired faces. Finally, Leo thought, they were ready.

They stood in a circle round the inert form of Isobel and

Leo prayed silently to a God that he didn't really believe in, but he hoped existed and took pity on this poor sinner below. Because he was desperate, truly desperate. If this place did mean anything, he hoped fervently that it meant something good.

The last trace of the sun had now gone and the moon was full and high in the sky. The stones cast grotesquely eerie shadows on the ground. Lard clicked on the ghetto-blaster again. Liberace had been replaced by the rather more contemporary B52s, and the funky notes of 'Love Shack' kicked out into the night.

They danced vigorously in a way that Leo hadn't done since the night of the Thornton Jones annual ball and his John Travolta impersonation. Leo's heart squeezed at the thought of it. That was also the last night that Isobel was well and he hoped that this ridiculous ritual they were performing would have some effect. He couldn't bear to see her like this – so weak and so fragile, so lifeless. She was completely still, prostrate in the middle of their ragged, disco-dancing circle.

Leo looked across at his friends strutting their stuff, sparklers in hand, whooping and hollering against the ancient powers of Stonehenge, and it all just seemed too far-fetched, too silly, too hopeful to work. Tears filled his eyes. 'Love Shack' was a great song, a classic, but he couldn't believe that it would open for them the gateway to the Land of Light. What they needed was a miracle. A bloody, bastardy 24-carat miracle. Leo sank to his knees. He'd failed. They'd all failed. They'd failed Isobel. And he had never felt so wretched in his life.

Lard and Grant stopped dancing too and stood in the great circle of stones, breathing heavily. They had been true and valiant friends and they had tried their best. Really they had.

Grant looked off into the distance and the inky black sky. 'Oh. My. God,' he breathed.

Leo followed his gaze. Mysterious pinpricks of light appeared in the sky, brighter than stars, multi-coloured, and they were swooping about, almost playfully. He stood up and joined his friends and they all stared in slack-jawed amazement.

'It's working,' he said, hardly daring to voice his thoughts. 'I don't believe it, but it's working!'

The lights came closer. They rushed about the sky like the Northern Lights on speed – bright kernels of illumination trailing shimmering gossamer strands – threading themselves in and out of the giant standing stones. The lights circled closer to the three friends, brushing against their arms and their hair, teasing them. They felt like warm breath.

The lads all started to cheer, indulging in some very unseemly American-style whooping and hollering. 'Woo! Hoo!' they all shouted. 'Woo bloody hoo!'

Isobel was still inert on the ground. A myriad of colours played over her body. The light intensified until it was almost blinding them. Leo turned away, covering his eyes. All at once, a million pinpricks of light rushed into the centre of Stonehenge with the ferocity of a raging waterfall. He did hope that this was what was supposed to happen. Leo felt a mixture of elation and downright fear as sparks showered over him. Those fairies, he thought, certainly knew their pyrotechnics.

'It's beautiful!' Grant cried out and started spinning, arms held out to the sky, letting the lights twine round him.

Leo laughed out loud and he felt lighter than he'd done in years. Lard was dancing again, kicking his legs in the air like a man possessed. The lights started moving faster and faster, blurring together in front of them, as if they were on a high-speed fairground ride. Faster. Faster. Faster in an insane frenzy. Leo couldn't make out Grant or Lard now. They were lost to him, gone in a kaleidoscope of colours.

And then the ground started to shake. Gently at first, then with more intensity. Leo couldn't keep his balance and he fell to the grass, landing near to Isobel. Crawling towards her, he pulled her close and lay over her, trying to protect her with his body. Leo hoped that they hadn't mistakenly called on some malevolent spirits in their attempts to get Isobel home, that they hadn't enticed forth some eight-headed beast with bad breath and a bad attitude. Perhaps it was more important than they thought for them all to be virgins. Flip.

The ground shuddered and shook again. Leo had never previously been involved in an earthquake, but he was pretty sure that this was one. Great cracks appeared in the ground and even the huge immovable stones seemed to shake to their core. Maybe it was too hard for them to cross time zones or astral planes or whatever the hell it was that they were trying to do. It seemed as if the whole place might split apart or implode. Leo cast his mind back to all the episodes of *Star Trek* he'd ever watched – their transporter equipment always used to get them into trouble. And, unlike

Captain Kirk, Leo was there without the aid of a bad toupee and a corset.

He heard Grant and Lard shout out. 'Whoa! Whoa!'

Out of the whirling lights, they crawled across to Leo and Isobel on their hands and knees. They all huddled together.

'I have no idea what we've started,' Grant panted. 'Forgive me, my friend, if this all goes horribly, horribly wrong.'

'I'm really beginning to wish we'd gone to the pub instead,' Lard cried.

Leo would second that. Then his mobile phone rang.

'Bloody hell, Leo. Talk about inappropriate timing,' Grant shouted above the growing noise of the wind.

'It's Emma,' Leo said, checking his caller display. 'Emma, can you hear me? *Emma!*'

'I need you, Leo. I really need you.' Emma's voice was faint, barely audible, and there was a load of extraneous noise on the line as if she were phoning from inside a washing machine.

They were the only words he heard before the line went dead. As if he didn't have enough cold shards in his heart, another one pierced him to the core. Emma needed him. And Emma never needed him. Something must be very wrong. He shouted back into the phone, 'Emma. Emma!'

The ground shuddered beneath them, the wind reached screaming pitch. As he tried to cling to the ground, Leo's mobile phone fell from his grasp, bouncing out of his reach.

And then, as suddenly as it had all started, everything simply stopped.

Chapter Seventy

It's way past midnight when I tear myself away from the hospital, leaving my father sleeping in the chair next to my mother.

When I finally get home, I'm crushed to find that there's no message on my phone from Leo and he hasn't tried my mobile either. Wherever he is, it seems that he hasn't picked up my call. More than at any other time, I need to hear a friendly voice. I need Leo to tell me that everything will be all right, that I can manage and, preferably, for him to rush round and take me in his arms. This time I need him to come through for *me* in a crisis, but it looks as if I'm going to be disappointed. Perhaps he simply doesn't care enough any more.

I look at Dominic's number on the telephone pad and briefly consider calling him as a substitute, but decide that he's really done enough for me for one day and, even though he told me that he rarely slept well at the moment, it really is very late.

With nothing much else to do, I fall into my bed, unwashed, unloved and still fully clothed to endure a night of fitful sleep filled with fragmented nightmares – Leo floating across the sky on a rapidly deflating balloon, my mother in a wheelchair bouncing out of control down endless flights of steps, my father as small as a child holding tightly to my hand, Dominic

Supergluing me back into a cardboard box. Dawn didn't come soon enough.

Now I'm pretending to eat a bowl of low fat, low sugar, low taste cereal while I decide how to approach the day.

First of all, I call my father at the hospital to check on my mother. There's no change, apparently, but she's still sleeping which is deemed to be a good sign. The more my mother can rest, the quicker her recuperation will be, seems to be the general opinion. I've discovered that you can easily spend your life worrying about nothing of any great importance, when family is all that really matters. I'll go to the hospital later, but as my next port of call I go into work.

When I enter the gallery, Caron looks at me aghast. I must look as bad as I feel.

'I saw the news,' Caron says.

'Oh.'

'They were loading you into an ambulance in nothing but red knickers and a bow.' Caron looks as if she can't believe what she's recounting. 'What on earth has happened? What were you thinking of? Have you gone mad?' my friend wants to know. 'You look terrible.'

Starting with my initial bright idea for the cardboard-box fiasco, I regale her with the whole story – the Superglue, the cat wee, the Fire Brigade, the television crew – paying particular attention to the part that Dominic had played in my rescue and rendering my friend suitably impressed by his prowess with scissors. Then I end by tearfully telling Caron about my mother's stroke.

'I called Leo,' I admit, nibbling at a fingernail. 'I didn't know what else to do.'

'Was that wise?'

'I don't care, Caron. I miss him. I want him back.' I must look suitably distraught as she doesn't even try to convince me otherwise. 'I don't know what he was up to all day yesterday but he should be in the office now.' My glance strays to the clock. 'I'll give him another ring.'

'I'll put some coffee on. You look like you need some.' Caron disappears into the back room.

I sigh as I slowly dial Leo's number, clasping the telephone receiver to my shoulder. What do I really want to say to him? Do I simply want to tell him about my mother's illness, or do I want to go for it and tell him that because of this, I've really and truly had a wake-up call? Having realised how easy it is for loved ones to slip away from you when you aren't looking, I've come to appreciate how much he means to me. Life without Leo would be inconceivable. I have an irrational fear that unless I tell him so right now, I may not get another chance.

Leo's office telephone rings and after a few moments is answered by a female voice that I don't recognise.

'Can I speak to Leo Harper, please?'

'I'm afraid that Leo isn't in work today.'

'Oh.' A pin bursts my bubble. 'Could you transfer me to Grant Fielding, please.'

'Unfortunately, he's not here either,' the woman says. 'Anything I can help with?'

'No,' I reply. 'It's a personal matter. It's his girlfriend.

Ex-girlfriend. Is their other friend, Lard, around?' I have no idea what Lard's proper name is.

'He hasn't turned up today either.'

The hairs on the back of my neck stand up. Call it feminine intuition, but I don't like the sound of this. 'Isn't that a little unusual?'

'We've got used to those guys acting off the wall,' the woman answers me with a brief accompanying laugh. 'But, yes, it is strange that we haven't heard from any of them.'

'Not at all?'

'No. Not a thing.'

'Thanks.'

'If you do hear from them,' the woman says in a quieter voice, 'tell them that Old Baldy is gunning for them.'

I hang up. He isn't the only one. I rub my hands over my red-rimmed, gritty eyes. Here I am in my hour of need, ready to forgive and forget, and now I've learned that Leo and his chums have bunked off somewhere without telling anyone – no doubt on a jaunt, or pulling some sort of stupid stunt. They are, probably at this very moment, teeing off somewhere in Ireland or Spain, clad in bad-taste shorts, golf club in one hand, beer in the other. Why did I ever think that Leo and I could get back together again? We're different kinds of people and always will be. I am sensible and responsible. Leo is not. I push away any thoughts of my recent cardboard-box escapade.

Caron comes back with my coffee and I sip it gratefully.

'Well?' my friend says.

'Leo and Grant have gone AWOL, it seems,' I tell her. 'They're all missing in action. Lard too.'

Caron frowns. 'I'm supposed to be having dinner with Grant . . .' Then she stops.

I raise my eyebrows. 'Oh really?'

'He called in to see you and you'd gone out with whatsisname, the boring one.'

'Atrocious Alec.' I shudder at the memory of my dire dating experience. 'Did you tell him that?'

'No, of course I didn't,' Caron says. 'We decided not to waste the evening and went out for a drink together. And something to eat. Then he came back to my place. For coffee. That's all. We got on very well,' she adds sheepishly.

'I see.'

'Is it okay with you?' Caron asks. 'I know he liked you, but you said you wouldn't touch him with a barge-pole.'

'Grant's lovely.' I shake my head. 'But he's too close to Leo. It would be like dating his brother. At least you know exactly what you can expect with Grant.'

'Maybe he'll be different with me.'

I raise an eyebrow. 'And maybe he'll turn up in time for your date from wherever he is.'

Caron pulls out her mobile phone. 'I'll ring him.'

But, sure enough, there's no answer from Grant's phone either. 'It sounds like it's been disconnected.' Caron's forehead creases with concern. 'There's just a weird static on the line.'

'If he is anything like Leo,' I warn, 'he'll have forgotten to pay his bill and he'll have been cut off. When are you supposed to be seeing him?'

'Tomorrow,' Caron says.

I give her a rueful glance. 'Then let's see if they've all turned up by then.'

Chapter Seventy-One

They were no longer in the middle of Stonehenge with a war of lights waging around them. The ground was still, as ground should be. But it was a lot softer than the ground they'd left behind.

Grant was the first to speak. 'Oh my word,' was all he said.

Leo was still lying over Isobel, protecting her body, and she still wasn't moving. They had, however – by some strange and perplexing miracle – arrived in the middle of a small wooded glade. Leo wasn't big on fairy folklore, but if he had to guess, he'd say that they'd somehow managed to turn up in the right place. He was prepared, however, to have that illusion dashed.

They all appeared to have landed unscathed – helped, no doubt, by the lush cushion of moss beneath them.

'Are you okay?' Leo asked the guys.

They both nodded at him.

The colours were so clear that they hurt the eyes. The sky was the hue of sapphires, the leaves like emeralds. Clear water rushed by in a small, tumbling stream which sparkled like diamonds. Leo wished that he had his sunglasses with him. Butter-coloured sunlight streamed through the trees, bringing the most perfect dappled shade. Even the air tasted like champagne and it was heavy, soporific and scented with jasmine. Leo's body was warm and he felt a buzz of euphoria inside. He'd once had a rush like this after smoking a joint and listening to Jimi Hendrix music. It wasn't an unpleasant experience then either.

The clearing was covered with tiny red toadstools – yes, exactly like the ones you saw in fairy stories. Sweet music that sounded like a flute was dancing gently on the breeze and mysterious flashes of light swooped around them. And Leo knew, instinctively, that this indeed was a magical place. He wondered what Isobel must have thought of dreary old, polluted South London in comparison with this. It made him realise how much she'd given up to come and spend time with the poor, bedraggled specimens of the human race.

She lay next to him now and he turned anxiously to her. 'Isobel,' he said, touching her cheek. 'We're here. I think we're here. Wake up.'

As Leo kissed her forehead, Isobel opened her eyes. 'The Land of Light,' she breathed. Tears rolled silently down her face. Colour flooded into her face, tingeing her once pale cheeks with a soft pink glow. She took his hand and squeezed it. 'You brought me home.'

'We did,' Grant said, brushing his arm across his eyes. Leo saw a tear escape. 'We bloody well did.'

Leo could hear the emotion choking his voice and he tore himself away from Isobel for a moment to go over and put his arms round his friend – in the most manly way he could manage. Grant had saved her. His friend had saved his love. Leo hugged him to his chest. 'Thank you,' he said, and they cried in each other's arms.

'Bloody hell,' Grant sniffed copiously, 'we'd better not tell them about this back at the office.'

They let go of each other self-consciously. 'No,' Leo agreed. 'You're probably right.'

Leo and Grant both wiped their eyes on their sleeves. Lard was sitting there looking shell-shocked and they went to hug him too – now that they'd got this emotion thing sorted.

'I need chocolate,' was all that Lard could manage to say. 'A Mars Bar.'

Isobel sat up and looked around her. The pinpricks of light became bolder, darting closer to them, and as they did Leo could see that they were tiny, iridescent fairies and silver butterflies no bigger than his thumbnail.

'How are you feeling?' he asked Isobel.

'Fine, Leo,' she said. Her skin was changing from flesh tones, taking on a more translucent quality. She seemed so serene. Happy. And, Leo supposed, relieved. If Leo had been her he would have been very worried about placing her survival in the hands of three fairly useless City types. But they'd made it. And no one was more amazed than Leo.

He patted his pockets but he hadn't got his mobile phone. Shame, but then two miracles in a day might be asking too much. 'Give me your phone,' Leo said to Grant. 'I have to call Emma.'

'Leo, this is the Land of Light. Remember? I'm not sure that the Vodaphone network stretches that far.'

His friend handed over his phone anyway and, sure enough, modern technology once again had met its limitations. Why was it that you could never get a signal when you most needed one?

'Then we have to go back,' Leo said.

'What?' Grant and Lard looked aghast.

'We have to go back.'

'But we've only just got here.'

'Emma needs me,' he said starkly. 'She's never ever needed me. Something must be terribly wrong.'

Chapter Seventy-Two

I never imagined that my mother could look so frail. Suddenly it's like looking at an old woman. Catherine has always been so regal in her bearing, now she seems so tiny in the hospital bed. Her hair, always so meticulously styled, appears thin and lank on the pillow. One side of her face is slack and there is a fine line of drool coming from her mouth. She'd be mortified to see herself like this and for me, and the rest of the family, it's frightening to see her so incapacitated.

Daddy is still being extraordinarily solicitous to his wife and, for once, I can tell why his patients love him so much. It's the first glimpse I've had of my father's legendary bedside manner. At home all we see is his gruff, complaining side and I rather like the softer father I've discovered. He's slept in the armchair next to Mummy all night and is now beginning to look as if he has. I've urged him to go home and, at least, shower and change. He's barely eaten either. Finally, he's agreed, but I know that he won't be away for long, so I've given him a list of useful things to bring in for my mother – toiletries and clean nightgowns being at the top.

My sisters Arabelle and Clara have arrived – their children having been despatched into the temporary care of various reliable friends. They won't be able to stay for too long, and I know that I wouldn't want to look after any of my nephews and nieces for any length of time; between them they can trash the most immaculate home within half an hour.

Arabelle is white-faced and dry-eyed. Clara, usually as constrained as me, has gone completely to pot and sobbed in my arms, terrified that our mother might never wake up. But around mid-morning Mummy rallies and we're all immensely relieved. My mother tries to speak, but it's impossible to understand what she's saying. It sounds as if she's been at the gin bottle for half of the night and I pray fervently that it will only be a short-lived loss for her.

Catherine currently has no movement down one side of her body too, but the doctor has reassured my father that this too could return with enough rest, enough physiotherapy and enough good luck. The private room is hot and crowded with equipment, and my sisters and I are squashed together. Already flowers are starting to arrive – great bouquets of lilies, carnations and gerberas. It seems that Henrietta Gooding has been straight onto the Kensington and Chelsea bush telegraph to transmit news of her friend's misfortune.

I smile to myself. All my mother's cronies love a good crisis – Catherine herself is no exception. And I so hope that she will be up and about and gossiping soon.

I kiss my mother on her forehead. 'I'll be back later,' I say. My sisters will have to leave shortly to be at home for their children and I become acutely aware that I have no one to rush home for. I'm the only one of my siblings without commitments and that's more painful than I had imagined. The hospital is only a short Tube ride from my flat, and the plus side of my unshackled lifestyle is that I can call in any time. My sisters aren't so lucky. I hug Arabelle and Clara and say goodbye, then I go out from the stifling heat of the hospital to the stifling heat of the London streets.

Caron is going to cover for me at the gallery again today and I know that if I want to take extended compassionate leave then I'll need to talk to Gregory, the gallery owner. I feel that if there's little that I can do for my mother while she's in hospital, then I'll probably be better occupying my mind with work. She might well need me more when she's allowed to come home.

I walk along aimlessly. There are things I know I should be doing, but I can't make my brain function clearly. A jumble of thoughts are swirling round my brain. And it isn't long before I find myself outside Leo's flat. I didn't mean to come here, but I don't know what else to do with myself.

Pressing the doorbell, I'm disconcerted to find that there's still no answer and I stand here not knowing quite what to do. It seems as if another lifetime has passed since I was here, trussed up in a box like a turkey. I rest my finger on the bell and lean against it, as if dogged insistence might make my missing ex-boyfriend materialise. When nothing happens, I sit down on the doorstep and begin to cry. I should write Leo a note or something, but I can't find the energy to search in my handbag for a pen or a piece of scrap paper.

'This is becoming a habit,' a voice says next to me.

Wiping my eyes, I look up. 'Dominic.'

He sits down next to me. 'I haven't seen Leo for a couple of days.'

'He seems to have disappeared off the face of the earth,' I tell him. 'He wasn't in work today.'

'Perhaps he's just taking a breather from the stresses and strains,' Dominic suggests. 'He might be having a great time somewhere and here you are pining away. You didn't do anything else silly with Superglue?'

'No.' I smile through my tears.

'Is he worth all this angst?' Dominic asks. 'It seems as if he's treated you very shabbily.'

'It's stupid, I know,' I say with a sniff. 'This isn't all about Leo though. My mother's ill.' My voice cracks. 'And I don't have anyone else to turn to.'

Dominic puts his arm round me. 'You have me,' he says, hugging me to him. 'Come with me and let's see if we can find you some medicine.'

So, not having a better idea, I take Dominic's hand and follow him down the hall.

Chapter Seventy-Three

Red wine, I agree, is very good medicine. After three large glasses of a particularly good Bordeaux, I'm feeling relatively little pain. My symptoms, whatever they were, have cleared up nicely.

Dominic grins in my direction. He's standing at the cooker, stirring an impromptu sauce to go with the pasta that's bubbling away in the other pan. This is a man who has a supply of fresh vegetables in his fridge. Courgettes, peppers, mushrooms, onions – a whole selection. There are three different types of yoghurt. The only thing that Leo has three different types of in his fridge is beer.

I look at Dominic over my glass of wine. It would be easy to fall in love with a man like this. It sort of helps that he's really rather handsome too. Dominic has a lived-in air. He wears fairly battered jeans, scuffed trainers and a black T-shirt that has seen better days. However, he looks as if he means to be scruffy, whereas Leo can wear a Paul Smith suit and still appear as if he's fallen straight out of bed.

'This is nice,' Dominic says. 'Cooking for one is infinitely more boring.'

'Did you do the cooking when Lydia was here?'

He nods. 'One of my many talents.'

'Rescuing damsels in distress being another?'

'I'm afraid that skill has only recently been added to my repertoire.'

'I'm very glad of it,' I say sincerely. I'm becoming too comfortable in Dominic's sofa. 'I feel very lazy sitting here. Can I do anything to help?'

Dominic shrugs. 'No,' he says. 'I can manage. Besides, I think you're in need of a bit of pampering, don't you? You've had a very traumatic few days. The pasta won't be long.'

I take the time to look around the flat, noticing that photographs of Lydia still grace most of the surfaces – as do photos of Leo in my flat. Whether you are male or female, it still takes a long time to let go of loved ones, it seems.

Dominic's cat, Chloe, eyes me with deep suspicion. I return the gaze and, knowing when she's beaten in the staring-out stakes, she slinks out of the room. This place isn't a bachelor flat – the décor definitely holds a female touch. The sofas are cream brocade, scattered with beige embroidered cushions – a dead giveaway. What man would ever think to buy embroidered cushions? I bet the bedroom will be decorated in a pastel shade – lilac or aqua, maybe even pink with highlights of teal. Each of the flats in Leo's block seemed to have a different layout – probably because it's a converted house. Here, the living area is one big room with a small dining-table in front of French doors that overlooks the garden. I wonder if this flat has a roof terrace like Leo's.

'This is a great place,' I say.

Dominic pulls a face. 'All Lydia's design,' he replies, only confirming what I thought. 'I have nothing whatsoever to do with anything that might smack of good taste. Unfortunately, I may well have to move out. Lydia's the biggest earner between us and I won't be able to afford to stay here on my own. I guess she'll want her share out of it too. At the moment, she's dossing down on her sister's couch.'

'Do you miss her?'

'Oh yes,' he says sadly. 'Very much.'

'Perhaps you can find a way to stay here?'

He turns away from me to stir the sauce. 'I'd take a lodger but we've only got one bedroom. And I'm afraid that my line of work isn't likely to earn me a quick million. Unfortunately, they don't dish out huge salaries to youth workers.'

'Is that what you do?'

My genial host nods. 'I manage a centre for delinquent teenagers. The Little Bastards as we fondly call them.'

'Very noble,' I say.

'And very badly paid.'

'But rewarding?'

Dominic nods again. 'Amid the paperwork there are rare occasions when we manage to get one of the kids off drugs or off the street or off the "At Risk" register. Then it's rewarding.'

'I work in an art gallery,' I say flatly. 'There's no merit in that.'

'People need beauty in their lives,' Dominic says. And for some reason that makes me cry again.

Dominic comes over to me and kisses my hair gently. 'It will get better. Just give yourself time.'

'It hurts,' I say. '*I* hurt. In places I never knew possible.'

'Pasta with Dominic's special sauce is a very good anaesthetic,' he tells me. 'Plus it feeds the soul. And if we're not very careful, it's going to be burned. Ready to eat?'

I nod, but even though a delicious smell of garlic scents the air, I have very little appetite.

'I thought we'd go out onto the roof,' he says. 'It's a warm night.'

'You have a terrace?'

'All Lydia's doing again,' he confesses. 'But it looks great up there. You'll see.'

He leaves me and is going back towards the kitchen area when a familiar pitter-pattering starts on the windows. Dominic lets out an exasperated sigh. 'Rain. How typical,' he complains. 'The British weather thwarting my best-laid plans. Sorry, but it looks like I'm going to have to set the table inside.'

'Do you mind if I go upstairs to have a look?'

'Help yourself.' Dominic nods towards a corridor at the other side of the room. 'Just don't be too long.'

'I'll be two minutes,' I promise. I walk through the corridor, past the bedroom – which is, much as I'd predicated, a shade of pale lilac with cerise pink highlights. Chloe lies curled up on the bed. She steadfastly ignores my approach and continues going through some sort of grooming ritual, probably sharpening her claws. Beyond the bedroom is a short, steep flight of stairs that leads to a heavy door. The key is in the lock and, turning it, I let myself out onto the roof.

The rain is coming in distinct, weighty splots, splashing

rhythmically on the terracotta tiles of Dominic's terrace and spotting them darkly like a Dalmatian dog. It's cooling on my head, which seems to be thumping with the start of a headache. Which I suppose isn't surprising after the events of the last few days.

Like the flat, the roof terrace is a tasteful affair. Steel tubs hold exotic-looking plants and help to screen the small wrought-iron table and chairs in the middle of the patio. A Chinese-style water feature trickles delicately in the corner, holding its own against the faint hum of traffic noise. Nets of fairy lights are strung out on the back wall of the flat and, even in the rain, it has an intimate, magical air. Definitely Lydia's touch again.

I gaze across to Leo's flat. His roof terrace isn't quite as attractive. There's a rusting bike, a few old plastic sacks held down by bricks. Some scattered weeds in lieu of sophisticated planting. And very little else. No intimate little dinner setting. No magic. The lack of a woman's touch is evident. Also, there are no lights on in the flat. Definitely deserted. It's worrying. Where on earth is he? He can't have simply upped sticks and moved in with this Isobel woman. That just isn't the sort of thing Leo would do. But then, even I'd be the first to admit that Leo hasn't been acting like his normal self recently. I will, however, kill him if I find out that he's whisked his new girlfriend off to some tropical paradise for a holiday, as he would never have dreamed of doing that for me.

From the bottom of the stair, Dominic's voice comes, 'Dinner's ready!'

I take one final look over the rooftops of London. It would

have been very romantic to have eaten dinner out here, under the stars. My eyes fill with hot tears. Out there somewhere is Leo, just beyond my reach.

Dominic pokes his head through the door. 'It's wonderful up here, isn't it?'

'Yes,' I say as brightly as I can manage. 'What a shame it's raining.'

We smile at each other rather sadly and I wonder if we're both wishing that we were with someone else.

Chapter Seventy-Four

'Maybe you could come to visit us some time,' Leo suggested. 'You know that I can't go back,' Isobel said quietly.

Tiny wings fluttered over her shoulders and she looked as if she might disappear at any moment, popping into the atmosphere like a soapy bubble. Even in this guise – full fairy mode – she really was extraordinarily beautiful. All trace of the contemporary young woman had gone, to be replaced by an ethereal, shimmering being. It was quite a transformation. In contrast, Leo felt too solid here, too substantial, too inextricably linked to reality. Truly the proverbial bull in the china shop. Being here was like climbing inside a Disney movie. Too cosy, too colourful, too cheery. Rather nice, but not quite real.

This was the moment he had been dreading and he had to force the question from his lips. 'Never?'

'No.' She looked up into his eyes. 'Not in human form. My powers are too weak.'

'Can't you take advanced fairying? At night school, or something? Upgrade yourself a bit.'

Isobel laughed, but at the same time she shook her head. 'The world is too harsh a place for me.'

'It is for me too,' he protested. 'I'm a sensitive soul on the quiet.'

'You're meant to be there, Leo. I'm not. You're stronger than you think.'

Leo traced his fingers over the palm of her tiny hand. 'Maybe one day there'll be a way. Maybe we miserable mortals will find the magic in our lives again. Maybe we'll believe in fairies once more.'

This time Isobel stayed silent.

His heart sank. 'That bad, hey?'

Leo's fairy friend nodded.

'I don't want to leave you,' he said. 'But you understand that I have to go back. Emma needs me.'

Isobel nodded.

The thought of Emma made Leo's heart contract. If she knew where he was, she'd be worried. She always worried about him. But how could she know? How could she know the things that Leo knew? Even though she thought she had the measure of him, she really had no idea what had been going on in his life.

And Leo was a very different person now from the one he once was.

Chapter Seventy-Five

I sit at my mother's bedside, her chill, frail hand clasped between mine. We're watching some terrible daytime television show together. I don't think that my mother has ever before seen daytime television. *The Paul O'Grady Show* would make her want to spill blood.

On the screen, women confront their boyfriends in high-pitched, shrieking voices about a series of misdemeanours real or imagined but often involving their best friends while a bouffant-haired presenter with long acrylic fingernails tries to keep them from punching each other. It's banal beyond explanation. Is this the best that modern-day relationships have to offer? Feckless men shacked up with tattooed harpies.

My mother is propped up in the bed, surrounded by piles of pillows. 'This is not fun,' she says, her speech still slurred by her stroke. 'Whatever happened to chivalry?' But now she sounds as if she's had three glasses of gin, not three bottles. 'I do worry about you.'

I laugh. 'What – that I'll end up on one of those shows?'

'Men don't want to settle down now,' my mother says. 'And I want you to be happy and married.'

'I don't know that the two go hand-in-hand now, Mummy.'

'It's lying here.' She sighs wearily and worries at the

bedclothes with her fingers. 'It gives me too much time to think.'

Catherine has been in hospital for a week now and has made remarkable progress. Due to her sheer dogged determination, she's regained some movement already in her right arm. She uses it now to flick through the channels on the television.

Over on the QVC shopping channel a stiff-haired woman is in raptures over a real cubic zirconia pendant. On the next channel, yet another house makeover programme is in full-flight – the presenter going giddy over some poorly constructed MDF wardrobe that will, no doubt, fall to bits a week after the camera crew departs. On another, a perma-tanned newsreader is recounting in sombre tones the story of a break-in by vandals at the ancient site of Stonehenge.

'What a bunch of idiots.' I tut at the screen. 'Haven't they got anything better to do?'

My mother clicks off the television. 'This is too depressing,' she says. 'What is the world coming to?'

'I'll bring you some more books in.'

'That would be nice, darling. I'm so bored.'

'It won't be for much longer. You'll be out soon,' I assure her. 'Giving us all hell.'

'Yes.' My mother sinks back into her pillow. 'Just you wait.'

'I have to go soon,' I say. 'I'm due at work.' Caron has been great, covering for my shifts this week but I don't want to take advantage of her, so I come in first thing in the morning to relieve my father for a few hours while he goes home and performs a few perfunctory household chores – the ones that previously he was so unused to having to do. He has become a dab hand with a duster. My father has been fantastic, rallying around Mummy to make her as comfortable as possible. I didn't expect my father to have a nurturing side to him, but now it's full on.

'Daddy's been marvellous,' I say to my mother. 'I thought he'd go to pot without you.'

'Your daddy is a tough old boot,' my mother tells me. She turns towards me, her lopsided face serious. 'You know that he's given in his notice at the hospital?'

'I didn't,' I admit. 'He talked about it, but I never thought he'd do it.'

'Me neither,' Catherine says, struggling to raise an eyebrow. 'They're letting him take early retirement. In three months' time, he'll be a free man. Apparently we're going to spend the rest of our lives travelling and having fun. Before it's too late.' My mother indicates a pile of holiday brochures on her bedside table. 'I see Charles flicking through them in the wee small hours.'

'That sounds great. I'm pleased for you both.'

'We don't know how long we'll have together, Emma,' my mother says. 'We want to make the most of it. You can make all the plans you want for the future, but you never know when the future can be snatched away from you. At least we've had a warning. It means that we can get our priorities right from now on.'

'You'll be up on your feet before long,' I pat her arm. 'They can't keep a good one down.'

'Have you heard anything from Leo yet?'

I shake my head. 'Not a thing. There's no sign of him at

his flat.' I've walked past often enough to know that. 'His mobile phone sounds as if it's been disconnected. It's just making strange crackling noises. Neither he nor his ditzy friends have turned up to work for a week now.'

'I'm sure there'll be a perfectly plausible explanation.'

'There never is with Leo,' I say. 'It's always something hare-brained. He'll probably try to convince me he was abducted by aliens.'

'Leo's a lot of fun.'

He *is* fun. There's no disputing that. 'I've been seeing someone else.'

'Really?'

I'm not sure that one almost romantic candlelit dinner for two is enough to be classed as 'seeing' someone, but I feel there's a spark of attraction there between Dominic and me that could be encouraged to grow. And he's normal. He's useful in an emergency.

'Is he nice?'

'Yes,' I say.

'You could sound a little more enthusiastic.'

'He's nice. He's normal. He's . . .'

'Not Leo?'

'No.'

'Everyone deserves a second chance, darling. I hope that you and Leo have one.'

I hope so too. If only I could find him.

Chapter Seventy-Six

Isobel led him away from Grant and Lard and they sat on the ground beneath the shade of a tree. She wrapped her arms around Leo and said, 'It'll soon be time for you to go.'

'Oh.' Leo knew that his place was back on earth with Emma, but it didn't mean that he was finding it any easier to leave. He seemed to have spent all of his life being detached from his most important relationships. Leo never saw his parents or his brother, he'd taken Emma completely for granted and yet with this small, mischievous fairy he'd finally found out how to connect on a deep emotional level. How to love unconditionally. Leo sighed into Isobel's hair and held her tighter. 'This is the hardest thing I've ever had to do. Are you sure you'll be okay now?'

Isobel met his eyes. '*We'll* be fine.'

'We?'

Isobel took his hand and placed it on her tummy. 'A part of you will always be with me.'

Leo's throat closed with emotion and tears rushed to his eyes. 'I'm going to be a daddy?'

Isobel nodded. 'A male child.'

Resting his head against her, Leo let the tears fall. 'A boy.' He imagined that he could see the new life growing inside her. Then a thought went through his mind and he sat up sharply, brushing away the tears. 'Wait. Wait. A boy? He's not going to be a gnome or anything?'

Isobel laughed. 'Our child will be an air spirit, Leo. Free and unfettered.'

'So your trip to London wasn't entirely wasted?'

'I met you, Leo. How could you think that it was anything other than wonderful?'

'But if I go back, I'll never see him. How will I know what he's like?'

'We'll be on the breeze as it blows in your hair. On your cheeks in the falling rain. In the sun as it warms your face,' she said. 'You'll know, Leo. You'll know.'

Leo didn't want to let her go. It was even harder now than before. Before, it was just about the two of them – now the equation was so much more difficult. 'You know that I have loved you,' he said. 'In my own stupid earthbound way.'

'Our love could only ever be a passing thing. There is someone for everyone, Leo. You have already found your love on earth.'

'Emma?'

Isobel nodded. 'She's your soulmate.' Then she lowered her eyelashes and looked coy. 'I have a confession to make.'

'Will I like it?

'Emma wished me into your lives,' she said.

Leo's eyes widened. That was a revelation.

'The alignment was right in the universe. That enabled me to respond.'

Rather like playing on the slot machines and coming up with three cherries in a row. Big payola. Emma, instead, got Isobel.

'She doesn't know it though,' Isobel admitted.

'It will certainly help to explain my behaviour over the last few weeks.'

'But you mustn't tell her.'

'There's always a catch with you fairies, isn't there?'

'Yes,' she said, and took his hand. 'Don't let her slip through your fingers, Leo. I have done as much as I can. Now it's up to you. Cherish her. Love her fully, as you know you can.'

'I'm going to try,' he said sincerely. 'I'm going to try my very best.'

'Then it's time for you to leave.'

'Can I kiss you one last time?' Cupping her face in his hands, he let himself drink in the taste of her lips.

Isobel stood up and led him by the hand back into the centre of the glade where Grant and Lard waited for him.

'Okay?' Grant wanted to know.

Leo nodded. And then Isobel handed each of them a gold chalice.

'Drink this,' she said.

Grant, Lard and Leo eyed the cups suspiciously. They were brimming with golden liquid that sparkled in the sunlight. They looked at each other in reluctant agreement and then each one took a cautious sip. Disappointingly, it tasted rather like Diet Pepsi.

They stood there for a moment until Leo said, 'Now what happens?'

Then everything went very, very black.

Chapter Seventy-Seven

I'm lurking outside Leo's flat again and now I'm getting seriously worried. A week has gone by and there's still no sign of him. Dusk is falling and there should be a light on inside by now. I sit on the wall outside and wonder what to do.

A few minutes later, while I'm still gripped by indecision, Dominic arrives home from work.

'Hey,' he says with a gentle smile. 'We must stop meeting like this.'

'Hi, Dominic.' My spirits lift on seeing him even though I didn't exactly expect to bump into him.

'At least you're waiting for me on the doorstep fully-clothed.'

'And not glued in a box.'

He laughs. 'It was very amusing,' he says. 'With hindsight.'

'And from your perspective,' I add wryly.

My rescuer laughs again and then says, 'What are you doing here?'

'I . . . er . . .' It doesn't seem polite to say that I've been hanging around waiting to see if Leo turns up. I've been meaning to call Dominic since our dinner together, but somehow I haven't got round to it. With visiting my mother in the hospital and fitting in work and all the other things I have to do . . . Suddenly they all sound like feeble excuses. I've found time to walk past here every day in search of my missing ex – so I could have dropped in to see Dominic any time, and it occurs to me that it's strange that I haven't. But then Dominic has my telephone number and he hasn't called me either when he said he would. I frown.

'I've been meaning to call,' he says as if reading my mind.

'That's okay.'

'No,' he says. 'I want to talk to you about something. I think you'd better come in.'

Wearily, I follow him up the stairs and into his flat, trying not to stare too much at Leo's door. Would one little ring on the bell hurt?

'Coffee?' Dominic says once we're inside.

'Please.' I'm suddenly overcome by exhaustion. Why is life always such a struggle? Do people ever manage to escape from the dreaded rat race and carve out a quieter, more peaceful existence for themselves?

Sitting down on the sofa, I look around me. This place is far too tidy for a guy who lives on his own. There isn't so much as a CD out of place and they look suspiciously like they're all in alphabetical order. Isn't that a bit spooky? Will someone so controlled be any good in bed? Then it occurs to me that all *my* CDs are arranged that way too. Suddenly that seems to be a bad idea. What does it say about me? Am I changing? Is it a positive step that I can now consider having my CDs arranged randomly? Perhaps I too have always been too uptight to be a good lover. What would it be like if two control freaks went to bed together? Think of the fights to be on top. I'm not even sure why I'm thinking along those lines. It's years and years since I've slept with anyone other than Leo and, somehow, I still don't feel in a rush to. While I grapple with my inner turmoil, Dominic chatters pleasantly about nothing while he makes the coffee and I let the conversation flow over me.

He comes and hands me my coffee. Then, instead of sitting next to me on the sofa, he deliberately crosses the room and takes up position in one of the armchairs.

'Thank you for a lovely dinner the other night,' I say. 'It was very kind. You must let me reciprocate soon.'

Dominic stares down at his mug. 'I don't think that's going to be possible.'

My friend sighs and looks at me from across the expanse of laminate flooring that separates us. 'Lydia came back,' he says. 'A few days ago.'

'It didn't work out with . . .'

'Gerry,' he supplies. 'No. Apparently he had too many bad habits. Lydia's managed to knock them out of me over the years. I'm almost perfectly house-trained now.' There's a slightly bitter edge to his voice. He too takes in the neatly-arranged cushions and the meticulously-spaced row of church candles. 'I don't think she could face going through that all over again.'

'She probably just realised she'd been a complete idiot,' I offer gently. 'You're a great guy.'

'She's out at the gym tonight.' He glances nervously at the clock. 'It won't be long before she's home.'

'Then I'd better be going.' I put my untouched coffee on the table beside me and stand up.

'I thought that maybe you and I could have . . .' His voice tails off. 'Well, you know what I mean.'

'I thought so too.'

'Put it down to terrible timing,' Dominic says with a shrug. 'But I've got to give this another go.'

'I hope she begged.'

'She did.' He gives me a tired smile. 'I've forgiven her. Life seems a lot better with her than without her. I decided that I wasn't ready to move on with someone else. Perhaps unwisely, I still love her.'

We kiss awkwardly on the cheek. I point at the door. 'I'm out of here,' I say with forced cheerfulness. 'I might just give your errant neighbour a knock on the way out.'

'I still love Lydia,' Dominic repeats. 'And you still love Leo.'

'That obvious?'

''Fraid so.'

'I hope it works out with Lydia,' I say. 'Tell her she's a very lucky woman.'

Dominic closes the door behind me and I stand in the darkened hall, gazing at Leo's door. Resting my finger on the bell, I let it ring and ring until the tip goes numb. Of course, there's no one there. Leo has disappeared into thin air. He's gone. Vamoosed. Has been spirited away. Where on earth can he be? And is he there with that other damn woman? I plod unhappily down the stairs to the front door. All I need now is my own happy ending.

Chapter Seventy-Eight

Everything was still very, very black. Leo could hear birds tweeting and there was a rasping sound by his ear.

Opening his eyes, Leo found that it made it too, too light again. He was lying on his back in a field. The rasping noise was a sheep chewing at the grass; on seeing Leo, it decided to lick his face instead. Pushing away the slobbering sheep, he forced himself upright. His legs, his arms, his everything, felt as weak as a kitten's. Blinking against the strong light, he looked around. They were back in the middle of the great circle of standing stones at Stonehenge, surrounded by sheep, and Leo was relieved that he hadn't ended up somewhere else in the wrong time and the wrong place like that unfortunate time-travelling bloke did every week on *Quantum Leap*.

Grant and Lard were lying on their backs beside him and they too were slowly coming back down to earth. Their hair was standing on end and Leo didn't suppose his was an exception. They had stupid grins on their faces and, of course, they were all covered in glitter.

His friends opened their eyes and took in their surroundings.

'We made it back,' Grant said with a grateful sigh. 'Thank goodness.'

'Are you okay, Lard?'

Lard checked his limbs. They all appeared to be intact. 'Fine,' he said. 'Never better.'

The sun was coming up, picking its way between the stones to reach its pinnacle, and the sky was aglow with a rich pink wash. Their green and pleasant land had never looked more beautiful.

'I was worried,' Grant admitted. He rubbed his hair, causing a glitter shower, and they all exchanged a knowing look. 'I thought we might get ourselves into some sort of trouble.'

Then, out of the exquisite silence, there was the sound of sirens. Two police cars pulled up by the perimeter fence and four rather burly policemen jumped out and ran towards them at full pelt, riot batons drawn. And Leo felt that their troubles might be just about to start.

He sighed, lay down on his back again and waited for the onslaught of officialdom. Had he really chosen to come back to this life over paradise? Leo heard Grant and Lard groan behind him. The policemen were still thundering their way across the field towards them.

Leo put his hands behind his head, crossed his ankles and said, 'Welcome home, boys.'

Chapter Seventy-Nine

It isn't something that I particularly want to do, but I can't help it, like some sad old moth to a particularly troublesome flame. I sit on my bed, surrounded by mementos of my relationship with Leo. A battered biscuit tin lies open next to me, overflowing with photos of us together and silly tokens of love.

I open a small tin can. A lurid green plastic snake shoots out and blows a raspberry. It makes me smile. I'm not sure that it did at the time. Perhaps I haven't always been fully appreciative of Leo's line in presents. Now they're my most cherished possessions.

The doorbell rings and I put the lid back on the biscuit tin, pushing it under my bed, before going to answer the door. We're having another girls' night in. Three lonely spinsters, too much Chardonnay, a DVD featuring Orlando Bloom and hours of discussing men without any of us currently having a relationship with one. Is this what I have to look forward to for the rest of my life?

Caron breezes in first, Jo following in her wake. I join the procession and we go through to the kitchen where Caron proceeds to pull cartons out of a carrier bag from Antonio's deli – a fine, expensive establishment just further down the street from my flat in Shad Thames. As well as being fine and expensive, it's also far too convenient and is the main reason why my oven has seen so little action during the time I've lived here and my bank account has seen so much.

Jo kisses me on the cheek. 'Okay?'

I nod bravely.

'Caron told me about Dominic.'

'Another one bites the dust.' I force a laugh. 'I'm beginning to think that I wear the wrong brand of deodorant.'

'So,' Caron says expectantly. 'Have you heard from the three missing reprobates yet?'

I shake my head. 'No. Not a thing.'

My friend's face falls. 'Bastards,' she says vehemently, before turning her attention to the food. 'For our delectation, I got tuna wraps, three sorts of salad, smelly cheese and . . .' she holds up her *pièce de résistance* like a trophy, 'coffee cake. Lots of it. Particularly good in times of crisis. Have you got any chocolate ice-cream?'

'Is that a stupid question?'

'Fabulous.' Caron claps her hands together, then scrunches up all the paper wrappers and throws them in the wastepaper bin. 'Where do you suppose they are?'

'Who knows,' I say. 'Aren't men always a law unto themselves? No doubt they'll turn up again one day as if nothing's happened.'

'Plates?' Caron demands.

'Plates.' I pull them out of the cupboard and put them down on the work surface.

My friend dishes out with a professional hand. 'I liked Grant.' Caron arranges the lettuce with the eye of an artist. '*Really* liked him. I had high hopes for him.' We all pick up our plates and go back through to the lounge, plonking ourselves down at the table by the window. 'I'm fed up of dating lame men. I should have realised that he'd be flawed because he's a friend of Leo's.' She lays a hand on my arm. 'No offence.'

'None taken,' I say.

'It's not difficult to find men. I could pick up a different guy every night of the week.' Jo is never one to mince words. 'But all they want to do is come home with you for casual sex. No one is interested in a serious relationship.

How do you find a good man without wasting too much time on the losers?'

'I've never been very good at that scene.' I've always been too uptight about my own body to consider sharing it with a stranger, and the thought of going through all that again fills me with dread.

'That's all there seems to be. Women grow out of it, but these days men don't seem to. They're all babymen now,' Jo says. 'Thirty-year-old toddlers. Grown men who behave like petulant infants and who have the same sense of responsibility. They're an embarrassment to their own gender.'

'Do you think it's our fault?' I say. 'Whenever Leo attempted to do anything remotely manly I always used to make fun of him. I guess it's no wonder he stopped trying. Perhaps they've no idea what their role is supposed to be any more.'

'I wonder if men judge us as harshly.' Caron pours out wine for us all. 'Let's face it, we want nothing less than perfection now in a partner. No baldies, no one with a beer belly rather than a six-pack, nothing less than a six-figure salary and definitely no kids from previous wives in tow. We want them to look all sporty and athletic, but not to spend hours away from us playing sports. We want them to have great careers without spending too much time at the office.'

'Whatever happened to unconditional love?' Jo wants to know.

'It sucks,' Caron says. 'Particularly if you're the one dishing it out.' She slugs back her wine. 'We are the generation of women who want it all.'

I sigh. 'And end up with nothing.'

'Bugger,' Jo says miserably. 'Now we're going to have to get seriously drunk.'

We raise our glasses and clink them together.

'We have become our own cliché,' Caron declares.

When Leo comes back – *if* he comes back – I'm going to win him again. I'm going to be soft and floaty and feminine. I'm going to bake him homemade cakes and start doing roast dinners. I'm going to turn the clock back thirty years and love him like my mother loves my father. I'm going to love him unconditionally. And there's no way that anyone – no matter how cute – will stand in my way. I smile sadly. 'I'll drink to that.'

Chapter Eighty

So, that was the end of the Great Stonehenge Escapade. Grant, Lard and Leo were bundled into the back of one of the police cars and were driven to the nearest nick.

Apparently their downfall was that they'd startled some Druids who were performing ancient rituals at dawn. Grant, Lard and Leo had dropped out of the sky about three feet in front of them, scaring them all to death. You would have thought Druids were made of sterner stuff. But no. They'd rushed off, gowns hitched up around their knees and had raised the alarm. Flying in the face of convention in this country, the police arrived pretty soon afterwards. If it had taken them the normal three days to turn up to an 'incident', then the three of them could have had it away on their toes and no one would have been any the wiser.

Except, of course, Grant, Lard and Leo were all captured in full glory on the gift shop's closed-circuit television system during their breaking and entering phase. And, of course, they'd left Ethel in the car park for all to see. Not marvellous at covering their tracks then. Somehow Leo didn't think they were cut out to be career burglars.

Now they were all in individual interview rooms, being 'interviewed'. There was no good cop, bad cop thing going on; the officers were just all pretty grumpy with them. This was mainly because Leo and his compatriots had decided that they would stick to the truth. And in this case, the truth was decidedly stranger than any fiction.

Leo's policeman, as he'd fondly come to think of him, was red and sweating in the face. He folded his arms. 'Run this past me one more time.'

'We were trying to get a sick fairy home.'

'To the . . .' the officer consulted his notes '. . . *Land of Light.*' This was said with a degree of cynicism often found in members of the constabulary.

'Yes.' The policemen were struggling with this because although Leo, Grant and Lard had forced their way into the gift shop, they hadn't actually stolen anything. Quite frankly, there wasn't anything worth stealing – unless your heart's desire was a *Welcome to Stonehenge* tea towel.

'Have you recently taken any illegal substances?'

Leo sighed. 'Not unless you count lavender poteen.'

'Don't get funny with me, sonny,' the policeman warned.

Leo felt as if he had the worst possible case of jet lag. All he wanted to do was lie down and sleep for a fortnight.

'The Druids said that you fell out of the sky.'

'Then perhaps you should ask them if they've been taking illegal substances too.'

'You're in very serious trouble, you know.' The policeman was looking exceptionally cross now.

'I'll pay for any damage we've caused,' Leo said. 'I'm very sorry about it, but it was an emergency.'

'What I want to know is, what were you doing there in the first place?'

'Trying to get a sick fairy home,' Leo and the policeman said in unison.

After three hours of interrogation and several cups of tea, the policemen decided that they had no option but to let them go. But not before exploring the possibility of getting them sectioned under the Mental Health Act for insanity and being a danger to the public at large. When they realised that wouldn't stick, they charged them all with criminal damage and let them go.

Such was the British justice system that when their case eventually came to court – shortly before they were old and grey and this was all a distant memory that they'd laugh about from time to time – they'd probably get a few hours of community service and a fine, which, of course, they could all pay with ease because they were relatively rich. And they'd all have a criminal record to add to their CVs, which far from hindering their career prospects as Leo had first feared, the City being what it was, it would quite probably enhance them. In the meantime, Leo would send a large cheque to the powers-that-be at Stonehenge, so that they could repair the damage to their tacky gift shop. In all honesty, the three lads would probably have done them a favour if they'd smashed the lot up. Who in their right mind would want to take home a Stonehenge fridge magnet as a souvenir, or a lifelike plastic replica of the magnificent stones? Although there were some rather nice Stonehenge shot glasses that Leo wouldn't have minded . . .

Then, he guessed, life would go on and the authorities would remain blissfully unaware of a fantastic opportunity to discover just how powerful the ancient monument in their keeping really was.

Grant, Lard and Leo met up by the front desk. They all looked as dishevelled as each other and just as exhausted. The police were already losing interest in them; it must have been time for their lunch-break. In step, the three miscreants plodded out into the car park.

'Did they rough you up?' Leo asked his partners in crime.

'You watch too many cop shows, Leo,' Grant told him with a world-weary huff.

'You're both okay though?' Leo's friends nodded at him. 'Apart from a slight tug from the long arm of the law,' he told them, 'I think we could class that as a successful mission.'

Grant put his hand on Leo's shoulder. 'At least Isobel is safe now.'

Suddenly it was all too much. Leo sagged to his knees on the dirty grit of the car park and, for the first time in his life, cried openly and loudly while Grant and Lard held him. And Leo started to realise just how awful he really felt.

Chapter Eighty-One

My father and I have bought a fold-down single bed from eBay – a revelation of virtual shopping for my mystified parent, whose retail outlet of choice is either Harvey Nicks or Harrods. My brother-in-law, Awful Austin, collected it in his Transit van and delivered it to the house yesterday. Between us we wrestled the bed into the downstairs study for my mother. It's still only a relatively short time after her stroke, but Catherine is making marvellous progress. Her balance still isn't great, however, and we know that when she's allowed to come home, the stairs might well be a problem for her to manoeuvre.

My father has cleared his study, packing away files and case studies with an air of finality. It's the first time in my life that I have ever seen his desk completely free of paperwork. Having made the decision to take early retirement, it's obvious to all that he now can't wait to leave. He's hired a cleaner too – a good one, it seems, as the place shines like a new pin.

My father sits down on the single bed which seems to take up much of the study.

'I'm sure we could have squeezed a double in here,' he says, rather optimistically.

'Nonsense,' I tell him. 'You and Mummy would have had to climb over each other to get out. The idea is to make it easier for her.'

'I know.' My father's voice wavers. 'But we've spent so few nights apart during our marriage. It seems wrong to be sleeping in separate beds under the same roof.'

Sitting down next to him, I give him a hug. 'I didn't know you were such a soppy old thing.' And it's true, my mother's illness has brought out a caring side to my father that I've rarely seen and it makes me realise that I don't really know my parents as people. My relationship with them has been entirely based on how they've interacted with me. But then how many people are best friends with their parents?

My father smiles self-consciously. I never knew that the love between them was so tender and it makes me feel proud to be their daughter.

'This won't be for long.' I cast a glance at the temporary bed. 'You know what Mummy's like. She'll be defying medical science by running marathons next year.'

'I do so hope that you're right, darling.' My father rubs the bridge of his nose. He's barely slept since my mother has been in hospital and he hasn't shaved as meticulously as he normally does – rushing home to perform small domestic tasks as quickly as possible, anxious not to be away from his wife's bedside for too long – white bristles push through his pink skin and he's nicked himself too many times. 'I do miss her,' he says, eyes brimming with tears.

I've never seen my father cry and that seems strange after

thirty years in his company. I guess that he's from the generation of men who perceive crying as a weakness. But he cries now, dabbing awkwardly at his tears with a cotton lawn handkerchief. 'I have spent the latter part of my life trying to make already beautiful women even more perfect. And I wonder what the point of it all was. Your mother is very proud of her looks; she was always asking me to do little nips and tucks, but I never would. I never thought she needed them. Now I look at her, with her face all slack down one side, dribble coming from her mouth and her clumsy movements, and do you know, Emma . . .' He takes my hand. 'Catherine has never looked more beautiful to me.'

I feel the tears come to my eyes too.

'Find someone to love like that, darling,' he says with a sniff. 'Even if it is that damn Leo.'

Chapter Eighty-Two

Leo called Emma as soon as he got home. Butterflies circled in his stomach and his mouth was dry. But on her home number, the wretched answerphone clicked in and Leo couldn't bring himself to leave a message as he didn't know what to say. He tried her mobile.

'Hello.'

'Emma. It's Leo.'

The phone went dead. He pressed redial and tried again. 'Emma?'

She hung up again. So he tried again and again and again, and every time he said, 'Hello,' Emma hung up. Though he didn't actually know what he would have said if she had been willing to engage in conversation, come to think of it. Leo, having raided his stock of mobiles, put his phone back into his pocket and slumped onto the sofa.

The flat seemed weird. Empty. Having Isobel there had definitely left some sort of imprint on it. Everything had stopped looking so perky and had gone back to being normal furniture and fittings. Even the cushions seemed to have lost their oomph. He suspected that his mirrors wouldn't talk to him any more. Maybe he'd up sticks and move. This place was starting to hold too many memories.

Grant came out of the kitchen bearing two mugs of tea. 'Mate,' he said, 'you look wrecked.'

'I've been calling Emma,' Leo told him, 'but she keeps hanging up on me.' All he wanted to do was lie in a nice, long, hot bath and make the world go away, but this was important. Emma's message had sounded urgent. He'd only been gone overnight, so hopefully he'd still be back in the nick of time to help out.

'Why don't you hit the sack for a while,' his friend suggested. 'After all that you've been through, you could do with a rest.'

Leo couldn't argue with that. 'I could try phoning her again.' He ferreted for his phone.

'You don't look in any fit state to speak to her now.'

'But she said she needed me.'

'It seems that perhaps our dear Emma has already changed

her mind about needing you,' Grant pointed out. 'You'd be no use to her in this state, anyway.'

'I should go down to the gallery. See if she's there.'

'Hitting the sack would be your best idea. You look like you haven't slept for a week.'

'I need to see Emma,' Leo insisted.

'You're hardly in a condition to present a rational argument,' Grant said. 'If you want her back, Leo, crashing in there looking like one of our homeless friends isn't the best recipe for success. Let me go down there on my way into the office and see how the land lies. If she's hanging up on you then she must have her reasons. I've got to talk to Caron too. I'm due to take her out for a wild night on the town. I'd hate to think that she'd been calling me while we were away for the night.'

Leo yawned, his eyelids grew heavy and his eyes rolled as sleep washed over him. He laid his head down on one of his subdued cushions. 'I don't want her to think that I don't care,' he mumbled. Because he did care, and Emma had to know that as soon as possible.

Chapter Eighty-Three

At Art For Art's Sake I've just taken delivery of the work for our latest exhibition. I'm busy unpacking cases and cases of delicate pottery painted with cartoon figures in strange sexual positions and scenes of mass torture in lurid colours.

Truly the produce of a warped mind and I wonder which of our fabulously wealthy clients will be snapping these up. The ones with a total taste by-pass, I conclude. It's making my eyes ache to look at them. Just the sort of thing I can imagine my parents having in their lounge. If they suddenly went insane, that is.

The majority of the wire-mesh torso sculptures have found new homes and have been shipped out by my ever-efficient friend, Caron, over the course of the last week. The rest are being packed and sent back to the artist, along with a cheque for his share of the loot. I think back to Rodin's statue of *The Kiss* in the Tate Gallery. My mother's right – that *is* art. Real proper art, with real proper people in it. Perhaps I should consider looking for a new job. Maybe I should consider a new life. Pack it all in and go to work in a scuba-diving centre in the Cayman Islands. I'm just arranging the new gallery layout and my new lifestyle when the door opens.

Grant stands there, looking sheepish.

I put down the pot I'm holding in case I'm tempted to throw it. A ten thousand pound temper tantrum is way beyond my meagre means – even to make a point. Then I'd be heading for the Cayman Islands out of necessity. Instead, for safety's sake, I place my hands on my hips out of harm's way. 'Look who's back from the dead,' I say sarcastically.

'Long time, no see.' He gives me a small, uncertain wave and inches his way further into the gallery.

'I take it that if you've turned up again – like the proverbial bad penny – then it means that Leo is back in circulation too.'

'Yes,' Grant says. 'That might be a correct assessment of the situation.'

'So? I think an explanation is required. I did consider going to the police to report you all missing.'

I think I see Grant flinch. 'Missing?'

'I've been calling Leo for over a week now and nothing, *nada*. His flat was empty. None of you were in work. Where on earth did you get to?'

'A *week*?' I'll swear that Grant blanches. He looks as if his knees have turned to jelly as he grabs hold of the nearest display case. 'We've been gone for a *week*?'

'Yes, you have. Are you going to tell me where you've been?'

He snorts as if he's surprised and says, 'A week?' once more.

'Well?'

'We just took a few days off together.' Grant tries – and fails – to look innocent.

'So? Did you have fun?' I ask.

'Not in the traditional sense of the word.'

'Where did you go?'

'Er . . . away.'

'Probably Ibiza or Las Vegas or Amsterdam.' I narrow my eyes. 'Anywhere that boys can behave badly would be my guess.'

Grant says nothing.

'Didn't you think to tell anyone where you were going?'

'It was a spur of the moment decision. Very last minute. We only thought we'd been . . . er, we only thought we'd *be* away overnight.'

'You are so irresponsible,' I chide. 'When normal people go on holiday, Grant, they tell friends and loved ones. They tell the people that they work with and work for. They don't just disappear off the face of the earth for days on end.'

'In Leo's defence, he has a lot on his mind.'

'And I don't?' I say. 'I've been pacing anxiously for days while Leo has been gadding about and has been just too busy to be bothered to call?' It's so typical of him and I wonder why I'd ever considered that I might want a relationship with him again.

'He's been trying to call you since the minute we got back, Emma. You keep hanging up on him.'

'I don't want to hear his feeble explanations.' What I actually want to do is hit him over the head with a frying pan.

'We did have our reasons,' Grant insists.

'And they were?'

'I can't tell you about them,' he says. 'But one day you'll understand.'

I sigh. 'If I ever start to understand anything Leo does, please shoot me.'

Grant stands there looking pathetic, hands in pockets, down-turned mouth.

'Caron has been worried about you,' I tell him gruffly. 'Fool that she is, she likes you. You had a date arranged and you never turned up.'

'Oh shit.' Grant looks crestfallen. 'I didn't do it on purpose, I swear.'

I put on my disbelieving face.

'I'll call her.'

I keep my face impassive.

'I will,' Grant promises me earnestly. 'I will. She's great. I hoped she might be here today. I'd love to take her out again.'

'Get in the queue, then,' I snap. 'In fact, go to the back of the queue.'

Grant hangs his head.

I sigh again – a relenting sigh rather than an exasperated one. 'You look like you need coffee.'

Grant nods and his smile reappears. He risks coming into the gallery fully and even sits on the chair at my desk. I go out to the kitchen, busy myself pouring some rather stewed coffee – if he thinks I'm making fresh coffee for him then he'd better think again – and take it out to Grant.

We sit for a moment sipping our bitter, too strong coffee quietly. 'Okay,' I say. 'I give in. Where is he now?'

'At home,' Grant tells me. 'He wanted to come down here, but I made him go to bed. He hasn't slept in a few days.'

Now I'm alert. 'He's not been sleeping?' Leo could sleep through an earthquake. 'What's wrong with him?'

'He's feeling pretty awful, Emma,' Grant replies, not meeting my eyes. 'You know that she . . . that Isobel's gone.'

'No.' I don't even try to hide my surprise. 'I didn't know. What happened?'

'You need to talk to Leo about that.'

My eyes turn to slits again. 'Is this all tied up with your disappearing act?'

'Yes.' Grant seems tired and there are dark shadows under

his eyes. He looks terrible. A month's sleep and a few vitamin injections wouldn't go amiss here either. 'We're worried about Leo, Emma. He's had a tough time. In the past few weeks he's had a lot of growing up to do.'

'That would be hard for him.'

'Go easy on him when you speak to him.'

'What makes you think I'm going to speak to him? My mother's been ill, Grant. Seriously ill. Where was Leo when I needed him?'

'He needs you, Emma. More than he realises. More than you realise.'

One of my father's 'pahs!' comes out of my mouth before I can stop it. Sometimes I'm too much my father's daughter. 'Every time I go all soft and squishy on him again, he does something stupid. I can't keep going on like this, Grant. My mind feels as if it's being tossed about in a tumble dryer. I can't think straight any more.'

'He still loves you, Emma. I think you feel the same. Would you ever consider taking him back?'

'Is hell ever likely to freeze over?'

Grant smiles sadly. 'So you do still love him?'

'What's that got to do with anything?' I say crossly. 'I'm immune to Leo's charms. I've moved on. I've met someone else.' I don't tell Grant that my particular someone else has just been reunited with his girlfriend. Instead, I flick back my hair and declare, 'I am *completely* over him.'

And, perhaps if I say it enough, one day it will be true.

Chapter Eighty-Four

'Here.' Leo beckoned the schoolboy towards him. 'Will you go into that shop and get me a bunch of flowers?'

The kid nodded. 'It'll cost you.'

'A fiver,' Leo said. 'On delivery.'

'Done,' the kid said. And Leo knew that he had been.

He handed over the money, including the purchasing fee, and moments later the kid came out of the florist's clutching a bouquet of pink-coloured flowers wrapped in cellophane. 'Great,' Leo said. 'Nice choice.'

He put the flowers behind his back and walked the ten minutes to Emma's parents' home, hideously self-conscious of the blooms he was bearing. He rang the doorbell and waited. Emma's father, Charles, opened the door. He was wearing an apron and rubber gloves.

Leo cleared his throat. 'Mr Chambers,' he said. 'Hi. Hello. I understand that Emma's mother has been unwell. I thought I'd pop in to give her my best wishes.'

Leo had never popped in to see Emma's parents before. They were not 'popping in' sort of people. The expression on Emma's father's face said that nothing had changed on that front.

'Come in, Leo,' Charles Chambers said, finding his manners. 'Come in.'

Leo followed Charles into the hall and then stood fidgeting uncomfortably.

'We've just finished lunch. Come through to the kitchen. I'm washing the dishes and having a tidy up. You can join us for a cup of tea.'

Leo followed him. Emma's mother, Catherine, sat at the table. She looked as if she had aged and was thinner and paler than when Leo had last seen her on the fateful night of her daughter's thirtieth birthday party.

'Leo,' she said warmly. His only fan in the Chambers household was clearly pleased to see him. 'To what do I owe this pleasure?'

'I wanted to come and see how you were.' Leo kissed her on the cheek. 'I'm sorry I didn't come sooner.' He handed over the flowers, grateful to be rid of them.

'Very nice,' Catherine said. 'My favourites. How thoughtful. Isn't Leo thoughtful, Charles?'

Charles didn't look entirely convinced.

'You're looking well.' That wasn't exactly true, but Catherine didn't look as awful as he'd expected. Or perhaps after his recent experience with Isobel, he was marginally better at dealing with illness than he had been.

'I'll be back to my old self before too long,' she assured him, patting his hand gently.

Leo realised that he'd taken his role in this family for granted too and he wanted to do anything he could to make amends. It was terrible to see Catherine looking a shadow of her former self and it made him think of his own mother and how little he'd seen of his parents in recent years. As soon as he left here, he'd call them and arrange to go to see them. But then, that alone could make them die of shock.

Charles switched on the kettle and then returned to his washing up. Leo joined him at the sink and picked up the tea towel. He dried the dishes as Charles washed.

'I've also come here with an ulterior motive,' Leo admitted to them. 'Emma isn't speaking to me. She won't return my phone calls.'

'And you want us to put in a good word for you?' Catherine said.

'Then you must be very desperate, Leo. When did my daughter ever listen to me? Or to anyone else for that matter.' Charles Chambers stripped off his rubber gloves.

'I'd like to become part of this family once again. If you'll have me.'

Catherine slowly shook her head. 'We'd love that, Leo. But there's nothing we can do for you. You're going to have to convince her all by yourself.'

'I know that we haven't always seen eye to eye, Mr Chambers, but I do love your daughter.'

'I don't doubt that, Leo,' Charles said. 'She loves you too. But do you make each other happy?'

'I'd like to think that we could, given another chance.'

'Well, there's one thing for certain,' Charles said with a heavy sigh. 'She's been damn miserable without you.'

Chapter Eighty-Five

The alarm clock went off yet again and Leo knocked it to the floor. Flipping onto his back, he stared at the ceiling. He kept hoping that, like Bobby Ewing on *Dallas*, he'd wake up in the shower and it would all have been a terrible nightmare and that none of it had really happened. But every morning he was in his bed facing harsh reality with no hope of a cop-out ending.

He'd been back in the real world now for over a week and it wasn't all that it was cracked up to be. Getting up and struggling through the day wasn't proving any easier. Leo wondered how long he could carry on with this feeling – or lack of it. He wasn't sure that numb and sick were classed as emotions.

Forcing himself out of bed, he padded through to the kitchen. Leo was looking too scary to go near a mirror – even he fully appreciated that. His hair was a disaster zone and he hadn't shaved at all over the weekend – somehow there didn't seem to be any point. His time was spent entirely alone, watching as many Disney films as he could find in the local video shop featuring fairies, while partaking liberally of red wine. How he missed Isobel and her mischievous little ways. She would know how to sort this out for him. She'd have made Emma return his calls with a wave of that wicked wand of hers. Instead he'd lost two great women

– and he wondered how he could have made such a mess of his life.

The sink was piled high with dirty dishes and Leo stood and surveyed the mess with disgust.

'Not so keen to spruce yourselves up now, eh?'

His dishes remained silent.

Leo sighed. 'Me neither.'

Going to the sink, he picked out the least dirty dish and then took a box of Kellogg's Frosties from the cupboard. There was no milk in the fridge – he already knew that as he had run out yesterday and couldn't be bothered to nip out to the shop. Leo quite liked black coffee anyway. Except that coffee was the other thing he'd run out of.

Sitting at the table with his dish, he went to tip out some cereal, but alas there was nothing in the box. Still, he hadn't much of an appetite anyway. Leo put his head on the table and, mercifully, sleep overtook him once more.

When Leo finally got to the office, Grant and Lard were already at their desks. They exchanged one of their glances as he entered.

'Leo!' Grant said. 'Where have you been?' He glanced at the clock. It was nearly eleven o'clock.

'I know. I know. Sorry. Sorry.' Leo slid into his chair and tried to busy himself with turning on his computer and other stuff that he really didn't care about.

Old Baldy came out of his office and glared at him. Their boss had been like a bear with a sore arse since Isobel had gone too. The fact that she'd been replaced by some pinch-faced temp with a tweed suit and librarian's bun couldn't be helping.

'On the late shift again, Mr Harper?'

'I know. I know. Sorry. Sorry. I'll be here on time tomorrow.'

'Nine o'clock, Mr Harper. Sharp. Or the number of your tomorrows will be severely curtailed.' And Old Baldy flounced back into his office.

'Bugger,' Leo muttered under his breath.

Grant and Lard waited until Old Baldy was engrossed in something else and then sidled over to Leo's desk. Lard put a Danish pastry down next to their friend.

'Breakfast,' Grant said. 'Eat it.'

Leo shook his head. No glitter. 'Cheers, mate,' he said, 'but I've already eaten.' He patted his stomach just to prove how full he was.

'You haven't,' Grant said.

'No.'

'Not for days.'

'I'm on a diet.'

'Yeah?' Grant said. 'And so is Lard.'

Grant and Leo looked up at Lard who was eating his customary Mars Bar with relish.

'I've got work to do, boys.' Leo tried to look interested in his computer while inside it felt as if his world was crashing.

Grant sat next to him and pulled his chair up close. 'This can't go on, Leo,' he told him softly. 'We are all in deep, deep doo-doo after our week's little unauthorised holiday, even though we only thought we'd been gone for one night. I'm not sure how we've managed to keep our jobs, but we have. If you don't buck up – and quick – Baldy will give you the bullet.'

Something inside Leo snapped. 'Do you think I care? Do you really think I care about whether stocks go up or down or bloody sideways?' He knew that he was shouting. People in the office were looking at him. 'What does it matter? *Why* does any of it matter?'

Grant lowered his voice further, the voice of calm in his storm. 'Leo. I'm your friend. Your best friend. I know what you've been through. I know what you're *going* through. I know the things you've seen. But, mate, you've got to get your act together.'

Leo turned and faced his friend. 'Why?'

Grant was clearly taken aback. 'Why?'

'Yes. Why?'

Grant looked at a loss for an answer. 'It's what we do,' he said. 'We carry on.'

'Grant,' Lard interjected, 'you know what she was like. You of all people know. You must be able to understand why he's so gutted.'

Leo raked his fingers through his hair.

'This isn't about Isobel though, is it?' Grant asked candidly.

Leo sighed and it wavered sadly on the air. 'Losing Isobel was bad enough, but I can rationalise that in some small part of my brain. She was a *fairy*, for goodness sake.' He lowered his voice. 'We were different beings from different places – it was never destined to last. I can cope with that. Sort of. But with Emma it's not the same. She's here. She's flesh and blood. There's no reason for us not to be together.

We're *meant* to be together. She's the sensible one. I thought she'd see that. I thought she'd want us to carry on just as we were. I miss her so much that even my fingernails hurt from the pain of it.'

'I wish I could wave a magic wand for you and make it all better.'

'But you can't,' Leo said. 'No one can. There's suddenly a bit of a wand shortage round here. I lost Emma, then I lost Isobel and now I've lost Emma again.' He felt like wailing out loud. How careless could one man be? 'I have to get through this on my own.'

'You have us,' Lard told Leo. 'You have your friends. We'll always be here for you.' He put his hand on his heart.

Leo and Grant raised their eyebrows at this.

'You said you were going to win Emma back, you prawn,' Grant said with more than a hint of exasperation. 'What have you done so far? Made a few whingey phone calls. Hung around outside the gallery and her flat when you know she's not there.'

'I went to see her parents.'

'That's it? The sum total of your effort?'

'Emma has made it very clear that I've blown it.'

'I know you're in the depths of despair and I hate to see you like this, but now you know exactly how Emma feels, mate. She's gone through all of this crap for you. Her finger-nails have been hurting too. Why should she trust you again?'

'I've changed.'

'How does she know that?'

'I don't know. It's rather difficult to show her how when she won't see me or speak to me.'

'So let's get back to basics. Why did you break up in the first place?'

'Because Emma felt we'd lost "the magic".'

'Then show her it, you idiot. For heaven's sake, Leo, you should by now know more about magic than most. Think about that.'

Leo's friend clapped him on the shoulder and he and Lard walked away. Leo sat and stared at his computer, utterly speechless. He stuffed the Danish pastry into his mouth and made himself chew even though he couldn't taste anything at all and might as well be eating a beer mat or his own underpants.

Grant's words reverberated round his brain. Leo had no idea that he could feel – or cause – this amount of pain. He was shocked to the core. Why was he never capable of showing Emma how much he loved her? Leo felt sick. Sick to his stomach. Sick to his heart. If it wasn't for the fact that Old Baldy would sack him if he even moved from this desk before nightfall, Leo would have gone to the bathroom and would have spilled his guts.

Chapter Eighty-Six

Leo was sitting alone in the dark, which he appreciated was a sad sack thing to do. Even worse, he was listening to Whitney Houston, but he did have a can of beer in his hand, which to Leo's mind sort of evened things out. He had got stuff to do, but he wasn't sure what, and he didn't know if he could be bothered with it anyway. He should probably iron a shirt for work tomorrow, but if he kept his jacket on then no one would see the creases.

The doorbell rang and he considered ignoring it, but it was ringing in a particularly persistent manner and whoever it was didn't seem to be in a rush to go away. Leo padded out to the hall.

When he opened the door, Grant and Lard were standing there grinning inanely.

'We have curry,' Grant announced cheerily. 'We have beer. We have a DVD of Manchester United's golden moments. We have all that is required for a good time.'

'Nearly all,' Leo said miserably.

'The lap dancer said she'd be along later,' Lard told him with a wink.

'Oh good.' Leo smiled at them tiredly. 'Come on in.'

In the lounge, Grant threw him a worried look. 'Whitney Houston?'

'It's a temporary phase.'

'I'm glad to hear it, mate.' Grant cut Whitney off in mid-warble and replaced her with the White Stripes.

'How are you feeling?' Lard asked sincerely. '*Really* feeling?'

'Fantastic,' Leo replied. 'I'm *really* feeling *really* fantastic.'

'You will,' Grant said, clapping him so heartily on the back that he nearly fell over.

They went through to the kitchen and Leo stood there being as useless as a chocolate teapot while Grant and Lard washed some plates and dished out heaps of biriani and onion bhajis and piles of poppadoms. Neither of them mentioned what a state his kitchen or, indeed his life, was in. Grant sang while he ladled out the vegetable curry and, call Leo slow on the uptake, but he then twigged that this forced *bonhomie* was all for his benefit. Part of the Rehabilitate Leo Plan. Even though he was still a miserable old git and he was absolutely sure that it wouldn't work, he was touched that they had gone to so much trouble on his behalf.

Succulent pieces of chicken tikka steamed gently in a silver-foil tray. No refined Indian gentleman popping up to serve it this time though. But for the first time in weeks, the smell of the spices pricked at Leo's appetite. He wasn't sure whether he'd eaten at all today, but suddenly he realised that he was starving.

'Can't you do something to help, you lazy bastard?' his dear friend Grant said over his shoulder.

'I'll get us some more beers,' Leo said, and turned his attention to the fridge to hide the fact that he felt like crying again.

Two hours later. Curry gone. And beer. All merry. Happy times. Happy times. Drink. Drink. Lots of drink. Sat in row on sofa. Watched football. With mates. Leo loved Grant. Loved Lard too. Great mates. The best. David Beckham. Also best. Loved Dave too. Loved Emma most of all. *Manchester United Golden Moments*. Top DVD. Much scoring. Naff off, Whitney Houston. Sloppy, sloppy, terrible music. All bollocks. Sorry, Emma.

'Goal! Goal! Goal!'

Mexican wave on sofa. Leo stood up. Wobble. Cheering. Cheering. Hoorah!

Leo. 'Boys. Boys. Sing-song. Sing-song.'

Grant and Lard stood up. Wobble. Wobble.

Leo. 'There's only one David Beckham!'

All. 'There's only one David Beckham! One David Beckham! There's only one David Beckham!'

Not so pissed. Saw Grant and Lard exchange relieved glance. Top mates. Ha! Old Leo was back. David Beckham saviour of all mankind. Emma sexiest bird on planet. Hurrah! Fell over. Ouff!

Seventeen cups of coffee and a little doze later and they were all a bit more sober and righteous. And who knew what it was, maybe the curry, the booze or the fact that Manchester United *were* the top team in the universe, but something had shifted inside of Leo and he knew that from now on, things could only get better.

Grant and Lard were at the kitchen sink and they were washing Leo's dishes. They were also wearing aprons which they had found who knows where. They must surely have been something to do with Isobel. Leo's heart squeezed at the thought of her and the fact that he was never likely to see her again – no bumping into her down at the shops or the pub, no catching a glimpse of her on a passing bus – but he didn't feel quite the amount of hopelessness that he previously had. Isobel had been an important part of his life and he'd never forget her, but he saw that it would be possible to let go. He'd learned a lot from her and he should put all this new knowledge to good use and not squander it as he'd squandered everything else in his life.

Before he was berated for his lack of domesticity, he started to cram the empty foil cartons and remnants of the curry into a black bin bag.

'You need a dishwasher,' Grant said.

'I do not.'

'You do.'

'You need to get out more,' Lard said.

'I do not.'

'You do.'

Now they were all sober and they realised that Leo wasn't about to top himself, they clearly thought they were safe to nag him again. He thought Grant and Lard would make a wonderful couple.

'You need a woman to look after you,' Grant said.

'I definitely do not!'

'You do!' Grant and Lard insisted in unison.

'Yeah?' Leo sat down at the table, resisting the temptation to open another beer. 'Look at the state of me. Miserable. Morose.'

'Manky,' Grant added. 'You might be crap at relationships, Leo, but you don't do great single either.'

'I'm not ready for another relationship.' He shook his head. 'I wouldn't want me. Who else would?'

Grant and Lard exchanged a demonic grin. 'Emma,' they said.

'No. No. No. Many times no.' Leo held up his hands. 'I have hurt that woman enough.'

'True,' they agreed.

'Anyway. What about you?' Leo frowned at Grant. 'I thought you and Emma were getting . . .' He rubbed his arms up and down himself in a seductive manner.

'Oh, Leo.' Grant sighed at him. 'When are you going to learn? If you could ever get your two brain cells to collide it would be a cataclysmic event.'

'Perhaps I should stand aside and let you get on with it.'

'She happens to be in love with someone else.'

Leo was horrified. 'Who?'

Grant turned to Lard. 'You hold him down while I knock some sense into that stupid thick skull of his.'

Leo gazed at them incredulously. 'She's still in love with me?'

They both rolled their eyes.

'She can't be,' he said. 'I'm such a pain in the arse. She has told me many times and in many different ways. She won't even take my calls.'

Grant and Lard gave him one of their special looks.

'I'm not saying it would be easy,' Grant said. 'You'd need a very cunning plan.'

'Emma wouldn't want me back with a bow tied round me.' A rush of warmth flooded into his body. Suddenly there was hope in his wounded heart. 'Would she?'

Chapter Eighty-Seven

I'm meeting Jo and Caron for lunch at their favourite haunt down by the River Thames, but I've got some time to kill and am stocking up on a few bits and pieces to see me through the weekend at my other favourite haunt – the Hay's Galleria. I've bought my friends a few little trinkets too, for being so fabulous over the last few weeks. I don't know how I would have managed without them.

The weekdays aren't too bad – when I'm busy at work and I often stay late researching and planning new exhibitions just to avoid going home – but the weekends loom large ahead of me and they're sheer torture. Friends are great, but they're not the same as having a partner waiting for you to slob around with.

I'm going to see Caron again tonight, but we aren't going out on the town. There's only so much enforced partying that I can stand and I've pretty much reached my limit. Instead, I'm planning to regroup and conserve my energies. Which essentially means that Caron and I are going to sit in and watch yet another DVD featuring an unattainable man. Jo, despite her disgust at men who want only casual sex, doesn't seem to be able to manage without it for any longer than a week or two either – so she's hitting the clubs with the intention of getting soundly laid. No doubt we'll hear about her tawdry escapades during the week.

This morning, I've been to see my mother who is now, thankfully, back at home, ensconced in her downstairs make-shift bedroom. I think that she still looks frail, but there's no doubt she's making a good recovery. My father is running round, catering to Mummy's every whim, like a teenager in love. It's both wonderful and heartbreaking to see. My mother has never been incapacitated in her entire life and it's strange to see her so dependent on other people. It's even stranger to see my father coping so well. If ever there's a silver lining on a cloud it's the fact that Daddy has somehow broken down his own emotional barriers and is now openly affectionate to his wife – and, even more bizarrely – to everyone else around him. He even smiled at the spotty teenager who delivered his newspaper today. There's no doubting that my parents are still deeply in love despite all that life has thrown at them. They have magic in their lives and there aren't many people who can count themselves so lucky. It gives me hope for the future. Even a future without Leo.

Leo has been home for weeks now and has given up calling me. And even though I kept hanging up on him when he did, I do really want to talk to him now. I could call him, but I haven't managed to summon up the courage to do that yet. Perhaps we're both too stubborn for our own good. It could also be that Leo has moved on, has found someone new, and this really is the end for us. I shift the weight of my carrier bags in my hands. We had such great potential and I still find it hard to believe that we managed to fritter it away so easily. We have both been stupid in taking each other for granted. But, when all is said and done, Leo is still probably more stupid than me.

* * *

Leo came out of the novelty gifts store, clutching at his bulging carrier bags. This was a complete trial for him as he wasn't a natural shopper. He was a man for a start and men just didn't have the right genes for it. This, however, was important shopping. So important that Leo had even scribbled down a list for himself. And he hadn't lost it. He wanted to get everything perfect, so nothing would be left to chance – or to his two cohorts. He must accomplish this feat alone. The amount he'd spent was making him feel dizzy and he decided he must consume some strong alcohol before he'd be capable of moving on to attempt phase two.

Leo headed towards the nearest bar in search of some medicinal Budweiser and as he did, he saw Emma coming out of one of the other shops. His heart nearly stopped beating. She was swinging down the middle of the arcade, smiling. He thought she'd lost some weight – which she'd like. But he had to say, she looked great. Happy and perky. Without him. And Leo wondered whether Lard and Grant had read this whole situation wrong. They were convinced that Emma still held a torch for him, but Leo didn't know if that was the case. She didn't exactly look miserable. He had to conclude that she'd usually looked an awful lot more miserable when he was with her. Was it insane to place his trust in two men who were just as clueless as he was when it came to reading what women want? Leo thought it might well be so. But they had helped him to get Isobel home and he supposed he could do worse than rely on their instincts again.

Emma was heading straight towards him. He felt like a rabbit trapped in the headlights, standing there with his arms chock-full of carrier bags. This was dastardly timing, indeed. He didn't want to bump into her now when he wasn't prepared. It reminded him of the day they saw each other here when he was shopping with Isobel and how it felt to see Emma with another man – a man he'd thought she was planning to marry. That left him more than breathless. He could never let that happen again. Leo felt panicky. Was this plan madness? Should he just shout out to Emma now and take his chances? They could maybe have lunch, a coffee – break the ice that had developed between them that way. Leo looked down at his carrier bags; he felt he'd come too far to veer from his chosen route now, although his courage nearly deserted him. She was a few metres away from him. Any second now they'd be face to face. A group of American students pushed their way past him, laughing and giggling, chattering in high-pitched East Coast accents. Leo lost sight of her in the tide of people, even though he stood on tiptoe and looked over their heads. By the time they'd passed by, he looked up and saw that Emma was walking away from him. And he thought that, for the moment, it was probably a good thing.

Chapter Eighty-Eight

Leo could do this. He could do this. He was pacing up and down outside the very smart florist's shop in the Galleria. It was true that he'd had a drink, but he was trying to curb his dependence on all things alcoholic. It had brought him nothing but trouble and was, obviously, along with money, the root of all evil. This situation, however, counted as exceptional circumstances and had required a few swift glasses of beer for courage. Leo made no excuses for his weakness.

There was a very lovely lady standing inside behind the counter in the florist's and she was looking at Leo as if he was a stalker. This was primarily because this wasn't his first time of pacing up and down outside. For half an hour now he'd been hoping that a suitably bribable child would pop up – but he was out of luck. This particular mission, it seemed, was going to be down to himself entirely. He chewed at his fingernails and he could feel sweat peppering his brow. Now he was making her look nervous. Leo knew what it felt like to suffer agonies of indecision.

With a deep breath he dived inside the shop. The woman looked suitably terrified and he was sure he could see her hand hovering over a panic button. This was possibly worse than buying underwear. 'I . . . I . . . I . . .' My goodness, he'd developed a stammer! 'I . . . I . . .'

'Yes?' She tried to give him an encouraging look.

'I . . . I . . .' Leo's hands had gone clammy and he was feeling faint. He wished he hadn't had a drink now. Leo was sure she could smell it on his breath. 'I . . . I . . .'

'You'd like to buy some flowers?'

'Yes.' A sigh of relief rushed out of his mouth. 'I'd like to buy some flowers.'

'Roses?'

Leo wiped his damp palms on his trousers. 'Roses would be lovely.'

She smiled at him and went over to a stand that had a display of a dozen different colours of roses in stainless steel vases. 'Is it for a romantic occasion?' she asked.

'Yes,' he said, with an over-enthusiastic nod. 'A romantic occasion.'

'Then I think red roses, don't you?'

'Yes,' he said. 'Red. Red is good.'

The florist smiled at him again. 'There,' she said. 'That wasn't so bad, was it?'

'No,' Leo said. 'That wasn't so bad.'

'And how many would you like?'

'About two hundred, I think.'

The florist went pale. 'Two hundred?'

'Yes. More if you have them.'

'Do you have any idea how much that's going to cost?'

'No,' he said. 'Whatever it is, it will be worth it. But I need them today.'

'I . . . I . . . I'll have to ring round our other shops,' she said. Now she'd developed a stammer. 'But I'm sure we can do that.'

'I'll take what you have now,' Leo told her. 'Can you have the rest of them delivered as soon as possible? I have things to do.'

'Yes,' she answered in a vaguely stunned way. 'I'm sure we can do that.'

Now she was looking terrified whereas Leo was gaining confidence by the minute. He handed over his address and an awful lot of plastic money. Then he took his leave of this lovely lady and strode outside the shop with a carrier bag filled with roses, heads peeping out. Leo had no idea why he had avoided this flower-buying lark for so long. It felt great.

Half an hour later and he was nearing home. Leo shifted his shopping against his chest. He was sure his arms were considerably longer than they were when he had set out, but he didn't care. Leo had worked his way through the greatest hits of Queen on his way home and was now on to 'It's a Kind of Magic' at the top of his voice. He even tried a few dance steps. It had worked for Gene Kelly, it could work for Leo. The sun was out. The birds were singing. Strangers smiled at his one-man concert rather than avoiding him. Old and faithful Ethel was parked patiently outside awaiting his return. Leo went over to her and kissed her roof. 'You and I are going to look irresistible,' he said. 'You just wait and see.'

Leo sprinted up the stairs – even though he was weighed down with a dozen different carrier bags – and just as he went to open the door, his lovely neighbour Dominic came out. 'Hello, lovely neighbour,' Leo said brightly. 'How the hell are you?'

'Fine,' Dominic said, looking decidedly shifty. 'I'm fine.'

'Good. Bloody hell, you look miserable, mate.'

'I'm fine,' he repeated. Then he shrugged. 'Lydia and I have had a bit of a tiff.'

'Bugger,' Leo said. 'Women. Thought she'd left you?'

'She's back,' Dominic said tightly.

Leo grimaced apologetically. 'Behind with the news. Haven't seen you in ages.'

'No,' Dominic said. 'But I understand you've been away.'

'And now I'm back,' Leo told him. 'Da! Da!'

'Good.'

Leo pulled a beautiful red rose out of his carrier bag with a flourish. 'Give this to Lydia,' he said. 'Tell her you love her.' And, just to show what a nice guy he was, Leo gave Dominic a big kiss on the cheek. He was sure he saw his neighbour flinch.

'How's Emma?' he asked croakily.

'Wonderful,' Leo said. 'Very wonderful. And very soon she's going to think I am too!'

'Give Emma my love,' Dominic said quietly. He clutched the rose to him. 'Tell her I send my love.'

Leo managed to stop himself from frowning.

'I will,' he said, and continued bounding on his way. 'I definitely will.'

And then his neighbour was gone, rushing away down the street as if his life depended on it, leaving Leo to wonder why Dominic would be sending Emma his love?

Chapter Eighty-Nine

It would be polite to change out of my tatty old T-shirt and sweats that have seen better days, but it's only Caron who's coming round for the evening and my friend has seen me in a worse state than this on many occasions. At least I'm clean. I languished in the bath, indulging myself in some of the lavender de-stressing bath oil that Caron bought me for my birthday. It's wonderful stuff, so I'm feeling very chill. All my make-up has been scrubbed off, along with a few layers of London grime, and I promise myself that I will do something wonderful with my hair tomorrow. For tonight, it can stay swept up in my scrunchy.

Padding barefoot through to the kitchen, I make myself a cup of green tea. A new health regime. No chocolate. No booze. I'm going to detox my body. Except, for tonight, I've bought in a box of chocolate Celebrations and a nice bottle of Rioja – so, apart from the green tea, I will start in earnest tomorrow. Honestly. *The X-Factor* is playing away to itself on the television.

The intercom buzzes. 'Hi,' I say. 'Come up.' And I buzz the door open. Turning off the television, I select a CD and click that on instead. Caron is bringing a soppy DVD which we'll watch later with a box of Kleenex to hand. Then I go to open the door to the flat.

'Hi.'

The last person I expect to see standing there is Leo. But he is.

He's wearing a dinner suit with a red rose in his lapel and looks breathtakingly handsome. Leo smiles at me and holds out an enormous bouquet of red roses wrapped in purple tissue paper. He leans jauntily on my doorframe turning up his smile, but something in his expression makes him seem surprisingly vulnerable and his eyes hold a worried look that I haven't seen before.

I examine the roses. They're exquisite. 'Thank you.'

'You're welcome,' Leo says.

I have wondered what this moment would feel like. I

imagined that I'd fall into Leo's arms, all the hurt and pain forgotten – but it isn't like that. I feel tense, affronted and Leo looks like a stranger to me. Perhaps I'm in shock. 'What are you doing here?'

'I've come to take you out,' he says brightly.

'Take me out?'

'If you'll let me.'

'I'm seeing someone else.'

'You're not,' Leo says. 'My spies have reliably informed me that you're still an unfettered, single woman.'

'Well, I could have been,' I sigh.

'But you're not.' Leo fiddles with the rose in his lapel. 'I saw Dominic today.'

'Oh.' I feel myself flush. 'Did he tell you what happened?'

'Er . . . yes. Of course he did. Man to man.'

'It was an experience.' I try very hard not to recall a vivid image of it. 'A dreadful experience. I'm going to have a lifelong aversion to cardboard and Superglue. And red underwear.'

Leo raises a puzzled eyebrow and I wonder how much Dominic has really told him.

'He said to send you his . . . regards.' Leo nods thoughtfully. 'His regards. He and Lydia seem very happy together. Very happy.'

'I'm sure they are.' I'm glad it's working out for the man who was briefly a good and caring friend to me. Dominic has forgiven his straying girlfriend and has taken her back. Am I willing to do the same?

I rake my hair and then realise what I must look like. Why couldn't Leo have warned me that he was going to drop back into my life unannounced? 'You'd better come in,' I say.

Leo comes into the lounge and sits down next to me on the sofa. It could so easily feel like old times, but something has changed in both of us. I can feel that there has been an unidentifiable shift somewhere and wonder whether it's in me or whether it's in Leo. And I also wonder whether it's for better or for worse. Would it ever be possible to get the old times back?

'You can't just turn up like this,' I tell Leo. 'Out of the blue. Couldn't you have phoned me? It's been weeks since I've heard anything from you.'

'I know, and I'm sorry. I thought you'd hang up on me again.'

'I can't just drop everything,' I say. 'I am expecting someone, as it happens.'

'Caron.'

'Yes.'

'She isn't coming,' Leo tells me.

A frown crosses my face. 'How do you know?'

Leo has the grace to look sheepish.

'Oh,' I say, penny dropping. 'You organised this with her? Caron who used to be my best friend, but the situation is currently under review.'

'Caron *and* Grant.' Leo checks his watch. 'They are currently enjoying a convivial meal together at a lovely Italian restaurant. I think they'll make a nice couple.'

'And what would you know about that, Leo? You've suddenly become a relationship expert?'

'Everyone thought that you'd missed me.'

'Oh, did they?' I fold my arms. 'Well . . . well, you can even miss toothache once it stops.'

Leo grins at me. He can read me like a book. 'Caron told Grant that you couldn't stop thinking about me.'

'Caron, who is now looking for a new best friend, said that?'

Leo reaches out and takes my hand. It's warm and familiar and sends a weakness to my knees that I hadn't expected. It's just like the first time I met Leo. His face is suddenly serious. 'I want to try again.'

'Oh.'

'You said that the magic had gone out of our relationship and I had no idea what you meant. Really I didn't. But I do now and I want to see if we can get the magic back,' he says.

'Oh. Oh.' My heart is pounding. 'And what about Ms Incredibly Gorgeous Isobel?'

'She's . . . er . . .' Leo looks sad. 'She's gone. For good. And she won't be coming back. You don't have to worry about that.'

'I can't be second choice, Leo.'

'It isn't like that,' he says. 'It was never like that.'

'Do you want to tell me what happened?'

'No.' Leo shakes his head. 'I'm not sure what happened myself. It's a very bizarre story. You wouldn't believe me.'

'I never believe you anyway, Leo.'

'I'll tell you when we've grown old and grey together.' He strokes my hand tenderly. 'Then you'll trust me.'

'If I agree to go out with you again, I'll be old and grey within two weeks.'

Leo grins at me. 'So you are considering it?'

In some ways it feels so good, so right for us to be here together again. Can I forgive and forget all that has gone on between us and start over with a clean slate? In striving for perfection, I've been less than perfect too and it looks as if Leo can forgive me. Aren't the strongest relationships made by people who are prepared to work through the bad times together?

Then I shake my head sadly. 'I can't do this, Leo.' I can't risk getting hurt again. Even though I'm hurting without Leo, it's a constant pain – not the rollercoaster ride that I was on before. 'I'm not sure that I can trust you with my emotions again.'

'You can.' Tears fill Leo's eyes. 'I promise you.'

'I can't risk it,' I say.

'Then it's really over?'

'I'm sorry.' My throat has closed, so I can't say anything else. I don't want to cry but I can't help it. Tears roll slowly down my face.

Leo stands up and I follow suit. He takes my hands in his warm ones. 'It's a terrible shame, Emma,' he tells me, 'because the new, improved Leo is a really great bloke.'

He holds me tight and kisses me like I've never been kissed before. Then he turns and walks out of the door while I stand and wonder what the hell I've done.

Chapter Ninety

Leo's car, Ethel, is parked on the road outside my flat under the spotlight of a nearby lamp post. She's decorated with a garland of tiny white lights and has swags of tinsel round the outside. Ethel is also wearing huge black false eyelashes on her headlights. Leo is already climbing into the driver's seat.

'Leo!'

He stops and looks back at me. I suddenly realised I couldn't let him go, so now I'm standing on the pavement feeling ridiculous. My eyes fill with tears and my throat is still constricted. Leo comes over to me.

'That looks pathetic,' I manage to say gruffly.

'Come on,' he says, tugging gently at my hand. 'Get in.'

'Where are we going? I can't go out looking like this.' Skanky sweats and scrunchy are not a good look. 'You're in your dinner suit.'

Brushing my cheek softly with his thumb, Leo says, 'You look beautiful just as you are.'

Leo opens the passenger door for me. The back seat of the car is filled with hundreds of red roses.

'Have you bought these all by yourself?' I whisper.

Leo nods. This is not the man I know and have loved. Someone must have taken him and waved a magic wand over him. By some divine intervention or top-rate miracle, Leo has turned into a proper boyfriend.

The perfume in the car is intoxicating. My head is reeling. I slide inside.

'I feel very silly,' I say without conviction. 'Can anyone see us? Where are we going?'

'Sit back and relax,' Leo instructs. 'Leave everything to me.'

He gets in the car next to me. Then we sit and look at each other for a moment, still in the silence, and I can see that Leo's eyes are full of love. Love for me. 'I have missed you,' I say tearfully. 'I've missed you a lot.'

My favourite Whitney Houston CD starts playing on the car stereo. Which is very strange because Ethel doesn't have a CD player. The stereo doesn't even appear to be switched on. Even Leo looks taken aback.

'How did you do that?'

'I didn't,' Leo says, bemused. 'It must be magic.'

He guns Ethel into life.

'Is all this magic going to make your driving any better?' I ask.

'No.' He shakes his head. 'It's magic. Not a miracle.'

'So some things never change?'

'No. I guess not.' He leans over and kisses me on the cheek. 'But some things do. You wait and see.'

Leo pulls out into the street and, in his usual style, kangaroos off down the road, shouting out of the window, 'Tally ho!'

We drive past a cyclist, way too close, causing him to swerve.

'I know you!' Leo shouts and gives the cyclist a friendly wave. 'Yoo hoo!'

He turns to me. 'I made him fall off his bike the night of your birthday party,' he confesses. 'Doesn't that seem like another lifetime ago?'

'Yes.' Another lifetime ago. In the past. Behind us.

In the rearview mirror I notice that the cyclist has fallen off his bike once more. He jumps up cursing and gives Leo the finger.

We both burst out laughing.

'Sorry!' Leo yells back at him. 'Sorry! Awfully sorry.'

Chapter Ninety-One

Lard pulled uncomfortably at his shirt cuffs. 'I've never been on a blind date before,' he complained.

'Shut up moaning,' Grant said, as they entered the restaurant. 'And be pleased that I care enough about you to arrange this.' He nudged Lard in the ribs and whispered, 'They're here.'

Caron and Jo were already seated at the table that Grant had booked. They both looked lovely. Not shimmery and sparkly, but grounded, substantial and beautiful women.

'Oh my word,' Lard said. 'I wish I'd worn my best undies now.'

Grant put his arm round Lard and hugged him. He'd developed a much stronger need for human contact and warmth since coming home. It was as if all his senses had been scrubbed out and were shiny and raw. His bond with Leo and Lard had strengthened from their experience and he knew that whatever happened to them in the future, it would never be broken. 'I told you I wouldn't let you down, my lovely little friend.'

The conversation in the restaurant babbled like the brook in the Land of Light, and Grant wondered if he would ever stop getting flashbacks to their visit there. It was like suffering from Post Traumatic Stress Disorder – little images could be triggered by such trivia. Except that the vision didn't frighten him or give him nightmares, but filled him with a powerful sense of love, loss and longing. When he saw flickering lights, would it always take him back to their weird and wonderful night at Stonehenge? Would these images always be imprinted so sharply on his brain, or would his memories fade with time? How much worse must it have been for Leo, to have loved and lost a being from another world? All he and Lard could do was try to support Leo and, when he felt alone and overwhelmed, let him know that, for a brief time, they had shared an earth-shatteringly surreal experience with him that had changed them all. Grant could see a kernel of compassion and humanity in the three of them that had never existed before.

Grant kissed Caron as he sat down. He was eternally grateful that she'd been able to forgive him for standing her up on their first official date and had agreed to give their stalled, fledgeling relationship another try. 'Hello again.'

Caron smiled shyly. Lard hovered nervously in the background and Grant pulled him into the nearest chair. 'Meet Lard,' he said by way of introduction.

'Why are you called Lard?' Jo wanted to know.

'I used to be chubby,' Lard confessed. He looked down at his new slim-line stomach – one of the bonuses of having persuaded a giggling Isobel to cast a spell on him. Now when Lard ate chocolate in vast quantities it only helped him to lose weight. The more Mars Bars he consumed, the more the pounds dropped off. It was a shame they couldn't bottle it and sell it.

'And now you're not,' Jo said. 'So what's your real name?'

'Tim,' Lard answered. 'My name's Tim.'

Grant looked at him in surprise. He was sure that he must have once known what Lard's real name was, but no one had called him that for years.

'So Tim,' Jo continued, 'if I let you buy me dinner, are you going to expect to sleep with me tonight?'

'No,' Lard said, faintly aghast.

'Shame,' she said. 'Let's eat. You can reconsider your answer later.'

Grant sighed with relief. They were going to be okay. Lard wouldn't stand a chance if Jo decided they were going to be an item. Which was good, because it meant that he could forget about keeping an eye on his friend and concentrate on his own date.

'It's good to see you.' Grant took hold of Caron's hand.

Caron filled his glass for him and they touched them together. 'To us,' she said.

'To us,' he echoed.

She sipped her wine and then said, 'I wonder how Emma and Leo are getting on? Do you think they'll still be talking to us?'

'I don't know,' Grant admitted. 'We've done all that we can to try to bring them together again. The rest of it is up to Leo and Emma.'

'I hope it's going well for them,' Caron said.

'Me too.'

'Leo's lucky to have a friend like you,' she said.

'No.' Grant shook his head. 'We're all lucky to know Leo. He's a very special guy. I have a lot to thank him for.'

It had been a strange few weeks, but life was gradually getting back to normal again and he was looking forward to settling down to more mundane pursuits once more. No fairies, no spells, no magic. He looked over at Caron; her eyes were shining in the candlelight. Perhaps it wasn't fair to class someone so stunning as a mundane pursuit. He smiled at Caron and felt a rush of warmth to his heart. And as for magic, well, maybe it was a bit rash to say no to magic. He hoped that he was always going to remain open to a bit of that.

Chapter Ninety-Two

It was a marvellous starry, moonlit night. Leo couldn't have asked for anything more perfect. And he'd seen some pretty amazing things in the past few weeks. They could hear nothing but the sound of the lapping waves on the beach, the rush of water over shingle. Leo didn't know what had really happened in the Land of Light or with the whole Isobel thing, but he did know that he felt more calm than he had in his entire life. There was a contentment at his core that had been missing before, and instead of charging aimlessly and foolishly through his life, he was going to start to appreciate the things he had. Leo Harper was going to stop and smell the roses.

Emma and Leo were sitting on a tartan blanket that he'd set out on the beach. Leo had whisked her down to Brighton – snuggled together in the beautifully-scented Ethel, eating up the miles with ease. This had always been one of their favourite weekend haunts and somewhere they hadn't visited in a long time. Now it was dark and the day-trippers were long gone, heading for the bars and restaurants, the renowned nightlife. The lights of the town sparkled in the distance and the huge framework of Brighton Pier provided their backdrop. They were alone, looking out over the vast sweep of ocean.

Leo had taken a lot of trouble in packing the picnic, trawling his brain to remember all of Emma's favourite foods. He realised that it felt great to do nice things for the person you love the most on earth.

The night was warm, but Leo had gathered some firewood and lit a fire on the beach. Cuddled up together, they were watching the sparks dance in the air. They'd both rolled up their trousers to their knees and had stripped off their socks so that they could toast their toes by the fire.

'Warm enough?' Leo asked.

Emma nodded, but he took off his jacket anyway and draped it around her shoulders. She didn't complain, just leaned against him, eyes closed. Leo undid his bow tie and let it hang. Tonight he had managed to tie it all by himself without the aid of a fairy and her magic wand. Isobel was right, he was perfectly capable of managing without her, and that thought somehow made him smile.

'What's wrong?' Emma squeezed his hand.

'Nothing,' he said. 'Nothing at all.'

'This is wonderful, Leo. Magical. Thank you.'

Reaching over to the picnic basket, he pulled out a bottle of champagne. He unwound the wire carefully and then let the cork fly – for once not having to worry about denting someone's ceiling or taking someone's eye out. As he did, a shooting star rushed across the sky.

'Did you see that?'

'Yes,' Emma said. 'That's the first time I've ever seen a shooting star. Aren't they supposed to be a good omen?'

'Make a wish.'

Emma's eyes met his. 'It already came true.'

Leo wondered if he would ever be able to tell Emma about Isobel. About why she'd been here. And how you should be very careful what you wish for. Maybe some time, but not now.

'Here . . .' Leo handed her two glasses and the champagne frothed over into them.

He took the wire fixer from the cork and twisted it around. Taking Emma's hand in his, Leo said, 'Emma, will you do me the very great honour of marrying me?'

Emma's eyes filled up with tears. 'Yes,' she breathed.

Leo slipped the champagne wire ring onto her finger. His fiancée admired it in the moonlight. 'It's beautiful.'

They stood up and wrapped their arms around each other.

'We need to make a toast,' Leo said.

Emma and Leo clinked their glasses together. 'To the moonlight, the madness and the magic. To us.'

They toasted each other, savouring the taste of the champagne. The wind picked up gently and lifted Emma's hair in the breeze. Lights sparkled in the sky, tiny pinpricks of colour that Leo knew instinctively he'd seen somewhere before. He turned to the fire; the flames flickered, showering sparks into the air. In the flames Leo saw an image of Isobel and she was smiling out at him. A tiny silver butterfly broke free of the flames and, as his eyes followed it, it fluttered away high into the sky until soon it was out of sight, vanished in the darkness. But he knew that Isobel was happy and Leo was happy too. She'd always be with him in spirit, but he had Emma – always his one true love – here on earth. And he was glad that he'd had the chance to know Isobel. He was glad that she had come along to open his heart, to blow it apart and to show him just how much he could love. She had managed to teach Leo a lesson that was well worth learning.

Punching his arm into the air, he cried out at the top of his lungs, 'Hoo! Hoo!'

Leo swept Emma up into his arms and twirled her around. She shrieked with delight. Then he ran down the beach, loving the crunch of the pebbles beneath his feet and the wind in his hair. They reached the sea and he carried Emma into the waves, letting the icy water rush over them both, gasping as the foam hit them.

'I love you,' Emma said, her mouth against his neck.

'I love you too.' Leo held her to him. 'We'll get it right this time. I promise you.'

'I'll hold you to it,' she warned. Then she jumped down and ducked him into the water, splashing and laughing. And Leo had never felt happier or more alive in all his life.

Chapter Ninety-Three

Everything is pitch black. Only the dying embers of the fire remain. The beach is completely deserted. Everyone sane is tucked up in their beds by now. But I never want this night to end. I'm loved. And I'm in love.

'I'm bloody soaked through,' I say, doing my best to sound cross.

'Sorry. Sorry. It was fun though.'

'It was *not* fun,' the future Mrs Leo Harper insists.

'Sorry. Sorry.'

'Just look at me.'

'I am.'

'I'm going to have to take *all* of my clothes off,' I say.

It may be dark but I can still make out the smile on Leo's lips – so I know he can see the smile on mine. '*All* of them?'

'Every last thing.'

'I could help you,' my husband-to-be suggests.

'Don't you come anywhere near me, Leo Harper. You are nothing but trouble.'

'Do I have to take all of my clothes off too?'

'Yes. Unless you want to catch your death of cold.'

'I'd rather take your clothes off first.'

'Ahh! Leo. Get off! That tickles. I'm serious.'

We help each other undress, laughing, loving. I'm still not sure what has happened between Leo and me, but it's finished now and behind us. We've learned from it and will move on. Leo covers my body with kisses. Tender, butterfly kisses. I have Leo back. The new, improved Leo. And I will cherish him as he deserves to be cherished.

'Come here, wifey,' Leo says. 'I want to show you what a thoroughly wonderful husband I'm going to be.'

I laugh and, holding each other tightly, we sink onto the brand new picnic blanket Leo has splashed out on. Another shooting star crosses the moon, leaving a trail of what looks like silver glitter in its wake. I blink back a tear. This really has been a magical night.

HAVE YOU READ THEM ALL?

Discover the bestselling books by

Carole Matthews

LET'S MEET ON PLATFORM 8

Teri literally runs into Mr Right in Euston Station – but he might not be Mr Available . . .

A WHIFF OF SCANDAL

Aromatherapist Rose's new life in a quiet village is thrown into chaos when someone catches her eye.

MORE TO LIFE THAN THIS

Sort-of-happily-married Kate is determined to find herself – but finds a distracting man called Ben first . . .

FOR BETTER, FOR WORSE

Although she arrives without a plus one, Josie finds herself torn between not two but three handsome wedding guests.

A MINOR INDISCRETION

When Ali's head is turned by another man, her marriage is on the rocks – but should they let a minor indiscretion come between them?

A COMPROMISING POSITION

After Emily's boyfriend posts compromising photos of her online, her best friend tries to mend her heart – but they both wind up falling for the same man.

THE SWEETEST TABOO

Sadie is flown to Hollywood by a producer who wants to win her heart – but he's not the only man in LA who has his sights set on her.

WITH OR WITHOUT YOU

Lyssa embarks on a trekking holiday in Nepal in a bid to get over a broken heart, but meets someone new instead . . .

YOU DRIVE ME CRAZY

Meeting in their divorce lawyer's office was bad enough – and then Anna and Nick's ex-partners show up . . .

WELCOME TO THE REAL WORLD

A new job as an opera star's assistant could be Fern's big break, but only if she can keep things strictly professional.

IT'S A KIND OF MAGIC

Emma wishes her long-term boyfriend would change – until he meets another woman, and she's the one to change him . . .

ALL YOU NEED IS LOVE

Single mother Sally is on a mission to give her son a better life – but is the charming Spencer Knight the answer?

THE DIFFERENCE A DAY MAKES

William and Amy move from the city to the countryside, but when tragedy strikes Amy finds herself living Will's dream . . .

THAT LOVING FEELING

When the man who left her at the altar arrives to shake up Juliet Joyce's tired marriage, she finds herself with a difficult choice.

IT'S NOW OR NEVER

Twins Annie and Lauren have very different lives – until they decide to make a change.

THE ONLY WAY IS UP

When Lily and Laurence suddenly lose everything, will they get back to their old luxurious life, or learn to love their new one?

WRAPPED UP IN YOU

After one too many questions about her love life, Janie books herself the holiday of a lifetime, and meets a gorgeous tour guide.

SUMMER DAYDREAMS

Nell is inspired to swap the chip shop for her own business making handbags, but success doesn't come without a price.

WITH LOVE AT CHRISTMAS

THE SEQUEL TO *That Loving Feeling*

Juliet Joyce loves Christmas, but this year everything is spiralling out of control . . .

A COTTAGE BY THE SEA

Grace and Flick jump at the chance to go on holiday to their best friend Ella's seaside cottage – but this week will change all their lives.

CALLING MRS CHRISTMAS

Cassie's love of Christmas turns into the perfect business. But when millionaire Carter enlists her help to make the day special for his kids, where will it lead?

. . . .

A PLACE TO CALL HOME

Ayesha and her daughter leave London for a fresh start, and find refuge with a reclusive popstar.

. . . .

THE CHRISTMAS PARTY

Louise has no time for romance, until she meets her company's rising star Josh, and the office Christmas party suddenly looks more tempting . . .

. . . .

THE CAKE SHOP IN THE GARDEN

Fay runs her dream cake shop from her garden, until love, life and family collide and she has to choose what matters most.

. . . .

PAPER HEARTS AND SUMMER KISSES

Single mother Christie has a flair for crafting and design, and it's not long before opportunity – and love – come knocking. But can she really have it all?

. . . .

CHRISTMAS CAKES AND MISTLETOE NIGHTS

THE SEQUEL TO *The Cake Shop In The Garden*

Baker Fay is called back to her old life, putting her relationship with Danny to the test . . .

. . . .

MILLION LOVE SONGS

Should Ruby break her no-strings-attached rules for Joe, with his beautiful ex-wife and two teenage kids, or let her boss Mason charm her?

. . . .

HAPPINESS FOR BEGINNERS

When handsome actor Shelby enrols his son in Hope Farm's school, Molly realises they're going to be a handful, but this could be the start of something wonderful.

. . . .

SUNNY DAYS AND SEA BREEZES

Jodie heads to the Isle of Wight, ready to leave London behind – but her new houseboat life isn't as solitary as she'd imagined.

. . . .

CHRISTMAS FOR BEGINNERS

THE SEQUEL TO *Happiness For Beginners*

Molly hopes a family Christmas will bring Shelby and his son together – but Hope Farm's animals aren't the only ones causing trouble this year.

. . . .

THE CHOCOLATE LOVERS' QUARTET

1 THE CHOCOLATE LOVERS' CLUB

For Lucy, Autumn, Nadia and Chantal, there's nothing chocolate can't cure – and with troublesome boyfriends and bosses, there's always plenty for their Chocolate Lovers' Club to discuss . . .

2 THE CHOCOLATE LOVERS' DIET

Lucy thought she had her happy-ever-after, but life is throwing a few more twists and turns at the Chocolate Lovers' Club.

3 THE CHOCOLATE LOVERS' CHRISTMAS

With Christmas just around the corner, the women of the Chocolate Lovers' Club have more to worry about than shopping for presents.

4 THE CHOCOLATE LOVERS' WEDDING

Lucy, Nadia, Autumn and Chantal are gearing up for the wedding of the year, but life keeps getting in the way.

SHORT STORIES

SUNSHINE, WITH A CHANCE OF SNOW

Beth is faced with her biggest challenge yet while on a beach holiday with her family.

A CHRISTMAS WISH

Broken-hearted Hannah is about to discover there's a little Christmas magic coming her way . . .

WINTER WARMERS

Curl up with a collection of three short, festive stories.

THE SILVER COLLECTION

A collection of heart-warming short stories.